The Medieval Shepherd: Jean de Brie's *Le Bon Berger* (1379)

MEDIEVAL AND RENAISSANCE
TEXTS AND STUDIES

VOLUME 424

The Medieval Shepherd:
Jean de Brie's
Le Bon Berger (1379)

Edited and Translated by
Carleton W. Carroll
and Lois Hawley Wilson

ARIZONA CENTER FOR MEDIEVAL

ACMRS

AND RENAISSANCE STUDIES

Tempe, Arizona
2012

THE ARIZONA CENTER FOR

MEDIEVAL &
RENAISSANCE

STUDIES

Published by ACMRS (Arizona Center for Medieval and Renaissance Studies)
Tempe, Arizona
© 2012 Arizona Board of Regents for Arizona State University.
All Rights Reserved.

Library of Congress Cataloging-in-Publication Data

Brie, Jean de, fl. 1379.
 [Bon berger. English]
 The medieval shepherd : Jean de Brie's Le bon berger (1379) / edited and
translated by Carleton W. Carroll and Lois Hawley Wilson.
     p. cm. -- (Medieval and Renaissance texts and studies ; v. 424)
 Includes bibliographical references and index.
 ISBN 978-0-86698-472-0 (acid-free paper)
 1. Sheep--Early works to 1800. 2. Shepherds--Early works to 1800. 3. Sheep--
France--Early works to 1800. 4. Shepherds--France--Early works to 1800.
 I. Carroll, Carleton W. II. Wilson, Lois Hawley, 1927- III. Arizona Center for
Medieval and Renaissance Studies. IV. Title.
 SF375.B713 2012
 636.3--dc23

                                                                    2012011948

Cover Illustration by Sue Kupillas.

∞
This book is made to last. It is set in Adobe Caslon Pro,
smyth-sewn and printed on acid-free paper to library specifications.
Printed in the United States of America.

TABLE OF CONTENTS

Acknowledgments   *ix*

General Introductory Materials   1
  Background of *Le Bon Berger*   1
  The Shepherd Himself   5
  The Growing Importance of Wool   7
  Written Records   9

Introduction to the Middle French Text   12
  Dating and Authenticity of the Text   12
  Sixteenth-Century Printings   13
  Language of the Vostre Text   22
  Style of the Vostre Text   26
  Editing Principles   28

Le Bon Berger, Middle French Text and English Translation   33
  Jehan de Brye, Le bon bergier   34
  Vostre's Table of Contents   38
  Chapter 1, *Prologue de la vie et estat de Jehan de Brie* / Prologue About   38
    the Life and Status of Jean de Brie
  Chapter 2, *De l'utilité et prouffit de cest traictié* / Concerning the Worth   56
    and Profit of this Treatise
  Chapter 3, *De l'onneur et estat du bergier* / Concerning the Honor and   64
    Profession of the Shepherd
  Chapter 4, *Des reigles generaulx de cest art* / General Rules Concerning   70
    this Art
  Chapter 5, *De la maniere de congnoistre le temps par les oyseaux, et de*   76
    sçavoir du beau temps ou de la pluye / Concerning the Way of Telling
    the Weather by the Birds, and to Know About Fine Weather and Rain

Chapter 6, *De congnoistre le temps par les bestes* / To Know About the   82
Weather by the Animals

Chapter 7, *De la consideracion des vens et lesquelz sont prouffitables* /   88
Consideration of Winds and Which are Beneficial

Chapter 8, *De la vie du bergier et des choses qui luy affierent* / About the   92
Shepherd's Life and the Things that Concern Him

Chapter 9, [*Du mois de janvier*] / Concerning the Month of January   106

Chapter 10, *Du mois de fevrier* / Concerning the Month of February   108

Chapter 11, *Du mois de mars* / Concerning the Month of March   116

Chapter 12, *Du mois d'avril* / Concerning the Month of April   122

Chapter 13, *Du mois de may* / Concerning the Month of May   124

Chapter 14, *Du mois de juing* / Concerning the Month of June   130

Chapter 15, *Du mois de juillet* / Concerning the Month of July   134

Chapter 16, *Du mois d'aoust* / Concerning the Month of August   136

Chapter 17, *Du mois de septembre* / Concerning the Month of September   138

Chapter 18, *De octobre* / Concerning October   140

Chapter 19, *De novembre* / Concerning November   142

Chapter 20, *Du mois de decembre* / Concerning the Month of December   144

Chapter 21, *De la maladie que on dist l'affilee* / Concerning the Malady   144
called Scours

Chapter 22, *Du poucet* / Concerning Pneumonia   146

Chapter 23, *Du bouchet* / Concerning Sore Mouth   146

Chapter 25. *Du clavel* / Concerning Sheep Pox   146

Chapter 26, *De la rongne* / Concerning Mange   146

Chapter 27, *Du poacre* / Concerning Oral Lesions   148

Chapter 28, *De bouverande* / Concerning Swollen Throat   148

Chapter 29, *De la dauve* / Concerning Liver Fluke   148

Chapter 30, *De l'avertin* / Concerning Staggers   148

Chapter 31, *De l'enfleure* / Concerning Bloat   150

Chapter 32, *Le runge* / Concerning Lost Cud   150

Chapter 33, *De l'yrengnier* / Concerning Cobweb Disease   150

Chapter 34, *Autre chapitre des remedes* / Other Chapter of Remedies   150

Chapter 35, *Remede du poucet* / Remedy for Pneumonia   152

Chapter 36, *Remede du bouchet* / Remedy for Sore Mouth   152

Chapter 37, *Remede du clavel* / Remedy for Sheep Pox   152

Chapter 38, *Remede de la rongne* / Remedy for Mange   154

Chapter 39, *Remede du poacre* [*et autres remedes*]; *La seignee des brebis*;   156
La maniere de chatrer et amender les aigneaux; *Du chien du berger* /
Remedy for Oral Lesions [and other remedies]; Bloodletting of Ewes;
Castration; Concerning the Shepherd's Dog

Poem and colophon   166

Textual Notes   171

Supplementary Comments   189

Appendix: Printer's Errors   207

Bibliography   211
    A. Works specific to Jean de Brie and *Le Bon Berger*   211
    B. General and Reference Works   212
    C. Other Medieval and Renaissance Texts   219

Index   221

Acknowledgments

Research and writing are essentially solitary activities, but one often needs the help of others to pursue them. It is a pleasure to indicate the individuals and institutions who have generously shared their knowledge, expertise, and materials with us during the preparation of this book.

We thank the directors and personnel of the numerous libraries whose materials we consulted: the Archives départementales de l'Oise, Beauvais; the Bibliothèque de l'Arsenal, Paris; the Bibliothèque nationale de France, Paris; the Bibliothèque du Musée Thomas Dobrée, Nantes; Guin Library, Hatfield Marine Science Center, Newport, Oregon; Hannon Library, Southern Oregon University, Ashland; the Jackson County (Oregon) Library System; Knight Library, University of Oregon, Eugene; Valley Library, Oregon State University, Corvallis.

The following individuals have helped us in various ways, and we are pleased to thank them publicly for their generosity: Barbara K. Altmann, Gabriel Bianciotto, Leslie C. Brook, Cynthia J. Brown, Maria Colombo Timelli, Kristen Figg, Jean-Marie Fritz, Michael Horvat, Tony Hunt, William Krueger, Norris J. Lacy, Margaret Meierhenry, Martine Meuwese, Mel Morris, James E. Perry, Rupert T. Pickens, Christine Reno, Samuel N. Rosenberg, Maureen Schroeder, Michelle Szkilnik, Jane H.M. Taylor, Claude Thiry, and Lola and Robert Work. We are grateful to Roy Rukkila and Leslie MacCoull, the editorial staff for Medieval and Renaissance Texts and Studies. We also thank the readers who evaluated our manuscript for MRTS; we are grateful for their helpful suggestions. And finally, we are grateful to Sue Kupillas for the cover illustration.

Two people deserve particular mention. The first is Rae S. Baudouin, whose paper, "Froissart's Pastourelle VII and Jean de Brie?," presented at the 1986 annual meeting of the Medieval Association of the Pacific (Stanford University), first introduced us to Jean de Brie. The second is Hart Wilson, whose marvelous computer skills and her generosity in using them were invaluable in bringing this project to completion.

We are especially grateful to our families for their support, which has been indispensable throughout this lengthy project.

General Introductory Materials

Background of *Le Bon Berger*

Because no original manuscript for this book has yet been found, many questions remain about its true date of composition or publication and even its authorship. We are left, at this point, with four printings, no two of which are exactly identical, and an 1879 edition based on one of these printings. The printings were made by four different establishments at various dates and even those dates cannot be completely verified. What is clear, however, is that the real substance of the book was supplied by someone who had been intimately involved with the raising of sheep and who wished to pass along the then "best practices," as they are now called, of sheep husbandry.

The authorship of *Le Bon Berger* is uncertain because of the many allusions it contains that could justifiably be considered scholarly, raising the question of how a "simple" shepherd could know these things. The life of Jean de Brie, as related in the first chapter of his treatise, may suggest a possibility for such knowledge but certainly does not assure it. He rose from a child given the care of tending geese in the country to an adult holding positions of trust and authority in his patrons' establishments, in Brie[1] and in Paris. In that environment he rose to relatively elevated positions of responsibility in the service of Arnoul de Grant Pont, treasurer of the Sainte Chapelle, and subsequently that of Jehan de Hetomesnil, king's councillor, Master of Requests of his household and canon of the Sainte Chapelle of the royal palace.[2] There de Brie may have had the opportunity for self-improvement or at least perhaps for observing the correct fashions for doing things and making sure that his book conformed to those fashions.

It is possible—even likely—that Jean de Brie dictated his text, and that it was written down by someone else.[3] In the dedication we find the statement that

---

[1] Cf. F. Lebert, "La Ferme de Nolongues et le bon berger Jehan de Brie," *Bulletin de la Société littréaire et historique de la Brie* 13 (1934): 133–38.

[2] H. Quignon, "Jehan de Brie, auteur du *Bon Berger* et son protecteur Jehan de Hétomesnil (xive siècle)," *Procès-verbaux et Mémoires de la Société d'Etudes historiques et scientifiques de l'Oise* 2 (1906): 173–77.

[3] Roger Grand and Raymond Delatouche, *L'Agriculture au moyen âge de la fin de l'empire romain au xvie siècle* (Paris: Boccard, 1950), 496; Frankwalt Möhren, "Analyse

Jean de Brie "a dit, nommé, **fait compiler et escrire** cest traictié" [has related, entitled, and had compiled and written this treatise] (2.08–10),[4] while in the concluding lines of chapter 2 we read "Par ces raisons et autres assez meilleur[e]s que
Jehan de Brie **ne fait pas mettre en escript** [. . .]" (26.04–06) [For these reasons
and others even better which Jean de Brie has not had written down . . . .] As
Holmér says, "Ces deux citations paraissent confirmer que Jean de Brie avait un
assistant en composant son traité, et que celui-ci était un lettré chargé de rédiger
les matériaux que Jean avait mis à sa disposition" [These two quotations seem to
confirm that Jean de Brie had an assistant in composing his treatise, and that
that person was a man of letters charged with writing up the materials Jean had
placed at his disposal.][5]

The assistant may have been Jean Corbechon (or Corbichon), from whom
Charles V had commissioned a French translation of *De proprietatibus rerum*
(*Concerning the Properties of Things*), by Bartholomew the Englishman,[6] as well
as Pietro de Crescenzi's *Ruralium commodorum liber*,[7] a sort of agronomical encyclopedia.[8] "Ce grand ouvrage, plein de faits, de conseils judicieux, de notions
pratiques excellentes, fut traduit en plusieurs langues et spécialement en français, par ordre du roi Charles V, sous le titre de *Livre des Prouffits champestres
et ruraux*"[9] ["This great work, replete with information, judicious advice, and
excellent practical notions, was translated into several languages, and especially
into French, by order of King Charles V, and called 'Livre des Prouffits cham-

---

sémantique structurale et contexte: Les dénominations du mouton dans des textes techniques," in *Actes du IVᵉ Colloque International sur le Moyen Français*, ed. Anthonij Dees
(Amsterdam: Rodopi, 1985), 119–42, here 133, 139 n. 52.

[4] The notation "2.08–10" stands for page 2, lines 8–10 of the Vostre printing (see below, 13–14). The passage in question can be found in our edited text, between the brack-
eted page indications [2] and [3]. Since the Vostre text contains 25 lines per page, these
lines are a bit closer to the "[2]" than to the "[3]".

[5] Gustaf Holmér, "Jean de Brie et son traité de l'art de bergerie," *Studia Neophilologica* 39 (1967): 128–49, here 148.

[6] Translated into French in 1372: Philippe Contamine, *La Vie quotidienne pendant
la Guerre de Cent Ans: France et Angleterre (XIVᵉ siècle)* (Paris: Hachette, 1976), 48.

[7] Paul Lacroix, in *Le Bon Berger, ou Le vray régime et gouvernement des bergers et
bergères, composé par le rustique Jehan de Brie, le bon berger: réimprimé sur l'édition de Paris
(1541)* (Paris: Liseux, 1879), xiv; Léopold Delisle, *Recherches sur la librairie de Charles V,
roi de France, 1337–1380*, 2 vols. (Paris: Champion, 1907; repr. Amsterdam: van Heusden, 1967), 1: 91–92, 230–35; Grand and Delatouche, *L'agriculture au moyen âge*, 496.

[8] This work is sometimes referred to as *Opus ruralium commodorum*. The author's
name appears in many forms: Petrus de Crescentius, Pierre de Crescens, etc.

[9] Paul Lacroix, *Sciences et lettres au Moyen Age et à l'époque de la Renaissance* (Paris:
Firmin-Didot, 1877), 127.

pestres et ruraux'.]"[10] But the identity of Jean de Brie's assistant—if indeed there was one—must remain a matter of speculation.

According to the opening paragraph of the work, *Le Bon Berger* is dedicated to Charles V, at whose behest the treatise was composed; it is dated 1379, said to be the sixteenth year of that king's reign (2.05, 2.13–14). He had acceded to the throne in 1364, and reigned until his death in 1380.[11]

Guérard describes Charles V as ". . . a unique exception, in the long royal line. Weak in body, of scholarly mien and tastes, a 'seated king' after so many fighters on horseback, he shunned the battlefield . . . was called the Wise, which, in the language of the time, meant the Learned, but also the Prudent."[12] He was famous for fostering learning.[13] He collected texts in Latin and Greek and subsidized their translation into French. In addition to ancient texts, his library included translations from other languages, and literary works of the French nation.[14] The Royal Library, founded by Charles in 1367, formed the basis for the French national library, the Bibliothèque nationale de France. Claire Sherman has reproduced a number of portraits of the king accepting books from various scribes, illustrating his interest in scholarly pursuits.[15] Regrettably, however, we have no proof of the assertion that he ordered the composition of *Le Bon Berger*. Works such as Calmette's *Charles V*[16] and Quillet's *Charles V le roi lettré* make no mention of our text. We must accept on faith the declaration of the dedicatory paragraph.

Why would the king of France have been interested in a book on shepherdry, the science of raising sheep? A quick look at the major imports and exports of England and France makes that interest apparent. Already established since Roman times, by the Middle Ages sheep-raising had long been honored in France. It was immensely more extensive than today, with more pasture available, including larger wasteland areas and fields of stubble accessible after harvest.[17]

---

[10] Paul Lacroix, *Science and Literature in the Middle Ages and the Renaissance* (New York: Ungar, 1964), 114.

[11] Jeannine Quillet, *Charles V le roi lettré: Essai sur la pensée politique d'un règne* (Paris: Librairie Académique Perrin, 1984), 351–52.

[12] Albert Guérard, *France: A Modern History*, rev. Paul A. Gagnon (Ann Arbor: University of Michigan Press, 1969), 104.

[13] F. Autrand, "France under Charles V and Charles VI," in *The New Cambridge Medieval History*, vol. 6, *c.1300–c.1415*, ed. M. Jones (Cambridge: Cambridge University Press, 2000), 422–41, esp. 423–26.

[14] Joan Evans, *Life in Medieval France* (London: Phaidon, 1969), 114.

[15] Claire Richter Sherman, *The Portraits of Charles V of France (1338–1380)* (New York: New York University Press, for the College Art Association of America, 1979).

[16] Joseph Calmette, *Charles V* (Paris: Arthème Fayard, 1945).

[17] P. Freedman, "Rural Society," in *New Cambridge Medieval History*, vol. 6, ed. Jones, 82–101.

Above all, it was the wool that was economically important.[18] Gimpel points to wool as the major raw material and explains that "tens of millions" of fleeces were processed every year.[19] He also mentions the "educational boom of the twelfth century" and the subsequent rise in demand for parchment, adding that selective breeding practices[20] must have taken place since the size of parchment increased over the twelfth and thirteenth centuries.[21] Southern asserts that the large-scale production of wool and cloth manufacture were what made western Europe an important export area in the Middle Ages, and compares that industrial impact with the production of coal in England.[22] Henisch reminds us that the importance of the wool economy can be seen even today at Chartres Cathedral on the left door of the north portal, where there are six figures that are involved in some facet of wool production.[23]

A book such as de Brie's *Le Bon Berger* was particularly important because any kind of systematic knowledge about agricultural practices was severely lacking in his time. His straightforward month-by-month recital of the practical aspects of sheep-raising from the shepherd's point of view certainly qualified to be included with the more learned treatises in the king's library.

Until the advent of merchants and manufacturers, records in medieval western Europe were kept mostly by clerics and did not reflect the practices of everyday life. Of the records kept, the most accurate were found in legal documents or agreements, the number of which greatly increased in the High Middle Ages. Written material such as the songs of poets, the wins and losses of the battles in the works of chroniclers, and records and ancient lore preserved by the church told very little of the functions that provided the staples of life. The people doing the actual work were either illiterate or too busy working to do more than pass on information by word of mouth, as de Brie recommends in Chapter 9. Cherubini points out that what records did exist were often untrustworthy and that "except in extremely rare instances, peasants have left no direct testimony of themselves, and reports from other levels of society—the clergy, nobles, merchants,

---

[18] Grand and Delatouche, *L'agriculture au moyen âge*, 489; P. Spufford, "Trade in Fourteenth-century Europe," in *New Cambridge Medieval History*, vol. 6, ed. Jones, 155–208, esp. 162, 167–69, 196–97, 202 on the wool trade.

[19] Jean Gimpel, *The Medieval Machine: The Industrial Revolution of the Middle Ages* (New York: Holt, Rinehart & Winston, 1976), 46.

[20] On these see F. Audoin-Rouzeau, "Compter et mesurer les animaux," *Histoire et mesure* 10 (1995): 277–312; R. Delort and F. Audoin-Rouzeau, eds., *L'élevage médiéval*, spec. no. of *Ethnozootechnie* 59 (1997).

[21] Gimpel, *Medieval Machine*, 45.

[22] R.W. Southern, *The Making of the Middle Ages* (New Haven: Yale University Press, 1953), 177.

[23] Bridget Ann Henisch, *The Medieval Calendar Year* (University Park: Penn State University Press, 1999), 85.

artisans—often give a distorted or at best an indirect picture of them."[24] Yet Lucas estimates that 90% of that society were peasants, the other 10% being divided almost equally between nobles and clergy.[25] Duby mentions an abundance of books about agricultural practices written for an educated lay public in the late thirteenth century.[26]

As trade increased, supported by a more settled and less nomadic lifestyle, the need for knowledge of profit and loss as well as the finer points of agriculture became obvious for the maintenance of large *seigneuries*. Hollister mentions the greater need for the skills of reading, writing, and mathematical calculation as important to expanding business, government, and church.[27] Jean de Brie's treatise provided precisely the sort of down-to-earth information needed for one of the most important economic activities of the time. It allows the modern reader to enter a rarely glimpsed aspect of the medieval world.

The Shepherd Himself

When one hears the word "shepherd," the mind's eye conjures up a solitary figure on a green hill with fluffy white sheep pasturing docilely at his feet, his faithful dog lying nearby. An idyllic scene, true, and "viewed from a safe distance, his work appeared to consist mainly of sitting in meadows, watching over gentle flocks, and whiling away the hours with a little music or flirtation,"[28] but that scene does not take into account the long hours of watching and waiting, the brushes with predators, nor the perils inherent in lambing. This view does not acknowledge his "unremitting watchfulness and skill."[29]

The shepherd meant income to the owners of the sheep he was tending, and he enjoyed the owner's protection since their profit and loss were of great economic importance. His honesty and attention to their interests gave him a

---

[24] Giovanni Cherubini, "The Peasant and Agriculture," in *Time, Work, and Culture in the Middle Ages*, ed. Jacques Le Goff, trans. Arthur Goldhammer (Chicago: University of Chicago Press, 1980), 113–38, here 131.

[25] Henry S. Lucas, *A Short History of Civilization* (New York: McGraw-Hill, 1943), 369.

[26] Georges Duby, *L'Economie rurale et la vie des campagnes dans l'Occident médiéval (France, Angleterre, Empire, IXe–XVe siècles): Essai de synthèse et perspectives de recherches*, 2 vols. (Paris: Aubier, 1962), 1: 170; idem, *Rural Economy and Country Life in the Medieval West*, trans. Cynthia Postan, 2 vols. (Columbia: University of South Carolina Press; London: Edward Arnold, 1968), 88.

[27] C. Warren Hollister, *Medieval Europe: A Short History*, 5th ed. (New York: Knopf, 1982), 149.

[28] Henisch, *Calendar Year*, 98–99.

[29] Columella, *On Agriculture*, trans. Harrison Boyd Ash (Cambridge, MA: Harvard University Press, 1960), 97.

certain status that, landless, he might not otherwise have enjoyed. In the case of de Brie, it gave him access to the household of his lord, both in the country and in Paris, and opportunities that he might never have had as a simple peasant. The shepherd was employed not only to be responsible for the animals' well-being, but also to make sure of their increase and to protect the value of their end products: wool, meat, pelts, and hides. He was often involved in breeding programs to upgrade his lord's sheep.[30] All of this meant that a higher level of decision-making was called for than in most occupations of the day, setting him slightly apart from his fellows, although his dress and his opportunity for education were the same. Because the shepherd's occupation was a lonely one, he was often suspect to villagers.[31] His practice of veterinary skills also differentiated him. At all times he needed to have the right medical equipment and the requisite knowledge to use it. Happily, we see that in de Brie's case the opportunity to have more contacts with his superiors led to opportunities for self-improvement. He was able to dictate this book and have it admitted to the royal library, tangible proof that de Brie was able to profit from these advantages. In so doing, he has provided us with this excellent view of the shepherdry of his time.[32]

Kaiser-Guyot remarks that "Rattaché à un centre d'exploitation agricole, responsable d'un troupeau de taille moyenne, le pâtre sédentaire pratique véritablement l'art de bergerie, tel que le traité de Jean de Brie le reflète. Sur les terres cultivées, il doit garder attentivement son troupeau, qui joue un rôle capital dans l'équilibre de l'économie agricole médiévale" [Attached to a central agricultural enterprise, responsible for a flock of medium size, the sedentary shepherd truly practiced the art of shepherdry, as the treatise of Jean de Brie reflects. On cultivated ground he must keep an attentive watch over his flock, which plays a role of capital importance in the medieval agronomic economy.][33] He had to be ready at all times to act upon his own initiative, to use his judgment in the field, to count and account for all his charges: sheep having no defense mechanisms of their own and a propensity for getting caught in hedges or suffering other mishaps.

In Chapter 8, de Brie details the shepherd's clothing and his tools and, no less importantly, his moral values and where he fits into the social and work order of his day. He also acknowledges two of his best management tools: his dog

---

[30] See G. Comet, "Animal Husbandry," and J. Langdon, "Animals, Domestic, Draught, and Wild," in *Oxford Dictionary of the Middle Ages* (hereafter *ODMA*), ed. R. Bjork, 4 vols. (Oxford: Oxford University Press, 2010), 1: 62–63, and G. Comet, "Stock Breeding and Selection," in *ODMA* 4: 1574–75.

[31] Henisch, *Calendar Year*, 95.

[32] See D. Hüe, "Le berger à la fin du Moyen Âge: remarques sur une figure trifonctionnelle," in *Remembrances et resveries: Hommage à Jean Batany*, ed. H. Legros et al. (Orléans: Paradigme, 2006), 117–38.

[33] Marie-Thérèse Kaiser-Guyot, *Le Berger en France aux XIVᵉ et XVᵉ siècles* (Paris: Klincksieck, 1974), 147.

and his crook. The collar that Varro describes in the first century B.C.[34] sounds very similar to the one that de Brie puts on his dog in the fourteenth of our era, though the description of his crook in this chapter varies greatly from what is often depicted today.

De Brie's work stands alone as a written testimonial to the practical aspects of sheep-raising at this time, but sheep appeared in the stained glass windows of churches and in calendars from the twelfth century on, reflecting their cultural and economic importance. Shepherds do not appear until much later and are shown in March in the sign of the Ram and also in June at shearing.[35] "The name often given to the tradition [of calendars] is 'The Labors of the Months' but in fact by the end of the medieval period it had become the cycle of occupations . . . ."[36] Because the calendars showed the peasants at work, they carried a double message. On the one hand they indicated to the faithful "la nécessité du labeur qui est une rançon du péché original (Genèse)" [the necessity of work, which is a ransom for original sin (Genesis)],[37] and on the other hand they were a representation of wealth and profit to be gained. By the end of the fifteenth century, there were Books of Hours and dramatic scenes glorifying shepherds — who after all did visit the Christ Child (Luke 2: 8–20) — as equal to the magi.[38]

The Growing Importance of Wool

It has been suggested that the transition from arable agriculture to animal husbandry in the form of sheep-farming in the late Middle Ages was inspired by its lower cost of production (and of wages in particular), since this kind of farming needed very few workers for its size. The primary factor that made the transition possible was the growing demand for wool.[39] "Les bêtes à laine, moutons et brebis étaient beaucoup plus nombreuses que les bovidés. Elles donnaient à la fois la viande, le cuir et la laine aux industries de la région" [Wool-bearing animals,

---

[34] Varro, *Roman Farm Management*, trans. Fairfax Harrison (New York: Macmillan, 1918), 254.

[35] Henisch, *Calendar Year*, 90, fig. 4–3.

[36] Bridget Ann Henisch, "In Due Season: Farm Work in the Medieval Calendar Tradition," in *Agriculture in the Middle Ages: Technology, Practice, and Representation*, ed. Del Sweeney (Philadelphia: University of Pennsylvania Press, 1995), 309–36, here 310.

[37] Perrine Mane, *Calendriers et techniques agricoles (France-Italie, XIIe–XIIIe siècles)* (Paris: Le Sycomore, 1983), 16. The allusion is to Genesis 3:19.

[38] Kaiser-Guyot, *Berger*, 133.

[39] See *Produzione, commercio e consumo dei panni della lanna (secoli XII–XVIII)*, ed. M. Spallanzani (Florence: Olschki, 1976); D. Jenkins, ed., *The Cambridge History of Western Textiles*, 2 vols. (Cambridge: Cambridge University Press, 2003); M. F. Mazzaoui, "Wool," *ODMA* 4: 1770.

rams and ewes, were much more numerous than cattle. At one and the same time they gave food, leather, and wool to the region's industries.][40]

It is paradoxical that a substance grown naturally on the backs of sheep, the least bellicose of animals, should provide the wherewithal that allowed kingdoms and armies to engage in conflict and to ruin the countries over which they carried on their campaigns. England's King Edward III financed a huge share of the Hundred Years War with taxes on wool. He extorted silver from his woolgrowers at the rate of two marks (26s. 8d.) in silver plate for every sack of wool they shipped.[41] Postan and Miller say that records show that between the thirteenth and fourteenth centuries this was annually about 35,000–40,000 sacks of wool, about 15 million tons.[42] Other than a few comments relating directly to agriculture in France during that particular time, it is not in the purview of this book to review the Hundred Years War (1328–1453) between England and France at any length except as it affected the shepherd and his profession. The war caused disruption of trade in wool, cloth, and dyes; losses in agriculture of feed from fields left fallow or torn up by clashing forces; money diverted or depleted from breeding programs as well as actual injury to animals and personnel; loss of record-keeping; and pestilence.

One of the conditions that favored raising sheep in de Brie's time was the amount of open space that could be utilized for their feed. The Black Death had decreased population and made more fallow land available, and because France was settled in a nuclear pattern, there were wide spaces between towns and baronies. One of the economic virtues of sheep was that they could take advantage of waste areas and fields, either fallow or harvested, where they could glean the grain that had been spilled, clean out weeds, and supply fertilizer for the revitalization of the next year's crop. Because of the more primitive reaping methods, there was a considerable amount of grain left on the ground. Although a boon to the foraging animals, this sometimes led to bloat, as de Brie mentions in his book.

As well as supplying meat, milk, cheese, and end products such as leather, parchment, tallow, lanolin, and strings for musical instruments and weapons, most importantly sheep also provided the wool that was a foundation of a booming trade at this time, one that bolstered the income of small families and manors alike and also fostered international trade. In addition, sheep products were easily transported, a bonus in that time. Large flocks were maintained and breeding was upgraded to produce better wool, mostly using Spain's fine-wool merinos.

---

[40] Yvonne Bezard, *La Vie rurale, dans le sud de la région parisienne, de 1450 à 1560* (Paris: Firmin-Didot, 1929), 164.

[41] John H.A. Munro, *Wool, Cloth, and Gold: The Struggle for Bullion in Anglo-Burgundian Trade, 1340–1478* (Toronto: University of Toronto Press, 1972), 36.

[42] M.M. Postan and Edward Miller, *The Cambridge Economic History of Europe*, vol. 2, *Trade and Industry in the Middle Ages* (Cambridge: Cambridge University Press, 1963), 180.

Over time different areas of France developed their own characteristic breeds. As we have seen, Henisch points to the figures on the north portal of Chartres cathedral, all of whom are engaged in wool production, as indicating the importance of wool and the cloth trade.[43] De Brie mentions how important even the snippets of wool are to his lord. The manufacture of cloth and woolen articles, whether from home spinning or commercial drapery, encouraged the growth of dyestuffs, some of which came from Mediterranean areas or from the north, red dyes, "kermes" from Spain and Portugal, or archil, a lichen, a violet dye from Norway, and blue woad from Picardy and elsewhere. The availability of wool led to the drapery trade and its further expansion through commerce. This expansion was in part due to the mechanical inventions that occurred and were implemented in the medieval era. Lynn White points out the importance of substituting mechanical labor for human effort and the immense changes thus effected: the use of water and wind instead of manpower, the discovery in the thirteenth century of the spring and treadle, with gear development in the fourteenth leading to a huge leap in productivity. "The spinning wheel is mechanically interesting not only because it is the first instance of the belt transmission of power and a notably early example of the flywheel principle, but because it focused attention upon the problem of producing and controlling various rates of speed in different moving parts of the same machine."[44] This was the beginning of the industrialization of the woolen industry that encouraged the rise of large flocks and the upgrading of the quality of their wool.

Written Records

In studying the more brilliant achievements of civilization, we often forget the common man, whose daily toil provided the economic and social bases of life. We think only of the deeds of great men and ignore traders, peasants, and craftsmen because we imagine they produced nothing important. This view has been popular with historians, but it is incorrect.[45]

The poets sang, the chroniclers totted up wins and losses on the battlefield, the church added canons and copied ancient lore, yet very little was done to make a record of the functions that provided the staples of daily life. The people tilling the land, planting, harvesting, and tending to domestic animals were either too busy or too unlettered to keep a written record of what they were doing and how, instead passing on information orally, as farmers around the world still do,

---

[43] Henisch, *Calendar Year*, 85.

[44] Lynn White Jr., *Medieval Technology and Social Change* (London: Oxford University Press, 1971), 119.

[45] Lucas, *Short History*, 369.

practicing what de Brie himself recommends in Chapter 9 of his book. Although there were a number of books circulating in Europe that had to do with agriculture, their audience was not the man on the ground who might have profited most. "The man who held the spade did not hold the pen."[46]

Lucas points out that the very foundation of medieval society was its agriculture, and he disagrees with those who claim that, because of this, they were "backward and static," saying that instead agriculture reflected a major change because it was an "advanced" form of economy and allowed people to give up a nomadic lifestyle.[47] Accurate information about shifts in agriculture is hard to assess because of its basic and non-intellectual appeal to historians, resulting in unevenness in reporting.

There were, however, books about agricultural pursuits. We have already mentioned Pietro de Crescenzi's *Ruralium commodorum liber*. This agronomical encyclopedia was not unique in its genre. As Evans states, "The work of Frenchmen of the later Middle Ages was less to increase the sum of learning than to make the sum more profitable."[48] According to Duby, "Tout homme riche entendait vivre de son bien et du travail de ses domestiques. Cette attitude d'esprit explique que l'intérêt pour la littérature agronomique n'ait en rien tiédi pendant les deux derniers siècles du Moyen Age, qu'il apparaisse si vif dans ces hôtels urbains où vivaient désormais beaucoup de notables" ["Every wealthy man expected to live off the produce of his own land and by the labour of his own servants. This attitude of mind explains why there was no waning in the interest shown in agrarian literature during the last two centuries of the Middle Ages and why it was eagerly perused in the town houses where so many notabilities now lived."[49]]

There was a much fuller documentation of charters and capitularies containing valuable information in the north of France, perhaps tied to the years of relative peace around 1450–1460.[50] Therefore the lack of early information may be attributed to several reasons, including the turbulent times. Fortunately, there are legal documents which do contain specific information about land use from which to draw conclusions. These are found in "'documents of practice'—donations, sales, exchanges, leases, and so forth,"[51] manifestations of what is termed "pragmatic literacy," which can be used as evidence for an accurate record of early agrarian life. Hollister points to a huge increase in documentation in the High

---

[46] Sweeney, ed., *Agriculture*, 7, citing Michael Camille, "When Adam Delved: Laboring on the Land in English Medieval Art," ibid., 247–76.

[47] Lucas, *Short History*, 369.

[48] Evans, *Medieval France*, 114.

[49] Duby, *Economie rurale*, 2:579; idem, *Rural Economy*, 317.

[50] Bezard, *Vie rurale*, 5.

[51] David Herlihy, "Land, Family and Women in Continental Europe, 701–1200," *Traditio* 18 (1962): 89–120, here 92.

Middle Ages, which he claims changed basic attitudes and encouraged a more "systematic" approach to all human endeavors, including farm management, adding that all across Europe, skills such as reading, writing, and mathematical calculation were becoming vital to the functioning of secular and ecclesiastical governments, urban businesses, and even agricultural enterprises.[52]

---

[52] Hollister, *Medieval Europe*, 149.

Introduction to the Middle French Text

Dating and Authenticity of the Text

Some scholars have disputed the authenticity or the date of our text. Henri Hauser asserted that the text was written "en pure langue du xvɪᵉ siècle" [in pure language of the sixteenth century],[1] but he offered no textual evidence in support of this statement, which was roundly criticized by Antoine Thomas, who called the affirmation "stupéfiante" [amazing, astounding.][2] Perhaps the most extraordinary analysis of our text is that of Charles Lenient, for whom the treatise is largely allegorical, partly satirical and partly political, "mélange de douce ironie et de conseils affectueux" [a mixture of gentle irony and affectionate advice];[3] it is "un appel à la paix, à la concorde, à l'usage modéré du pouvoir chez les grands, à la docilité chez les petits, après les abus, les misères et les folies du règne précédent" [a call for peace, for concord, for the moderate use of power on the part of the great, for docility on the part of the humble, after the abuses, calamities and follies of the preceding reign.][4] For Lenient, the treatise may even have been dictated in part by the king himself.[5]

In his "Notice sur Jehan de Brie" Paul Lacroix wrote that, in the absence of a manuscript, one must be satisfied with the abridged version made from it at the beginning of the sixteenth century (*Le Bon Berger*, ed. Lacroix, vɪ); later he refers to what we have as an analytical excerpt (xv). But, as Holmér points out, Lacroix gives no indication of the reasons that made him consider the surviving version of *Le Bon Berger* an abridgement.[6]

Holmér presents the tentative conclusion that the text that has come down to us "constitue un remaniement de la rédaction primitive, composée en 1379 par Jean lui-même" [constitutes a reworking of the earliest text, composed in 1379 by Jean himself.][7] Möhren echoes this idea: "La langue du texte paraît tellement rajeunie qu'il vaut mieux parler d'un remaniement que l'on ne peut que dater du

---

[1] Henri Hauser, "Une Bévue du Bibliophile Jacob sur Jehan de Brie," *Revue d'Histoire Littéraire de la France* 19 (1912): 407–8, here 408.

[2] Antoine Thomas, "A propos de Jehan de Brie," *Romania* 42 (1913): 85–87, here 86.

[3] Charles Lenient, *La Satire en France au Moyen Age*, 5th ed. (Paris: Hachette, 1912), 224.

[4] Lenient, *Satire*, 225.

[5] Lenient, *Satire*, 222, 225; cf. Mickaël Wilmart, "L'homme face à la mort de l'animal: Pratiques, savoirs et croyances des bergers du xɪvᵉ siècle d'après la traité de Jean de Brie (1379)," in *La Mort écrite: Rites et réthoriques [sic] du trépas au Moyen Âge*, Actes de la Journée d'études du groupe «Questes» (Paris-Sorbonne), 26 avril 2003, ed. Estelle Doudet (Paris: Presses de l'Université Paris-Sorbonne, 2005), 137–53, here 140 n. 7.

[6] Holmér, "Jean de Brie," 146.

[7] Holmér, "Jean de Brie," 148.

début du xvıᵉ siècle" [The language of the text appears rejuvenated to such a degree that is preferable to speak of a recasting or adaptation which can be dated only from the beginning of the sixteenth century.][8]

It is, of course, regrettable that we have no manuscript of this text and must rely instead on printed versions much more recent than the date of composition found in the dedicatory opening (2.13). We accept that date at face value, however, conceding that Vostre or his typesetter may indeed have "rejuvenated" the language to some extent. This text is in any case much closer to the original text than that published by Lacroix, based on the Jonot printing of 1541/2 but with many modernized spellings.

Sixteenth-Century Printings

Le Bon Berger is preserved in four sixteenth-century editions. Each of these exists in a single copy; our efforts to find additional printings or additional copies have proven unsuccessful. Lacroix felt that the manuscript "a dû certainement faire partie de la bibliothèque des rois Charles V et Charles VI, et . . . fut peut-être acheté par le duc de Bedford avec les principaux manuscrits de cette célèbre bibliothèque" [must certainly have been part of the library of Kings Charles V and Charles VI, and . . . may have been purchased by the Duke of Bedford, along with the principal manuscripts of that famous library],[9] and speculated that it might yet be found in some English library.

The 16th-century printings

For each we give the siglum, the name of the printer, the place and date of publication, if known, and the present location and catalogue number (shelf-mark) of the surviving copy. We then give various details: format and foliotation; wording and layout of the title page; number of lines per full page of text; running headers; the presence or absence of catch-words; woodcuts, if any; historiated initials and any other decorations; colophon or other end-matter. Finally, we list bibliographical references, in short-title form and in chronological order.

V   Simon Vostre. Paris, undated, probably between 1486 and 1520 (Holmér, "Jean de Brie," 130–32).

Paris, Bibliothèque nationale de France, Rés. S 1001.

Small in-8° gothic, 52 ff.

Title page: Jehan de brye Le bon bergier. The beginning of the dedication follows immediately, below the woodcut.

Twenty-five lines per page.

---

[8] Möhren, "Dénominations du mouton," 133.
[9] Lacroix, *Le Bon Berger*, vi.

No running headers.
No catch-words.

Woodcuts: Title page, presentation scene, shepherd (with dog and crook), king, two observers.

No historiated initials or decorative borders. A four-line decorative initial *A* at the beginning of the text; two-line initials marking chapters and other textual divisions.

Colophon:
⊄ Cy fine la vie du bon bergier Jehan de
brie nouuellement imprimee / pour Symon
vostre libraire demourant a la rue neufue
nostre dame a lymage saint iehan leuange-
liste.

Bibliography: Jacques-Charles Brunet, *Manuel du libraire et de l'amateur de livres*, 5ᵉ éd. (Paris: Maisonneuve & Larose, n.d.; repr. Mayenne: Joseph Floch, 1965), 1: 1256; Lacroix, *Le Bon Berger*, x; *Catalogue général des livres imprimés de la Bibliothèque nationale* (Paris: Imprimerie Nationale, 1923), 77: 657; Holmér, "Jean de Brie," 129.

T   Widow of Jehan Trepperel and Jehan Jehannot. Paris, undated, probably between 1512 and 1522 (Holmér, "Jean de Brie," 130–31).
Nantes, Musée Dobrée, imp. 328.
Small in-8° gothic, 52 ff.

Title page: IEhan de brye le bon bergier.

Twenty-five lines per page (page breaks are almost always identical to those in *V*).

No running headers.
No catch-words.

Woodcuts: Title page, presentation scene, shepherd (with dog and crook), king, two observers. *T*'s woodcut may have been copied from *V*'s. It is extremely similar, but slightly less carefully executed.

No historiated initials or decorative borders. Two-line or three-line initials marking chapter headings and other textual divisions.[10]

---

[10]   Forty-one three-line initials, 15 two-line initials.

Colophon:

> Cy finist la vie du
> bon bergier Jehan de brie Nouuelle-
> ment imprimee a Paris par la veuf
> ue feu iehan trepperel et Jehan
> iehannot demourans en la
> rue neufue nostre dame
> a lenseigne de lescu
> de france

Bibliography: Brunet, *Manuel*, 1: 1256; Lacroix, *Le Bon Berger*, vii; Louis Polain, *Catalogue de la Bibliothèque du Musée Thomas Dobrée*, vol. 2, *Imprimés* (Nantes: Musée Thomas Dobrée, 1903), 185–87; Holmér, "Jean de Brie," 129; Roméo Arbour, *Dictionnaire des femmes libraires en France (1470–1870)* (Geneva: Droz, 2003), 504.

J   Denys Jonot [*sic*, for Janot], Paris, 1542.
Paris, Bibliothèque de l'Arsenal RES 8 S 7784.[11]
Small[12] in-16 gothic, 72 ff.

Title page:

> Le vray regi-
> me & gouvernement des Bergers
> & Bergeres:compose par le
> rustique Jehan de Brie
> le bon Berger.
>
> M. D. XLJJ.
>
> A Paris: en limprimerie de De
> nys Jonot imprimeur
> & libraire.

Twenty-one lines per page.
Running headers, all pages except for "Table " and "Le prologue":
    left: Le gouuernement
    right: des Bergers
No catch-words.
Two- or three-line initials mark some chapters and other textual divisions; in other cases space was left for an initial to be added by hand but none was executed.

---

[11] Holmér indicates that the shelf-mark of this volume is A 112 ("Jean de Brie," 129).
[12] The pages measure about 72mm wide by 113mm high (2 13/16 by 4 1/2 inches).

No colophon.

Explicit: Fin de Jehan de Brie le bon berger.

Bibliography: Brunet, *Manuel*, 1: 1256 (who states that this edition had first appeared undated, around 1530); Lacroix, *Le Bon Berger*, VII–X (Lacroix used this printing for his 1879 edition); Holmér, "Jean de Brie," 129.

B   Jean Bogart, Louvain, 1594.
Nantes, Musée Dobrée, imp. 329.
Small in-8° gothic,[13] 48 ff.

Title page:

Le

Vray regime

et gouvernement

des bergers et berge-

res: compose par le rv-

stique iehan de brie le

bon Berger.

[woodcut]

A Louvain.

De l'Imprimerie de Jean Bogart, Impri-

meur iuré, l'An M. D. XCIIII.

Twenty-nine lines per page.
Running headers, all pages except for dedication, "Table" and "Le prologue":
    left: Le gouuernement
    right: des Bergers.
Catch-words, all pages.

Woodcuts: Title page; chapters 2, 3, 5, 6, and 7.

Historiated initials: Prologue; chapter 5. Three-line initials marking chapter headings and other textual divisions.[14]

Decorative border: Dedication (p. 1).

Explicit: Fin de Jehan de Brie le bon berger.

---

[13] Brunet observed that the use of gothic characters in this printing was remarkable, given the time of publication (*Manuel*, 1: 1256, cited by Lacroix, *Le Bon Berger*, x).

[14] In three cases, where the initial falls at the beginning of the second-last line on the page, it is only two lines high.

Imprimatur: Ce livre contenant le vray regime des Bergers se polra imprimer sans offense de la Religion Catholicque. Nicolas de Leuze à Fraxinis, Licentié en Theologie, commis à la visitation des Livres.

No colophon.

Bibliography: Brunet, *Manuel*, 1: 1256; Lacroix, *Le Bon Berger*, x; Polain, *Catalogue*, 187; Holmér, "Jean de Brie," 130.

Textual groupings

These early printings fall into two groups, *TV* and *BJ* (Holmér, "Jean de Brie," 130). Although our listing of variants from *J* is incomplete (cf. "Editing Principles", below), the partial variants reveal many cases where *B* and *J* share a reading different from that shared by *T* and *V*. Many of these involve relatively minor differences in vocabulary, usage, or word-forms, but some are more substantive, involving a significant difference in vocabulary. A few examples:

42.18[15] sert *TV*, sort *BJ*
44.21 feroit *TV*, seroit *BJ*
48.10 les vens *TV*, les ungs *BJ*
66.15–16 repairent *TV*, reviennent *BJ*
72.25 souloient *TV*, fait *BJ*
91.24 vertu *TV*, nature *BJ*
96.21 male *TV*, malade *BJ*

In some cases, *BJ* share a reading we feel is more correct than that shared by *TV*. See the rejected readings for 25.22–23, 53.03, 54.03, 69.10, 89.03, 91.22, 92.18. In other cases it is *BJ* that are in error, e.g., 42.03, where the printers did not realize that *nulz hommes mortelz* was a singular subject, and printed the plural verb *pourroient*. There are several cases where a word or expression present in *TV* is omitted by *BJ*. On the other hand, *BJ* add a heading not present in *TV*, immediately preceding the title of Chapter 21.

---

[15] Page and line references are to Vostre.

Additional Remarks on the Bogart and Trepperel Printings

The Trepperel Text

Evidence suggests that the Trepperel printing was based on the Vostre. Not only is the overall page layout the same, 25 lines per page, but from page 5[16] to the end of the text almost every page begins with the exact same word in the two printings[17]—even when a word is divided between the last line on one page and the first line on the following page.[18]

Other indications that *T* is based on *V* include:

Shared Errors:
   8.24 *piees* (*pies* B)
   13.11 *foue* (for *fouc*, found elsewhere)
   41.12–13 *meilleurs et* repeated (these words are not repeated in *B*)
   53.03 erroneous paragraph sign ("℃") and *Et* (not present in *B*)
   53.23 *contres* (*contre* B)
   72.25 *souloient* (*fait* BJ)
   92.18 *praignent* (*preigne* BJ)

Typography:
   48.02 use of *vv* (lower-case *v*, twice in succession) in *vvest* (*vuest* B)
   60.05 use of letter *l* plus round *r* to improvise the letter *k* (upper-case *K*, *B*)
   Particular spellings (not treated as errors):
   72.07 *er* (but *air* elsewhere in both texts; *air* here in *B*)
   98.02 *blecez* (*blessez B*)

On the other hand, there are numerous cases where *T* corrects *V*'s erroneous readings, as an examination of the variants will show. A few examples:[19]

   6.18 vie a estat *V*, vie et estat *T*
   8.09 ser merites *V*, ses merites *T*
   10.23 duue *V*, dune = d'une *T*

---

[16] Since the *V* text begins on the title page, we count the title pages in *B* and *T* as page 1.

[17] The sole exception is pages 54–55, where in *V* the word *ne* ends page 54 and in *T* it begins page 55. *V*'s page 62 contains, exceptionally, 26 lines of text, but *T* omits several words present in *V* (see variants to chapter 10) so that *T*'s page 63 begins at the same place as *V*'s.

[18] This is true even when some of the line breaks within a page differ or when *T* omits one or more words present in *V*.

[19] Page and line references are to *V*; line numbers in *T* are either the same or differ by 1.

11.15 des dix *V*, desditz *T*
68.04–05 laquelles *V*, laquelle *T*
68.19 receu et mengié *V*, receue et mengee *T*
71.23 chmaps *V*, champs *T*
78.02 Junig *V*, iuing = juing *T*
84.13 refroidiees *V*, refroidies *T*
85.07 mediciue *V*, medecine *T*
97.03 chastris au masle *V*, chastris ou masle *T*

T sometimes presents more modern word-forms than those found in *V*:[20]

2.17 cest *V*, ce *T*
7.25 prendent *V*, prenent *T*
31.14 prendent *V*, prennent *T* (also 86.25)
47.08 traiant *V*, tirant *T*
61.12 abortir *V*, avorter *T*
64.12 puist *V*, puisse *T*
78.20 char *V*, chair *T* (also 84.15)
84.09 es (= *en* + *les*) *V*, aux *T*

T's syntax is occasionally more modern than that of *V*:

25.12 ou livre Ezechiel *V*, ou livre de E. *T*
27.09–10 a croistre et multiplier *V*, a croistre et a m. *T*.

The Bogart Text

The language of *B* is frequently more modern than that of *V* and *T*. This involves primarily the form of individual words. The third-person plural present indicative of *prendre* is generally *prendent* in *V* (13.12–13, 23.18–19, 26.25, etc.) and *prennent* in *B* (but we find *prendent* in *B* 12.12 = *V* 12.23). The third-person singular present subjunctive of *pouoir* in *V* is *puist* in eight cases and *puisse* in three; *B* prints *puist* in six cases and *puisse* in five. The third-person preterite of *vouloir* is *voult* in *V* 1.03 but *voulut* in *B* 2.03. (Both printings have *voulut* in *V* 29.09–10, *B* 28.06.) *V* uniformly prints *sçavoir* (nine occurrences), whereas it is *savoir* in *B*. Similarly, *sçaira V* 4.20, *saura B* 4.25. Where *V* prints *amer*, 26.21, *B* 25.13 has *aymer*. In some cases the older verb in *V* is replaced by a more modern one in *B*: *traiant V* 47.08, *tirant B* 45.18; *repaire V* 63.13, *revient B* 59.06; *repairent V* 66.15–16, *reviennent B* 61.26.

Similarly for various nouns: *magistre V* 18.23, *maistre B* 19.14; *flours V* 22.12, *fleurs B* 21.23; *acteur V* 24.20, *auteur B* 23.22; *Genesis V* 27.06–07, *Genese B* 25.24;

---

[20] The following lists are not exhaustive.

char V 78.01, *chair B* 71.23. The preposition *emprez V* 25.14 becomes *aprés* in *B* 24.11. In five cases out of six, the adverb *mains* in *V* is replaced by *moins* in *B*. The contracted form *ou* (= *en* + *le*), frequent in *V*, is generally replaced by the more modern form *au* in *B*, although *B* sometimes retains the earlier form. *B* simply omits the particle *mont*, found in *V* 24.19 and perhaps considered archaic by the time *B* was printed. In one respect *B*'s syntax is more modern than that of *V*: in 45.06, 45.09, 76.17, and 97.07 *B* omits the *si* preceding the verb *est* (*B* 43.10, 44.01, 70.20, 89.04). On the other hand, *B* retains the construction "possession-by-juxtaposition" in the four instances mentioned in our discussion of the language of the Vostre text (25).

The Bogart printing presents a greater number of significant variants with respect to *V* than does *T*. In several cases *B* abridges the text by omitting a phrase. There is no obvious reason why these passages are markedly shorter in *B* than in *V*.[21]

17.25–18.07 [. . .] Saint Augustin avec Pamphile le martir, duquel Saint Euzebe de Cesarie escript la vie, fist trente milliers de volumes de Livres et vainquit tous les dessus nommez en labour de faire livres, car il en escript tant de jour et de nuyt que a peine le pourroit on croire qui ne l'auroit veu ; et que Ptholomees [. . .] *V*, [. . .] Sainct Augustin et Pamphile le martyr en assembla infinitement de volumes de livres Et que Ptholomeus [. . .] *B* (16.24–25).

22.09–11 pour faire les ouvrages que on dit *de haulte lice* de plusieurs ymages et pourtraitures de bestes [. . .] *V*, pour faire les ouvraiges et pourtraictures de bestes [. . .] *B* (21.21–22).

24.25–25.02 [les sages laboureurs] font tenir et gesir leurs oeilles aux champs de jour et de nuyt pour engresser les terres *V*; *B* omits the phrase *de jour et de nuyt* (23.28).

On the other hand, several passages appear to involve a deliberate revision of the text, often suggesting a point of view in conformity with that of the Roman Catholic Church:

13.10–12 tout aussi Saint Mathieu blasme les pasteurs qui font dommage a leur fouc et les appelle faulx prophetes et loups ravissables *V*, tout aussi sont blasmez les pasteurs qui font dommaige et sont loups ravissables *B* (12.24–25). St. Matthew (the allusion is to Matthew 7: 15) is not mentioned, the verb *blasmer* changes from active to passive voice, and the reference to *faulx prophetes* disappears from *B*.

---

[21] Initial page and line references are to *V*; references to *B* follow, in parentheses.

20.06–08 Dieu le tout puissant fist et crea les peres de ce monde des cieulx et des elemens *V*, Dieu le tout puissant fist et crea ce monde des cieulx et des elemens *B* (19.06–07). The reference to *les peres* disappears from *B*.

26.17–18 Ce [the fact that sheep-herding is an honorable occupation] peult on prouver apertement par nature et par la Saincte Escripture *V*, Ce peult on prouver appertement par la Saincte Escripture *B* (25.10–11). The reference to nature disappears from *B*, so that Holy Scripture alone is cited in support of the author's claim.

28.08–09 Jacob's stratagem for producing spotted or mottled sheep (Genesis 30: 32–42, 31: 8–10) is referred to as *sa malice* in *V*, whereas in *B* it is *son engin* (26.22), possibly because *malice* had connotations of deviltry or evil magic.

29.02–06 The story of Judah and Tamar (Genesis 38: 11–26) is modified so that she is introduced not as *sa femme* (*V*) but simply *une femme* (*B* 27.12) and whereas she is his spouse in *V*, she becomes *sa belle fille* (*B* 28.02). *V*'s version was apparently unacceptable to whoever was in charge of producing *B*.

58.19–59.03 In comparing the hats of prelates and those of shepherds, the author observes that the latter are folded over in front, so that the shepherd can bring to his master any wool he has cut from the sheep in his charge, whereas the hats of prelates do not have such a fold, and he speculates that this is because prelates keep for themselves any profits from their charge: Et peult estre que ce est pour ce que ilz [*les prelas*] ne veulent pas reporter aucun prouffit a leur maistre qui les a commis au gouvernement ou ilz sont, car les prelas tondent et prendent voulentiers et retiennent tout le prouffit pour eulx mesmes. Et se aucuns en y a qui en reportent aucun prouffit a leur maistre, ce est pour estre promeuz en plus hault degré par le moyen de symonie, si comme l'en dist. This criticism of prelates disappears from *B* (55.07–08).

91.24 Icelle herbe [*tume*] est de telle vertu *V*, de telle nature *B* (84.16–17). *V*'s *vertu* could be seen as relating to magical powers.

Finally, the statement following the poem, at the very end of *B*, makes it perfectly clear that the text had been examined from a Roman Catholic point of view.

Language of the Vostre Text

i. Possible vestiges of the Old French case system

"As early as 1314 one sees the case system broken down . . . . Only a vague sense that an *-s* should be placed on some singular forms and omitted on some plural forms remained. Hence in the rare instances in which the declension system is found, the use is often incorrect. From the beginning of the fourteenth century, in the majority of cases, the Modern French usage was already in force."[22] Christiane Marchello-Nizia asserts that in the fourteenth and fifteenth centuries one may say that there may not be a single manuscript totally lacking in traces of declensions ("Au xive et xve siècle, on peut dire qu'il n'existe peut-être pas un seul manuscrit totalement dépourvu de traces des déclinaisons").[23] We can, of course, deduce nothing of Jean de Brie's usage in this respect—or in any other—from the printed text of his work, given the gap of over a century between the two. Yet we can find just a few traces of the Old French case system in *V.*

The clearest example of what seems to be the Old French singular subject case is *nulz hommes mortelz,* followed by a singular verb, in 42.02–03 (a reading shared by *T,* whereas *B* has these forms with a plural verb). We also find *nulz* as singular subject in 15.14, but in this case *BT* both have *nul.* Another apparent example of the Old French singular subject marker is *inconveniens,* 10.21 (whereas *BT* have *inconvenient*). We find *mesmes* as a singular subject in 30.03–04, but the same form is also used as a plural subject (13.13–14) and as a singular introduced by a preposition (15.13 and 57.02). Finally, among the numerous proper names, two present the distinctive *-s* (discounting *Charles,* which survives in that form): Moÿses (four occurrences, 16.21 and three in 29.12–21) and Ovides (7.23 and 16.06). Several of the names in the long list of "ancient wise men" (15.23–16.10) end in *-s,* but it is difficult to know whether this relates to the singular subject marker.

ii. Other remarks concerning the language of the Vostre edition

Pronouns

The subject pronoun for the third person plural is *ilz* in 38 cases, but in 21 cases we find the older form, *il.* The more modern spelling *ils* does not occur in Vostre. Marchello-Nizia says that *ilz* dominates from the middle of the fourteenth cen-

---

[22] Rosalyn Gardner and Marion A. Greene, *A Brief Description of Middle French Syntax,* Studies in Romance Languages and Literatures 29 (Chapel Hill: University of North Carolina Press, 1958), 1.

[23] Christiane Marchello-Nizia, *Histoire de la langue française aux xive et xve siècles* (Paris: Bordas, 1979; repr. Paris: Dunod, 1992), 97; eadem, *La Langue française aux xive et xve siècles* (Paris: Nathan, 1997), 121.

tury, and that *il* is the usual form in texts composed in a more archaic style or with literary pretensions (*Langue*, 223-24). Our edition preserves *V*'s usage throughout.

For the impersonal subject pronoun, *V* uses both *on* (85 occurrences) and *l'en* (69), as well as a single instance of *l'on*. The form *l'en* is especially frequent after the word *que*; we find just two occurrences of the elided form *qu'on*, one of which is in the poem following the text proper. But *l'en* is not always preceded by an unstressed *-e*: it occurs after various other vowels (*fait l'en* 23.09, *dont l'en* 55.24, *a l'en* 73.15, etc.). Cf. Marchello-Nizia, *Langue*, 224-25.

The reflexive pronoun before an infinitive or a present participle is in a state of flux, but *soy* predominates in our text: *en soy eslevant* 41.21; *il se doit humilier et soy faire comme le plus petit* 55.10; *pour soy esbatre* 59.18; two more examples are to be found in 81.04 and 99.15. The text of 95.23 shows the rivalry between the two forms: *pour soy escourre, car, a se escourre . . ..* Further, we find two occurrences of *eulx* before an infinitive: *ne eulx mettre a obeissance* 32.08; *les aigneaux ne peussent eulx empoudrer* 76.24.

Adjectives
Several descriptive adjectives occur with identical forms before masculine and feminine nouns — adjectives which later developed distinctive feminine forms. Chief among these epicene adjectives is *grant*, which occurs 23 times before feminine singular nouns, whereas *grande* occurs but once (17.06). Several adjectives ending in *-ant*, identical to the present participles of corresponding verbs, also modify feminine singular nouns. The most frequent of these is *nuysant*, which occurs eight times in this context, e.g., *la chaleur est nuysant et contraire* 33.08; [*la pluye*] *leur est . . . nuysant et dommagable* 35.08. Similarly, *La raison et la cause mouvant* 21.24; *autre quinzaine ensuyvant* 67.03–04; *eaue courant* 70.24–25; *une herbe nommee chaillie leur est moult prouffitable et nourrissant* 80.04–06. We find three examples of adverbs corresponding to epicene adjectives: *forment* 9.11, 11.03, 37.18; *loyaument* 8.21; *vulgaument* 44.13. On the other hand, there are several cases of adverbs based on the feminine form of adjectives ending in *-ale*: *especialement* 70.07, *generalement* 30.21–22, *principalement* 27.19–20 and 38.21, and *specialement* 26.22.

Older word-forms and particular spellings
The third-person present subjunctive forms of *aler* are *voist* (41.15) and *voisent* (34.21, 66.14); the modern forms *aille* and *aillent* do not occur in our text. The third-person present subjunctive of *dire* is *die* (39.07), not *dise*. The third-person singular present indicative of *trouver* is *treuve* (18.12, 91.13); the third-person plural present indicative of *prendre* is *prendent* (7.25, 12.23, etc.). The third-person singular future of *laisser* is *lerra* (48.09). The infinitive *veoir* appears six times (22.13, 43.16, etc.) — never the modern *voir*.

We find the spelling *-ga-* where Modern French uses *-gea-*: *dommagable(s)*: 35.08, 45.11, 48.15, 72.24; similarly, *-go-* occurs in *changoit* (12.20) and *mengoires* (14.24). In 11 cases out of 15, *V* prints *menguent* for the third-person plural present indicative of the verb *menger*; in the singular, we find two occurrences of *mengue* and one of *menge*.

Spellings with *-ie-*, where Modern French uses *-e-*, particularly in verbs, are frequent: *blecier* (31.03–04, 63.01, 74.01), *couchier* (44.07, 63.19), *destachier* (53.22), etc.; nouns exhibiting the same spelling include *bergier* (128 occurrences), *conseillier(s)*, and *traictié* (nine occurrences). A few words show a hesitation between the two forms: *menger* and *mengier* (14 occurrences of the former, four of the latter); *pechié* and *peché*, *tournier* and *tourner*, *trenchier* and *trencher* (one occurrence of each form of these three pairs). On the other hand, some verbs that ended in *-ier* in Old French appear without the *-i-* in *V*: *ayder* 67.20–21, *baillee* 15.21, *croiser* 100.18, *esloigner* 63.04, *laisser* (ten occurrences, as well as one of *lesser*, 31.13; no occurrences of *laissier*), *seicher* 91.12.

We may note a fairly large number of nouns printed *-cion*, rather than with the modern *-tion*: the general pattern is *-cion* following a vowel (including nasal vowels) and *-tion* following a consonant. Twenty words follow the former pattern, e.g., *abitacion*, *addicion*, *intencion*; ten words follow the latter pattern, e.g., *confection*, *corruption*, *digestion*. Exceptions to this distribution are *disposition* and *usurpation* (*-tion* following a vowel), *proporcionnees* (*-cion* following a consonant); we find both *discrecion* and *discretion* (two occurrences of each), but this is the only word that occurs with both endings.

Two more spellings that may be seen as older forms are *enluminer* (4.06–07) and *esperit* (4.06, 20.21, 72.25–73.01).

The use of binomials (or paired synonyms),[24] a stylistic trait already much in evidence in Old French texts of the twelfth and thirteenth centuries, is relatively frequent in our text as well. This most often involves verbs, either infinitives or conjugated forms:

> le pasteur doit **eschever et obvier** de tout son pouoir (34.16)
> le droit naturel que Nature a **aprins et enseignié** a toutes bestes (13.22–23)
> les aigneaux **se meurent et perissent** souventesfois (65.03)
> sans **oster ne separer** d'avec la mere. (65.22)
> les aigneaux sont **separez et ostez** d'avec leurs meres (66.25–67.01)
> pour elles **ayder et secourir** (67.20–21).

In some cases one of the paired verbs is more archaic and the other more modern:

> quant les mouches ou les guepes les **poingnent et piquent** (41.09–10)

---

[24] We thank the anonymous reader who suggested the use of this term.

l'en ne doit pas **tirer ne traire** le lait (65.08)
le bergier doit **clorre et fermer** les huys et fenestres (75.12–13).

There are a few cases of linked nouns or adjectives:

les brebis [sont] moult **griefves et pesantes** des **aigneaux et faons** (60.06–07)
en plusieurs **lieux** ou en plusieurs **places** (91.22–23)
ne fait pas **plaine ne parfaicte** cure (93.24).

In addition, we find cases of nearly synonymous terms, where a general word and a more precise one appear together:

Et sera cest ouvrage **mis et divisé** par chapitres (4.16–17)
le bergier ne les doit pas **mettre ne les bouter** es estables (32.12)
par les corps du ciel est **causee et faicte** toute la mutacion (44.23–24)
affin qu'il y puist **mettre et enveloper** son argent (50.06)
et doit estre **mis et attachié** (52.11–12)
le bergier doit **porter et çaindre** sa panetiere (53.07)
la bouterole ou l'en **met et fiche** le mance (56.16)
ilz sont **mis et establez** (67.02–03)
une maladie et maniere de rongne qui **prent et tient** es museaux (88.15)
ou elle est **mise et reposee** (91.24).

The two terms involved in such pairs are sometimes so close in meaning that they can be reduced to a single term in the translation, with little or no loss of meaning.

Finally, certain words may be seen as echoing the vocabulary of an earlier time. Thus, *repairer* (five occurrences, 9.11, 32.09, 63.13, 66.15–16, 75.09) co-occurs with forms of *retourner* (eight occurrences, 4.20–21, 9.10, 29.10, etc.) and *revenir* (five occurrences, 8.15, 68.11, 74.11–12, 77.13, 93.13–14). The older verb and the more modern are found in the same context. Speaking of his experience in tending hogs, Jean de Brie tells us that "au vespre, au **retour** des champs et de leur pasture, s'en **repairoient** si forment et radement . . ." (9.10–12). Similarly, *traire* (three occurrences) is found alongside its modern equivalent, *tirer*: l'en ne doit pas **tirer** ne **traire** le lait du piz a la mere de l'aigneau (65.08).[25] On the other hand, the adverb *moult* occurs 44 times, whereas *beaucop* occurs but once, and that in the poem, of doubtful authorship and which may not have been part of the original text. As Baldinger shows, *beaucoup* is rare in the fourteenth century and supplants *moult* only in the sixteenth century (cited by Möhren, "Dénominations du mouton," 139, n. 53).

---

[25] Further observations concerning the language of the text may be found in the Textual Notes.

Syntax

With certain restrictions, the idea of possession could be expressed in Old French by the simple juxtaposition of two noun phrases, e.g., *la fille le roi*, "the king's daughter". We find just four instances of this structure in *Le Bon Berger*: *ou livre Ezechiel* 25.12; *en la tunique Aaron* 50.25; *la nativité Saint Jehan Baptiste* 91.19; *la nativité Nostre Dame* 99.08. Marchello-Nizia notes that this form is not exceptional in Middle French, but that it faced strong competition from the construction with *de* (*Langue*, 398; cf. Gardner and Greene, *Syntax*, 6). In contrast, our text contains numerous examples of the possessive structure with *de*, e.g., *ung des conseilliers du roy* 14.12; *l'ostel **de** messire Arnoul de Grant Pont* 19.03; *ou service **de** maistre Jehan de Hetomesnil* 19.19.

In conclusion, we may say that the Vostre text of *Le Bon Berger* is typical of Middle French documents, in that its language is in transition, and preserves archaic traits at the same time as it announces later, more modern, linguistic features.

Style of the Vostre Text

Jean de Brie composed what must be one of the first "how-to" books ever written. This book is not in the least romantic; it contains none of the action or intrigue of romance. It is a straightforward manual on how to raise sheep for the best return on your money. De Brie's timing was perfect because there was a tremendous wool industry at that time and the gentry were looking for what would now be termed "cash crops". Land was available, the labor force plentiful, and the climate suitable.

As one might expect, given the stated purpose of the book, its basic style is unadorned prose, and self-conscious literary effects are essentially absent. At most it is illuminated by the occasional proverb, or a reference to a biblical or mythological source.

In fact, we find two contrasting writing styles in *Le Bon Berger*, and our translation attempts to remain faithful to each. The book begins with a pro forma stylized dedication to the king, followed by the author's claim that his work is something new, a *nouvelleté*. The tone becomes more personal in Chapter 1, where the author relates his own history, insisting that his experience qualifies him to speak of his subject with authority. He again stresses the novelty of his text, saying that not one of the wise men of old, *les anciens sages hommes*, whose names he presents in an extensive list, "ever wanted or dared to deal with the present material or, by chance, did not wish to reveal to their dear companions and friends the glory of this great science." Chapter 2, "Concerning the worth and profit of this treatise", and Chapter 3, "Concerning the honor and profession of the shepherd", continue the author's justification of his work, the latter including numerous references to biblical shepherds.

In Chapter 4, "General rules concerning this art", the author begins to discuss specific matters dealing with sheep husbandry, and his style changes accordingly,

becoming straightforward and workmanlike. As Holmér has said, this treatise is "très riche en informations toutes spéciales et abondant en mots rares" [very rich in specialized information and abounding in rare words.] [26] De Brie's usage reflects his personal experience and he used the local or more homely names to discuss various aspects of the natural world. In his modern French translation of the text, Michel Clévenot was content to retain de Brie's medieval names for many of these terms. [27] We have attempted to identify the names of birds, plants, and the illnesses of sheep, and to find equivalents in modern English.

Yet Jean de Brie can sometimes surprise us. At the end of his Prologue, for example, following the conventional exordium already mentioned, the author concludes his Second Prologue with the eminently practical suggestion that anyone who needed to find his place should "place a stone or other marker to find the chapter." This may be due to a change of "voice", where we hear Jean de Brie himself, rather than his collaborator.

Proverbs or proverbial expressions:

Rouge vespree et blanc matin font esjouyr le pelerin (44.13–14)

[T]el est amy a la despense qui ne l'est pas a la defense (54.16–17)

Others occur in the concluding poem, though this may not be by Jean de Brie (see Textual Notes).

Biblical references:

In addition to those in Chapter 3, mentioned above, de Brie quotes various saints:

Saint John (4.10–13, 13.07–09)

Saint Matthew (13.09–14)

Saint Paul (49.05–08)

— and other biblical sources, such as the book of Ezekiel (25.12–14).

Mythological or allegorical elements:

Fortune (10.21–23)

Phoebus and the four horses of the chariot of the sun (41.17–44.18)

The influence of the heavenly bodies and the planets (44.18–24)

Classical references (mainly in Chapter 1):

Ovid (7.23)

Virgil (10.04)

the "ancient wise men" (15.23–16.25)

Varro and others (17.16–18.11)

---

[26] Holmér, "Jean de Brie," 128.

[27] Jean de Brie, *Le Bon Berger*, trans. Michel Clévenot (Paris: Stock, 1979; repr. Étrépilly: Les Presses du Village, 1986).

Metaphors and similes are rare in our text, but we do find a few. In Chapter 1 de Brie speaks of having learned his trade in *la droite fontaine de ceste science et doctrine du fait de la bergerie,* "the true fountain of this wellspring of skill and learning about the art of shepherdry" (15.06–07). In Chapter 5 he says the magpie, when it comes to prognostications, *est une droite sebille,* "a genuine sibyl" (38.16–17). In Chapter 8 the shepherd and his ointment case are compared to the notary and his writing table (51.14–17), and in an extended comparison, the shepherd equipped with his crook is compared to a bishop or abbot with his crozier or the man-at-arms with his lance or sword (54.20–56.14). In Chapter 13 our author even incorporates a traditional springtime image, saying that in May the earth *a lors vestu sa belle robe qui est aorné[e] de plusieurs beles florettes de diverses couleurs,* "has put on her beautiful gown, adorned with many lovely little flowers of diverse colors" (73.10–12).

Because this book was written to provide first-hand information and expertise, supplementary comments (marked "‡") illuminate de Brie's account for the modern reader, especially his specific descriptions of plants and illnesses. Other authors, both ancient and contemporary, are also cited, demonstrating the extensive length of time that sheep have been used profitably for the physical and financial benefit of mankind.

Colloquial names for animals, plants, birds, and illnesses are prevalent in all cultures and it has been a challenge to reach back in time and correctly identify each of them. Every effort has been made to do so. On-the-ground experience in managing a farm flock for over twenty years has also been relied upon. The translators will welcome any helpful suggestion where there may have been a misappellation.

Editing Principles

Editions *B, T,* and *V* have been examined *in toto,* by means of microfilms and prints, and all significant variants are indicated. The Janot printing, *J,* presented a problem, in that no photographic copy could be procured. A partial examination, *in situ,* allowed the verification of most of the passages for which we have emended the Vostre text, as well as a few others of particular interest. It is likely that a systematic comparison of *J* with *V* would yield additional variants.

The notion of "significant variant" is, of course, relative. As we have said in our edition of *Le Chevalier deliberé,* one person's significant variant may be another's graphic variant, and vice versa.[28] Our approach here is much the same as it was for that later text: to exclude what we considered to be mere variations in spelling and to include all other sorts of variants. One exception to this: where

---

[28] Olivier de la Marche, *Le Chevalier deliberé (The Resolute Knight),* ed. Carleton W. Carroll, trans. Lois Hawley Wilson and idem, MRTS 199 (Tempe: ACMRS, 1999), 29.

V prints *si comme*, *B* generally has *comme*. This case presents itself so frequently[29] that we decided to exclude it from the critical apparatus. In doubtful cases we have favored inclusion, believing that even orthographic variants may sometimes be of interest.

Intervention and non-intervention

The editor needs to find a middle ground between absolute fidelity to the source (with whatever errors and incoherences it may contain) and the wish to present a readable, intelligible text. Vostre's printing of *Le Bon Berger* is relatively free of gross errors, but we have nonetheless emended where we felt it was necessary to do so. All emendations are clearly indicated in the critical apparatus at the foot of the page, between the text and the variants, and take the following form:

$$\text{et } BT] \text{ a } JV$$

—which is to be interpreted as follows: Where our edited text reads *et* (the reading found in *B* and *T*), *V* has *a* (a reading shared by *J*). This presentation allows the reader to see clearly the reading to be found in each of the early printings.

We have occasionally undertaken to correct the text by inserting a single letter or a short word, even though no printing supports the resulting form. Such corrections are placed in brackets, e.g., "les anciens sages homme[s]" (15.22), "chandelle[s] et oinctures" (23.21), where the plural is better suited to the context. Some of these corrections involve adjectives and past participles, to make them agree with the modified noun (see, for example, 26.05, 35.01, and 41.12), but there are other cases where no such simple correction can be made, and we therefore retain *V*'s reading and discuss the situation in a textual note.

In a few places *V* prints a plural verb with a singular subject, or vice versa. (Curiously, several of these cases of subject-verb disagreement appear in the other printings as well.) We find just one case of a plural subject with a singular verb: *descent*, where the subject is *yraignes et vermines* (90.10).[30] These are not to be confused with compound subjects, two singular nouns linked by *et*, where a singular verb is usual, agreeing with the nearer of the two subject nouns. Examples include "La raison et la cause . . . est" (21.23–24), "Le suif et la graisse est bon et prouffitable" (23.20–21), and "le traictié et la doctrine en est bonne et prouffitable" (26.08–09).

---

[29] Specifically, *T* shares *V*'s reading *si comme* 24 times out of 25 (the sole exception being 45.18), whereas *B* has *comme* (without *si*) 20 times and reads *si comme* in just four places, corresponding to *V*'s 15.23, 16.21, 91.02, and 94.11. (One occurrence of *si comme* in *V* falls within the passage omitted by *B*, 58.19–59.03.)

[30] Another occurs in line 14 of the concluding poem: "les inconveniens / Qui peult venir aux pastoureaux"—but this may be for metrical reasons.

The opposite situation, a singular subject with a plural verb, occurs several times, e.g., in 66.03–04: "la longue demeure de plus de quinze jours avec la mere souloient engendrer . . .".[31] Since subject-verb agreement is so fundamental to French grammar, and a disagreement in this domain is so jarring, we have emended to restore the expected agreement.

Textual notes

Emendations and various other textual matters are discussed in the textual notes, and are signaled by an asterisk in the text. In the case of *il* with a plural verb, we have noted the differences among the various printings, but this combination occurs frequently enough that we have not felt it necessary to point out each such occurrence in the notes. Similarly, we find a number of places where *V* prints *quil*, where *qui* is intended. We have systematically emended to *qui*, believing that *qu'il* would often lead to misreadings; we have noted the variant readings, but have not encumbered the notes by repeatedly mentioning "*quil* for *qui*". We have treated two occurrences of *sil* for *si* in the same way.

Diacritical symbols and elision

We add an acute accent to the letter *e* in final syllables whose vowel is /e/, to distinguish it from unstressed *e* (not, however, in the feminine endings -*ee* and -*ees*). The cedilla is used as in Modern French, to indicate that the letter *c* represents /s/ before the vowels *a*, *o*, and *u*. Following the advice of Lepage[32] and the group from the Ecole nationale des chartes,[33] we have used the *tréma* (dieresis) very sparingly, primarily in proper names. We have maintained *V*'s usage concerning elision, so that, for example, one finds both *qu'elle* and *que elle*.

Spelling and abbreviations

We have introduced the customary distinctions between *i* and *j* and between *u* and *v*; we have expanded all abbreviations, including number-words, without indicating their presence in our text. We have followed Omer Jodogne's recommendation[34] and print *pouoir* and *pouoit*.

---

[31] Other cases of a singular subject with a plural verb occur in 66.04, 72.12, 72.25, 76.15, 85.05, and 92.18.

[32] Yvan G. Lepage, *Guide de l'édition de textes en ancien français* (Paris: Champion, 2001).

[33] Ecole nationale des chartes, *Conseils pour l'édition des textes médiévaux*, fasc. 1, *Conseils généraux* (Paris: Ecole nationale des chartes, 2001).

[34] Omer Jodogne, "*Povoir* ou *pouoir*? Le Cas phonétique de l'ancien verbe *pouoir*," *Travaux de linguistique et de littérature* 4 (1966): 257–66.

Capitalization and punctuation

Capitalization follows modern usage, marking proper names and common nouns with allegorical value. Numerous capital letters beginning clauses (but internal to the sentence) in *V* are replaced by lower-case. We have reproduced *V*'s two-line capitals marking textual divisions. We use lower-case forms for compass directions but capitalize the names of the winds and those of the signs of the Zodiac. Punctuation follows modern usage and is added to clarify the reading of the text as we understand it. *V* makes fairly ample use of the virgule (/), generally representing a minor pause; the period; and a sort of paragraph sign (⫟). Words divided between two lines are often marked by a sort of slanting equal sign, functioning as a hyphen, but there are slightly more cases where no punctuation marks the divided word: a tally of all odd-numbered pages shows 43% of divided words marked with this symbol, versus 57% unmarked.

Le Bon Berger

Jehan de Brye, Le bon bergier

A la gloire, a la[1] louenge et a l'onneur du tresbon et Souverain Pasteur, le createur de toutes choses, lequel voult[2] souffrir jusques a la mort pour la redemption et delivrance [2] de ses[3] oeilles de l'umain lignaige. Et pour obeir reverem-
ment a la voulenté et commandement du* tresexcellent prince en haultesse, en
noblesse, puissance et amour de sapience, de prudence et de science, Charles le
Quint, Roy de France, nostre sire, regnant tresglorieusement et en grant* felicité,
Jehan de Brie, natif de Villers[4] sur Rongnon,[5]* en la chastellerie[6] de Coulommiers en Brie,* a dit, nommé, fait compiler, et escrire[7] cest[8] traictié de l'estat, science et pratique de l'art de bergerie et de garder oeilles et bestes a laine, qui fust*
fait en l'an de grace mil trois cent soixante dix neuf, et le seziesme[9] du regne dudit
seigneur, environ la feste de Penthecoustes.

Suppliant humblement a la clemence et benignité de la royalle majesté que
cest[10] traictié vueille recevoir en gré, sauve la correction dudit seigneur et de sa
tresgrande[11] et sage discretion, dont la bonne renommee queurt par le monde.

Prologue[12]

S elon l'usage et commune observance des anciens, aucuns qui faisoient escrips
ou[13] traictiez souloient mettre et assigner les causes de leur procés, c'est assavoir la cause [3] materiele, la formele,[14] la cause efficiente et[15] la finale, quel
tiltre le livre aura, et a quelle partie de philosophie on* le doit supposer, et quel
prouffit il en peult ensuivir. Mais Jehan de Brie ne fait force de toutes les causes
que on y vouldroit assigner, fors que seulement de obeir de toute sa vigueur et de

2.03 du tresexcellent prince] de t. p. *BTV*

---

[1] a la *om. BJ*
[2] voulut *BT*
[3] de ses] des *B*
[4] Villiers *BT*
[5] Rougnon *B*
[6] chastellenie *BT*
[7] dict, nommé, faict, compilé et escript *BJ*, dit nommé fait et compillé *T*
[8] ce *BJT*
[9] siziesme *B*
[10] ce *T*
[11] sa grande *T*
[12] Le prologue *B*
[13] et *T*
[14] la formele *om. T*
[15] a *B*

Jean de Brie, The Good Shepherd

To the glory, praise and honor of the most good and Sovereign Shepherd, the Creator of all things, for which He was willing to suffer until death for the redemption and deliverance of His sheep of the human race. And to obey reverently the wish and command of the most excellent prince in highness, nobility, power and love of wisdom, prudence and science, Charles the Fifth, King of France, our Lord reigning most gloriously and with great felicity, Jean de Brie, native of Villers sur Rongnon, in the castlery[1] of Coulommiers in Brie, has related, entitled, and had compiled and written this treatise regarding the nature, science and practice of the art of shepherdry and the care of sheep and wool-bearing animals. It was made in the year of grace 1379, the sixteenth year of the aforementioned lord's reign, around the feast of Pentecost. Asking humbly the mercy and good will of His Royal Majesty, that he might receive this treatise in good part, subject to the correction of the aforesaid lord and of his very great and wise discretion, whose good renown runs throughout the world.

Prologue

According to the usage and common observance of the ancients, people who used to write or make treatises were accustomed to put down and assign the bases of their causes, that is to say the material cause, the formal, the effective and the final; what title the book was to have, and to which field of philosophy one should assign it, and what profit could come of it. But Jean de Brie does not attach importance to all the causes one might wish to assign to it, except for obeying his lord with all his might and his power to the accomplishment of

---

[1] "The jurisdiction of a castle" (*Oxford Universal Dictionary*).

tout son pouoir* a l'acomplissement du plaisir de celuy qui ceste[1] oeuvre a com-
mandee et voulu estre ainsi traictiee, lequel Dieu par sa grace tiengne longuement
en tressaine[2] vie et[3] bonne prosperité. Et toutesfois pour ensuyr aucunement le
propos des anciens qui se travaillierent pour nous monstrer et enseigner doctrine,
nous mettrons tiltre a ce livrest[4] ou petit traictié, et sera appellé nouvelleté, pour ce
que de nouveau et nagueres il a receu nouvelle forme de la matiere de quoy il est,
si comme* l'euvre presente le monstrera. Et se aucun demandoit a quelle partie de
philosophie il sera supposé, on peult respondre qu'il sera attribué et[5] supposé a la
philosotie, ou philosophie de bergerie. Et en verité on le pourroit et deveroit* par
raison appliquer a toute philosophie raisonnable, moralle et naturelle.

[4] Le prouffit de cest ouvrage est moult grant et bon a la chose publique,[6]
si comme cy aprés sera plainement declairé, dont pour l'utilité il devera estre
chierement gardé. Si soit le nom de nostre seigneur Jesucrist appellé a cest commencement, et le Saint Esperit vueille enluminer[7] et enseigner tellement le fai-
seur que ceste oeuvre prengne bon moyen et bonne fin.

Autre prologue

On doit entrer en la bergerie par l'uys, et qui[8] y entre par ailleurs, il est larron,
si comme Saint Jehan le nous dist* ou[9] diziesme chapitre. Si[10] entrerons par
l'uys a l'ayde de Dieu et procederons briefvement pour oster l'ennuy qui par prolix-
ité pourroit venir aux lisans ou aux escoutans. Et sera cest ouvrage mis et divisé par
chapitres, et les chapitres par parties et par pieces pour le mieulx declairer et donner
a entendre, a fonder l'intencion du docteur et proceder par ordre. Et qui n'y sçaira[11]
retourner, si y mette une pierre ou autre enseigne pour trouver le chapitre.

---

[1] cest *T*
[2] tressaincte *B*
[3] tressaine vie et *om. T*
[4] livre *T*
[5] attribué et *om. T*
[6] publiques *T*
[7] illuminer *B*
[8] que *B*
[9] au *B*
[10] Nous *B*
[11] saura *B*

the pleasure of him who has commanded this treatise and willed it to be this way, may God by His grace keep him for a long time in most excellent health and good prosperity. However, to follow in some degree the direction of the Ancients who strove to show and direct us to knowledge, we will give a title to this little book or small treatise, and it will be called a novelty because it has received once again and recently a new form of its subject, as the present work will show. If anyone should ask to what field of philosophy it might be assigned, the response can be that it will be attributed and assigned to *philosotie*, or the philosophy of sheep husbandry. In truth, it could and should be reasonably applied to all philosophy that is reasonable, moral and natural.

The value of this work is very great and for the public good, as will later be plainly declared, for which usefulness it should be dearly preserved. May the name of Our Lord Jesus Christ be called upon at this beginning and may the Holy Spirit consent to illumine and teach the author in such a way that this work will have a good form and good result.

Second Prologue

One should enter a sheepfold by the door, and whoever enters any other way is a thief, as Saint John tells us in the tenth chapter.[‡] So we will enter by the door with God's help and proceed succinctly to remove the boredom that can come to readers or listeners through prolixity. This work will be arranged and divided into chapters, the chapters into parts and pieces to best explain and make clear, to establish the base of instruction, and to proceed in order. And for anyone who would not know where to find his place again, let him place a stone or other marker to find the chapter.

Le premier chapitre* de ceste doctrine sera de l'estat et de la vie de Jehan de Brie dessus nommé.* Le deuziesme. De l'utilité et [5] proufit de cest present traictié. Le tiers. De l'onneur du bergier, et comment l'estat de bergerie est grant et honnorable. Le quart. Des reigles generaulx* que le bergier doit tenir et garder en cest art. Le cinquiesme. De la maniere de congnoistre le temps par les oyseaux pour sçavoir du beau temps ou de la pluye. Le siziesme. De congnoistre le temps par augurement de bestes et par certains signes. Le septiesme. De la consideracion des vens et lesquelz sont prouffitables, ou non. Le huytiesme. De la vie, meurs et estat du bergier et des choses qui luy affierent et appartiennent pour son mestier. Le neufviesme chapitre. De la garde des moutons, des chastris, des brebis portieres et autres, des aigneaux et des bestes antenoises par toutes les saisons de l'an, et premier du moys de janvier. Le diziesme. De fevrier.* Le unziesme. De mars. Le douziesme. De avril. Le treziesme. De may. Le quatorziesme. De juing. Le quinziesme. De juillet. Le seziesme. De aoust. Le dixseptiesme. De septembre. Le dixhuytiesme. De octobre. Le dixneufviesme. De novembre. Le vingtiesme. De decembre. [6] Le xxi^e chapitre sera[1] de la maladie que l'en* appelle *l'affilee*. Le vingtdeuziesme. D'une autre que l'en dit *le pousset*. Le vingtroiziesme. Du bouchet. Le vingtquatriesme.[2] Du clavel.* Le vingtcinquiesme. De la rongne. Le vingtsiziesme. Du poacre. Le vingtseptiesme. D'une maladie que l'en appelle *bouverande*.[3] Le vingthuitiesme. Des dauves.[4] Le vingtneufviesme. De evertin.[5]* Le trentiesme. De enfleure.[6]* Le xxxi^e. De la maladie du ronge perdu par herbe que on dit *poncel*.* [Le] xxxii^e. De [la] maladie que l'en appelle *yrengnier*. Le xxxii^e. [*sic*] Des cures de chascune des maladies dessusdictes et des remedes.[7] [Le] xxxiiie. Des oingnemens et de la maniere de la confection.* [Le] xxxiiiie. Des saignies et de la maniere de seigner et amender les petis aigneaux.*

Prologue de la vie et* estat de Jehan de Brie

Plusieurs gens par importunité et jactance se efforcent de acquerir gloire mondaine et de[8] faire exaulser et valoir leur nom des proesses et des biensfais d'autruy. Aucuns autres en y a qui acquierent nom de maistre sans cause et

6.18 vie et estat *BT*] vie a estat *JV*

---

[1] Le xxie ch. sera *om. B*
[2] Le vingt et quatriesme *T*
[3] De bouveraude *B*
[4] De la dauve *B*
[5] De l'avertin *B*
[6] De l'enfleure *B*
[7] des cures et remedes des maladies dessusdictes *T*
[8] de *om. B*

Chapter 1: The first chapter of this treatise will be about the estate and the life of the aforementioned Jean de Brie. Chapter 2: About the usefulness and benefit of this present treatise. Chapter 3: About the honor of the shepherd, and how the estate of the shepherd is great and honorable. Chapter 4: About the general rules that the shepherd should hold to and preserve in this art. Chapter 5: About the way in which to recognize the weather by birds, in order to know fine weather or rain. Chapter 6: About recognizing the weather by the omens of animals and by certain signs. Chapter 7: About consideration of the winds, which are profitable and which are not. Chapter 8: About the life, mores and estate of the shepherd, and of the things which attach and are due to him for his vocation. Chapter 9: About the keeping of sheep, wethers, breeding sheep and others, of lambs and yearlings throughout all seasons of the year; and first about the month of January. Chapter 10: About February. Chapter 11: About March. Chapter 12: About April. Chapter 13: About May. Chapter 14: About the month of June. Chapter 15: About the month of July. Chapter 16: About August. Chapter 17: About September. Chapter 18: About October. Chapter 19: About November. Chapter 20: About December. Chapter 21: About the malady called scours. Chapter 22: About another called pneumonia. Chapter 23: About sore mouth. Chapter 24: About pox.[1] Chapter 25: About mange. Chapter 26: About oral lesions. Chapter 27: About swollen throat. Chapter 28: About liver fluke. Chapter 29: About staggers. Chapter 30: About bloat. Chapter 31: About the malady of lost cud from the plant called poppy. Chapter 32: About cobweb disease. Chapter 32: About the cures for each of the aforementioned maladies and some remedies. Chapter 33: About ointments and how to make them. Chapter 34: About bloodletting and methods of bleeding and altering little lambs.

Prologue About the Life and Status of Jean de Brie

Many people through chicanery and boastfulness seek to achieve worldly glory and to make their names exalted and valued from the prowess and accomplishments of others. Others acquire the name of "master" without justification

---

[1] This becomes Chapter 25 in the body of the text and the other chapters follow sequentially.

sans ce qu'ilz en soient dignes ne qu'il[1]* ayent aucun degré de science. Et soubz
[7] couleur exquise, si comme de faire office de notaire ou de[2] procureur, sont
appellez l'ung maistre Pierre, l'autre maistre Robert. Si les peult on figurer et
comparer[3] a ung savetier qui fait solliers vieux, et est appellé maistre Lorens ou
maistre Guillaume, combien qu'il ne sache faire denree de bon ouvrage. Aucuns autres sont parez et aornez plus de peaulx et des oeuvres aux peletiers que[4]
des Escriptures ne de la science des livres. Et voulentiers et communement font
fourrer leurs habis de pennes de escuireux, ou d'autres bestes que l'en* appelle
rampaille,[5] et n'ont cure de fourreures des aigneaux ne des brebis, et peult estre
que ce font eulx[6] pour mieulx ravir et pillier, car les rampailles ont les dens et les
ongles plus trenchans et plus agus[7] que n'ont les oeilles, qui sont debonnaires.[8]
Telles gens, ainsi fourrez et emplumez pour monstrer leur renardie,[9] peult on
figurer au corbeau qui[10] emprunta estranges[11] plumes pour aler a une assemblee,
et pour ce n'en fut* il oncques[12] meilleur ne plus sage. Et quant il eut rendu ses
plumes, si comme dit Ovides,[13] il demoura noir et sale selon sa premiere nature.
Toutes telles manieres de gens prendent[14] nom de maistre par [8] abus et usurpation, et contre eulx proprement est dicte la parabole dessus proposee : Qui ne entre par l'uys en la bergerie, il n'est pas loyal bergier. Mais, Dieu mercy, il n'est pas
ainsi ou[15] cas present, ne Jehan de Brie ne se veult louer ne vanter, ne[16] il ne quiert
avoir gloire du bien fait ne de la proesse d'autruy. Et toutefois* est il[17] bien digne
d'avoir nom de maistre par ses* merites et par le comble de sa grant science, eu[18]
consideracion et regart a l'estat de sa personne par ce qui[19] s'ensuit.

---

[1] ilz *T*

[2] de *om. T*

[3] et comparer *om. T*

[4] p. plus que *T*

[5] rampailles *T*

[6] eulx *om. B*

[7] ont les dens plus agues *T*

[8] debonnaire *BT*

[9] couardie *T*

[10] que *B*

[11] e. des estranges *T*

[12] pourtant il n'en fut o. *T*

[13] Ovide *B*

[14] prendront *B*, prenent *T*

[15] au *B*

[16] ne *om. T*

[17] il est *T*

[18] en *B*

[19] qu'il *B*

and without being worthy or having any kind of skill. With excellentpretense, in performing the office of notary or procurer, they are called Master Peter or Master Robert. They can be compared to a cobbler who makes old shoes and is called Master Lawrence or Master William although he does not know how to produce well-made goods. Others are adorned and decked out more with skins and the works of furriers than with the writing and learning of books. They willingly and ordinarily trim their clothing with squirrels' plumes or with other beasts that are called *rampaille*,[1] not caring for the fur of lambs or ewes; perhaps they do this in order to be better able to ravage and pillage, for these animals have teeth and claws that are more biting and sharp than those of ewes, which are gentle. These people, thus furred and finely feathered to show their slyness, can be compared to the crow who borrowed another bird's feathers to go to a gathering but for all that was neither better nor more wise. When he had given back the feathers, as Ovid says,[‡] he was still as black and dirty as he was before. All such manner of people take the name of master through deceit and usurpation and against them the parable earlier proposed is properly told: He who does not enter the fold through the door is not a loyal shepherd. But, thank God, the present case is not like that, nor does Jean de Brie wish to brag or boast or seek vain glory from the good deeds or prowess of others. And yet, he is fully worthy of the name of master by his merits and by full measure of his great skill in consideration and regard to his personal status because of what follows.

---

[1] *Ramper*: "*Ramper* a d'abord signifié, conformément à son sens étymologique, 'grimper' (v. 1150)" (Rey *Dictionnaire*). [*Ramper* originally meant, consistent with its etymological sense, to climb using hands and feet.]

Il est vray et soit chose notoire et sceue a tous que ledit Jehan de Brie, demourant a Villers[1] sur Rongnon, le huytiesme an de son aage, ou[2] temps que les
peux reviennent es chiefz des enfans qui[3] ont esté teigneux et que ilz commencent a muer leurs premiers[4] dens* et que il[5] ont encore[6] leur folle plume et ne sont
prenables d'aucune loy, fu* lors institué et deputé a garder les oues et les oysons
audit* lieu de Villers,[7] lesquelz il garda bien et loyaument a[8] son pouoir* par
l'espace de demy an et plus,[9] en defendant yceulx oues et oysons des escoufles, des
huas, des pies,* des corneilles et d'autres choses a eulx contraires ou nuysibles.

Et tel[9]lement se porta oudit[10] office de la garde a luy commise, que pour le bon
raport de sa personne, il fust en autre estat et fust mené en la ville de Nolongne[11]*
hors dudit Villers[12] et yllec luy fust baillee la cure de garder les pourceaux, lesquelz
il garda au mieulx qu'il[13] peust* par l'espace d'ung an ou environ. Et convenoit qu'il
les menast aux champs tous batans et a force, car ce sont rudes bestes et de mauvaise
discipline. Et au vespre, au retour des champs et de leur pasture, s'en repairoient si
forment et radement que ledit Jehan, qui[14] lors estoit jeune, ne les pouoit* arruner,
retenir ne aconsuyr, et souvent ne sçavoit se il en avoit perdu aucuns, ou se il avoit
son droit compte. Et celle cure estoit et fust moult dure, greveuse et intolerable
audit Jehan, assez plus que n'estoit la garde des oues et des oysons. Sur ce pourroit
on assigner et dire plusieurs bonnes raisons prouvables es[15] Escriptures, en philosophie naturele et es livres des proprietez des choses et des bestes, desquelles ledit
Jehan se passe pour continuer ceste matiere.

Aprés l'estat ou office de garder les pourceaux, ledit de Brie, en acroissant
son estat de estre promeu aux hon[10]neurs terriennes,* fust estably et ordonné
audit lieu de Nolongne pour mener les chevaux a la charrue au devant du bouvier
ou charretier pour haster et exciter les chevaux, si comme Virgile l'enseigne en

8.24 pies *B*] piees *TV*

---

[1] Villiers *B*
[2] du *B*
[3] que *B*
[4] premieres *T*
[5] ilz *BT*
[6] encores *B*
[7] Villiers *B*
[8] et *B*
[9] au plus *B*
[10] audit *B*
[11] Nolongue *T*
[12] Villiers *B*
[13] ilz *B*
[14] que *B*
[15] et *T*

It is true, manifest and well-known to all that Jean de Brie, living at Villers-sur-Rognon, in the eighth year of his life, at the time when lice come back to the heads of children who have had ringworm, when they begin to shed their first teeth and still have their downy hair, and are not accountable to any rules, was then appointed to take care of geese and goslings in Villers, which he tended as well and loyally as he was able for a period of six months and more, defending those geese and goslings from buzzards, kites, magpies, crows and other harmful things.

He carried out the job assigned to him so well that, because of his good reputation, his status improved and he was taken to the town of Nolongne outside Villers and there he was awarded the job of tending pigs, which he watched after as best he could for the space of a year or thereabouts. He had to hit them hard when leading them to the field, for they are intractable, ill-disciplined beasts. In the evening, on the way back from grazing in the fields, they came back in such a rush that Jean, who was young then, could not hold them back nor keep up and often did not know if he had missed any or if he had the right count.[‡] This task continued to be most hard, annoying and intolerable to Jean, much more than herding geese and goslings. Many good and demonstrable reasons may be cited about this from Scripture, from natural philosophy, and from books about the properties of things and animals,[‡] which Jean will forego in order to keep to his subject.

After the occupation of guarding the pigs, de Brie, his standing increasing by being raised in earthly honors, was appointed and sent to Nolongne to lead the plow horses in front of the drover or plowman in order to urge them on, as Virgil teaches in his *Bucolics*, where he deals with the cultivation and

son livre des *Bucoliques*,[1] ou il traicte de cultiver et labourer les terres — ouquel[2] office a la charrue ledit de Brie ne demoura que par trois mois seulement, pour ce que l'ung des chevaulx luy passa dessus le pié dextre et le bleça tellement que il en fust malade par l'espace d'ung mois ou plus, et ne peult* continuer ne excercer iceluy office, causant son essoine[3] de maladie.

Et quant ledit Jehan fust tourné a guarison de son pié, attendu que il se estoit[4] bien porté et que il estoit bien digne d'avoir aucun estat convenable a sa personne, l'en luy bailla la garde de dix vaches a lait de la maison de Nolongne,[5] lesquelles il garda bien par l'espace de deux ans continuellement. Et plus les eust gardees de sa bonne voulenté, se inconveniens[6] n'y fust entrevenu. Mais Fortune, qui nully ne veult ne laisse demeurer en seur[7] estat, en eut envie et par importunité d'une* des vaches, qui estoit desree et demandoit les toreaux, ou elle estoit enyvree de mauvaise her[11]be ou bruvage, le hurta de ses cornes moult orgueilleusement et impetueusement et abatit ledit Jehan a terre soudain et le bleça forment,[8] tellement qu'il ne peult plus garder les vaches.

Et quant il fust relevé et en convalescence, il vint audit hostel de Nolongne dire que jamais il ne garderoit les vaches. Et nonobstant son empeschement il fust receu honnorablement, et lors luy fust baillee la garde de quatre vingz aigneaux debonnaires et innocens, qui ne hurtoient ne bleçoient. Lequel Jehan, qui des lors avoit esprouvé, comme dit est, aucunes des fortunes et tribulacions[9] de ce monde, auxquelles* il avoit resisté par sa pacience, receut voulentiers la garde desdictz* aigneaux, et fust aussi come leur tuteur et curateur, car il[10] estoient soubz aage et mineurs d'ans. Et pour ce que ledit Jehan n'est pas noble et que il ne luy appartenoit pas de lignage, il n'en peult avoir le bail, mais il en eut la garde, gouvernement et administracion quant a la nourriture. Et iceulx[11] aigneaux ledit Jehan traicta et garda moult amiablement et charitablement par l'espace d'ung an et plus. Et soubz son gouvernement, selon la coustume du pays, furent nourris, tondus, empoudrez, oings et [12] saigniez par bonne industrie, et gardoit ledit Jehan son droit compte chascun jour et les defendoit des loups et de[12] autres males bestes.

11.15 desdictz (des dictz *B*, des ditz *T*)] des dix *V*

---

[1] Bucoliques ou Georgicques *B*
[2] auquel *B*
[3] son estat *B*
[4] c'estoit *T*
[5] Nolongnes *T*
[6] inconvenient *BT*
[7] cest *B*
[8] fort *T*
[9] et tribulacions *om. T*
[10] ilz *BT*
[11] ceulx *T*
[12] des *BT*

working of the earth. De Brie's job with the plow lasted only three months because one of the horses stepped on his right foot and hurt him so badly that he was sick for the space of a month or more and could not continue in this job because of his debility.

When Jean's foot was healed, since he was in good standing and worthy of having another position suitable to him, he was given the safekeeping of ten milk cows belonging to the house of Nolongne, which he cared for continually for two years and would willingly have continued if a difficulty had not come about. But Fortune, who does not want to leave anyone in a settled state, was jealous and, employing the perverseness of one of the cows who, either in heat and seeking the bull or else intoxicated from bad plants or water, struck him with her horns most arrogantly and impetuously, hurling Jean suddenly to the ground and wounding him so badly that he could no longer tend the cows.

When he was back on his feet and convalescing, he went to the house of Nolongne to say that he would never again take care of cows. In spite of this difficulty, he was very well received and was then given the care of eighty gentle and innocent lambs, which neither attacked nor wounded. Jean, who before then had experienced, as has been recounted, some of the vicissitudes and tribulations of this world, which he had withstood with patience, willingly took on the care of these lambs and was also their tutor and overseer, because they were under age and young in years. Because Jean was neither noble nor did he belong to a well-known family, he could not have their complete charge, but he had the care, direction, and administration of their feeding. These lambs Jean handled and cared for most amicably and kindly for a year and more. According to local custom, under his direction they were fed, shorn, dusted, salved, and bled with good diligence, and Jean kept a correct count each day and protected them from wolves and other harmful animals.

Et aprés la garde d'iceulx aigneaux, consideré que ledit Jehan croissoit en aage de adolescence et en science de bonne doctrine pour garder bestes, et avoit ja onze ans, lors luy fust baillee la garde de six vingz moutons autrement dis *chastris*,[1] lesquelz estoient chastes[2] par default de[3] membres genitaulx et n'avoient aucune coinquinacion a femelle. Et les garda continuellement par trois ans ou environ si bien et deuement que il n'en fust aucune complainte, et que par ses fais louables[4] et bonnes oeuvres, la bonne renommé de sa[5] science, sens et[6] discretion en ceste doctrine acroissoit de jour en jour ou[7] pays de Brie et es lieux de[8] environ. Et ne faisoit pas comme mercenaire, car il aymoit le prouffit de son maistre et[9] l'acroissement de ses bestes, et ne les changoit pas, si comme l'en dit que font aucuns faux[10] pasteurs qui en donnent une oeille grasse pour deulx* maigres, et en prendent[11] le prouffit pour eulx et ne leur chault fors[12] que ilz en[13] rendent leur nombre, et aucuns autres en y a qui fendent les [13] grasses oeilles par le ventre et en ostent le suif et la gresse et appliquent a leur prouffit furtivement et laissent les bestes maigres et languereuses par[14] leur coulpe.[15] Certes, soit en espirituel ou en temporel, il n'est pas bon pasteur ne vray qui n'ayme le salut et le bien de ses oeilles. Et aussi que Saint Jehan blasme en ses Evangiles[16] les pasteurs qui n'entrent pas es bergeries par l'uys, tout aussi Saint Mathieu en ses Evangiles[17] blasme[18] les pasteurs qui font dommage a leur fouc* et les appelle faulx prophetes[19] et loups[20] ravissables qui prendent[21] la substance de leurs oeilles et eulx mesmes les devorent.

---

[1] chastrés *B*
[2] chastrés *T*
[3] de *om. B*
[4] f. moult l. *T*
[5] la *B*
[6] et *om. B*
[7] au *B*
[8] de *om. B*
[9] et *om. B*
[10] faux *om. B*
[11] prendrent *T*
[12] fors *om. B*
[13] en *om. T*
[14] maigres a [*sic*] l. et par *B*
[15] coupe *B*
[16] son Evangile *B*
[17] Saint M. en ses E. *om. B*
[18] sont blamez *B*
[19] a leur fouc . . . prophetes *om. B*
[20] et sont loups *B*
[21] prennent *B*

After the care of these lambs, since Jean was growing into adolescence and in the good technical knowledge of caring for animals and was already eleven years old, he was offered the care of 120 sheep, otherwise called wethers,‡ which were chaste because of gelding and having no sexual contact with a female. He watched over them so well and devotedly for about three years that he received no complaint and, by these praiseworthy deeds and good work, the good renown of his knowledge, sense and judgment in this skill grew from day to day in the region of Brie and in the surrounding areas. Nor did he do this for his own gain, for he cherished the profit of his master and the increase in his animals and did not switch them, as is said that some false shepherds do, giving one fat ewe for two skinny ones and taking the profit for themselves, caring only for having the right number. There are others who split open the stomach of the fat sheep and take out the suet and fat and add to their profit on the sly, leaving the animals skinny and listless by their misdeed.

It is certain that in the spiritual or the temporal sense he is neither a good shepherd nor true who does not love the health and well-being of his sheep. Just as in his Gospels Saint John censures the shepherds who do not enter the fold by the door, so Saint Matthew in his Gospels condemns the shepherds who harm their flock, calling those who take the substance of their ewes and devour it themselves false prophets and ravening wolves.

Ou[1] temps que Jehan de Brie estoit de l'aage de quatorze ans, il garda deulx cens brebis portieres a Messy,* emprez Cloye,* par l'espace de deux ans ou plus, ouquel[2] par experience, qui est la souveraine maistresse des choses, il aprint par grant cure la theorique et la pratique, la science et maniere de nourrir, garder et gouverner bestes a laine, et le droit naturel que Nature a aprins et enseignié a toutes bestes, non pas seulement aux raisonnables, mais[3]* a toutes autres bestes qui naissent et sont en l'air, en terre, et en la [14] mer, et qui font[4] generacion, l'a enseigné et monstré audit Jehan, avec l'usage et continuacion qui moult y ont aydé et valu.

Et aprés, tout aussi[5] que l'en doit monter aux honneurs de degré en degré et aussi comme l'en sceust pourveoir de estat a ceulx qui en sont dignes selon leur science, meurs et discrecion, tout aussi[6] ledit Jehan de Brie, sans symonie, fust estably et institué a porter les clefz des vivres, garnisons et choses de l'ostel de Messy appartenans a messire Mathieu de Pommolain, seigneur lors du Tueil* et l'ung des conseilliers du roy nostredist* seigneur* es enquestes de son parlement a Paris, lequel office de clavier ledit de Brie fist et excerça par trois ans ou environ continuellement.

Item : Ledit Jehan, en augmentant son estat selon ce[7] que raison et nature le duisoit[8] et que il venoit[9] a ans de discrecion, fust nourricier par sept* ans continuelz, en ladicte ville de Messy, des oilles,* bestes a laine, moutons, chastris,[10] portieres,[11] aigneaux et antenoises, qui sont bestes d'anten, c'est a dire de plus d'ung an d'age,* et leur appareilloit litiere es estables, fourrage et rateliers, et prouvende es mengoires, et autres vivres et choses necessaires moult curieusement. Si [15] doit on avoir vraye presumption que en faisant et continuant les offices et fais dessus declairez et autres qui sont des dependences et appartenances dont cy aprés sera dit plus plainement,[12] ledit de Brie, comme bon et vray estudiant, fust enseigné, instruit et imbut[13] en la droite[14] fontaine de ceste science et doctrine du fait de la bergerie, de laquelle fontaine les ruisseaux seront dirivez

14.18 par sept *T*] pars ses *V*, par ses *B*

1 Au *B*
2 auquel *B*
3 a toutes bestes . . . mais *om. B*
4 qui font *om. T*
5 ainsi *B*
6 ainsi *BT*
7 ce om. *T*
8 devoit *T*
9 vint *T*
10 chastrez *B*
11 portiers *T*
12 dont sera dit plus amplement *T*
13 induit *T*
14 en ladicte f. *T*

When Jean de Brie was fourteen, he took care of 200 breeding ewes at Messy near Cloye for the space of two years or more. From experience, which is the greatest teacher, he learned through great application the theory, practice, science, and manner of feeding, tending and managing woolbearing animals, and the natural law shown and taught to all animals, not only those who reason, but to all other beasts that are born and live, in the air, on earth, and in the sea. This was taught and demonstrated to Jean with practice and perseverance, which are greatly helpful and valuable.

Afterward, just as one should rise in honors, step by step, and status is provided for those known to be worthy in their learning, morals, and judgment, just so Jean de Brie, without simony, was established and appointed to carry the keys of the foodstuffs, provisions and household appurtenances of the house at Messy belonging to Sir Matthieu de Pommolain, then lord of Tueil, and one of the councilors of our lord the King in the court of inquests of his parliament at Paris. This office of keybearer de Brie performed on a continual basis for about three years.

Jean, increasing his status by what reason and nature taught him and because he had come to the age of discretion, was a foster father for seven full years, at Messy, to woolbearing sheep: rams, wethers, bearing ewes, lambs, and yearlings (which are females of a year or more of age).[1] He provided them most carefully with bedding in their fold, with forage and feedracks, with feed in their troughs, and other foodstuffs and necessary things. So one should really presume that, performing continually the aforementioned offices and deeds and others that belong thereto, of which hereafter will be told more plainly, as a good and true student, de Brie was taught, instructed and immersed in the true fountain of this wellspring of skill and learning about the art of shepherdry. From this spring streamlets will be drawn and poured forth

---

[1] Möhren makes a valiant effort in his article to bring consistency to the use of sheep labels: *belier*, *mouton*, etc. The only ones about which there is never confusion are *chastris*, for obvious reasons, and *antenoises*. Although *chastris* may sometimes be lumped with *belier* and *mouton*, the *antenoises* are always discrete.

et declairez en cest[1] tractié si[2] plainement et proprement[3] que ung asne, qui est fole beste et rude, y pourroit mordre et en avoir[4] vraye congnoissance, mais que il sceust aussi bien lire et entendre que feroit ung homme.

De ce mesmes

Nulz[5] ne soit si presumptueux que il tiengne ceste doctrine pour fable, car elle est moult noble et digne de grant louenge pour la haultesse du grant entendement de l'acteur. Et doit on entendre grant amour et vraye obeissance en ce que ledit de Brie l'a voulu bailler, manifester et declarier au roy nostre sire, et a nul autre ne l'eust il baillee. Et peult on vrayement[6] considerer que[7] les anciens sages hommes,* desquelz nous avons moult de biens, si comme furent Hermes, Platon, Xenocrates, Aristoteles, Pytagoras, Salomon, Possedemus,[8] Asclepiades,[9] Ypocras, [16] Zenon, Eraclitus,[10] Dyogenes, Chritolaüs, Auximenes, Hypater, Hermogenes, Cricias, Empedocles, Permenides, Boetos, Xenophantes, Epycurus, Socrates, Clyo, Theostratus,[11] Epymenon, Byaspenis, Jules Cesar, Boeces,[12] Virgiles,[13]* Omers,[14] Ovides,[15] Caton, Cyceron, Tulle, Macrobes,[16] Seneque, Xenoplyn,[17] Euclides, Peryander, Mellissus, Secons, Buridans,[18] et plusieurs autres philosophes sages et de[19] grant renommee de science ; et Jupiter, qui fust si soutil homme en l'isle de Crete que il trouva et enseigna la maniere de prendre les oyseaux volans en l'air, les poissons nouans en la mer et es eaues doulces,

15.22 hommes *BT*] homme *V*

---

[1] ce *T*
[2] cy *T*
[3] clairement *T*
[4] auroit *T*
[5] Nul *BT*
[6] vrayement *om. T*
[7] qui *B*
[8] Possidemus *B*
[9] Asclipiades *T*
[10] Heraclitus *B*
[11] Theophratus *B*
[12] Boece *B*
[13] Virgile *B*
[14] Omere *B*
[15] Ovide *B*
[16] Macrobe *B*
[17] Xenophon *B*
[18] Buridant *B*
[19] de *om. B*

in this treatise so plainly and suitably that an ass, which is a foolish and ignorant beast, could chew on it and have some true knowledge thereof—providing he knew how to read and understand like a man.

Concerning the same

Let no one presume to take this teaching as fiction, for it is most noble and worthy of great praise because of the author's depth of great understanding. Great love and true obedience should be understood, since de Brie wished to grant, show and declare it to our lord the King and would have given it to no other. One can truly consider that the ancient wise men from whom we have much wealth, such as Hermas, Plato, Xenocrates, Aristotle, Pythagoras, Solomon, Posidonius, Asclepiades, Hippocrates, Zeno, Heraclitus, Diogenes, Critolaus, Auximenes, Hypater, Hermogenes, Critias, Empedocles, Parmenides, Boetos, Xenophantes, Epicurus, Socrates, Clio, Theophrastus, Epimenides, Bias of Priene, Julius Cæsar, Boethius, Virgil, Homer, Ovid, Cato, Cicero, Tullus, Macrobius, Seneca, Xenophon, Euclid, Periander, Mellisus, Secons, Buridan, and many other wise philosophers greatly renowned in knowledge, and Jupiter on the island of Crete, whom many foolish people thought to be a god, and who was such a clever man that he discovered and taught the way to capture birds flying in the air, fish swimming in the sea and in fresh water,

et les bestes sauvages des boys et des forestz, et duquel plusieurs folles gens
cuidoyent qu'il fust dieu ; le roy Oetes,[1] qui par science fist faire le mouton a la
toison d'or ; ceulx qui firent faire le dieu Hamon en Lybie en forme de mouton,
ne autres qui ayent traicitié ou[2] temps passé des hystoires, si comme Moÿses,[3] qui
fist le Penthateuque; Esdras l'escrivain, Neemias, Solius,[4] Pierre le Mengeour,
ne[5] aucuns des hystoriographes du temps passé ; neys* le chetif Helynant, moine*
de Froitmont, qui n'avoit dont [17] il peult acheter seulement du parchemin pour
escrire ses faictz de ses croniques,* ne vouldrent ou n'oserent oncques traictier de
ceste matiere presente, ou par aventure ne le vouldrent pas dire ne reveler a leurs
chiers compaignons et amys pour la gloire de ceste grande* science. Si la doit on
bien nommer nouvelleté.

Et ne soit merveille a aucun de ce que dit est cy dessus, ne murmure n'en soit
faicte contre ledit de Brie, car il ne procede pas par vanterie, par jactance,
ou par orgueil pour acquerir vaine gloire, ne pour cuyder que il sache plus que les
autres, mais seulement pour conforter et soustenir ses opinions en raison et en[6]
verité. Et jasoit ce que Marcus Terencius Varro a son temps escript* aux Latins
plusieurs livres sans nombre ; et Calaterius fust moult exaulsé de la multitude
de ses livres qu'il escript aux Grejois ; et que Origenes en labour de ses escriptures surmontast tant les Grejois comme les Latins ou[7] grant nombre de ses oeuvres; et que Saint Hierosme, si comme l'en dit, fist des livres jusques au nombre
de six milliers;[8] et que Saint Augustin avec[9] [18] Pamphile le martir, duquel[10]
Saint Euzebe de Cesarie escript la vie, fist trente milliers de volumes de livres et
vainquit tous les dessus nommez en labour de faire livres, car il en escript tant
de jour et de nuyt que a peine le pourroit on croire qui ne l'auroit veu ; et que
Ptholomees,[11] roy de Egypte, qui fust surnommé Filadelphus et qui tout passa,
en fist faire a son temps soixante dix milliers[12] de volumes, et tint par long temps
les soixante dix interpretez* qui lors estoient—neantmains, l'en ne treuve pas ne

---

17.16–17 son . . . escript] leur . . . escrivirent *BTV*

---

[1] Octes *T*

[2] au *B*

[3] Moyses . . . Neemias *om. B*

[4] Solinus *B*

[5] et *B*

[6] en *om. T*

[7] au *B*

[8] fist des l. plusieurs *B*

[9] et *B*

[10] duquel . . . l'auroit veu] en assembla infiniment de volumes de livres *B*

[11] Ptholomeus *B*

[12] en fist assemble son temps plusieurs m. *B*

and wild beasts of woods and forest; King Æetes, whose skill produced the sheep with the golden fleece; those who had the god Hamon made in the form of a sheep in Libya; and others who in times past have dealt with histories, like Moses who made the Pentateuch; Esdras the scribe, Nehemiah, Solinus, Peter the Glutton [Comestor], and other historians of the past; even the needy Hélinand, the monk of Froidmont, having nothing with which he could buy parchment on which to write the deeds of his chronicles — none ever wanted or dared to deal with the present material or, by chance, did not wish to reveal to their dear companions and friends the glory of this great science. Thus this treatise may indeed be called a novelty.

And what has been said above should not be astonishing to anyone nor should any muttering be made against de Brie, for he does not act from boastfulness or self-promotion or from pride in order to garner vain glory, nor from thinking he knows more than anyone else, but only to reinforce and support his opinions in reason and truth. And even though in his day Marcus Terentius Varro wrote numberless books to the Romans, and Calaterius was most praised for the great number of his books that he wrote to the Greeks; Origen in the work of his writing surpassed the Greeks as well as the Romans with the great number of his works; and Saint Jerome, it is said, made books up to the number of six thousand; and Saint Augustine, with Pamphilus the martyr, whose life Saint Eusebius of Cæsarea wrote, made thirty thousand volumes of books and outdid all of the above in the work of making books, for he wrote so many day and night that one could scarcely believe it not having seen it; and Ptolemy, king of Egypt, who was surnamed Philadelphus, in his time surpassed everyone in having seventy thousand volumes made, and who then for a long time had seventy translators — nevertheless, one does not and could not find this

pourroit trouver cest present tractié en aucun de leurs livres, si semblera bien que ce soit nouvelle chose. Et pour le bien publique, ledit Jehan de Brie, du commandement du souverain seigneur et prince des Crestiens, a entrepris en soy le fais et la hardiesse de ce faire, car audit seigneur, a sa haultesse et noblesse, tous secretz de sciences doivent estre interpretez et manifestez, referez[*] et revelez.

E t en oultre, quant ledit de Brie eut esté ainsi licencié et magistre[1] en ceste science de bergerie, qu'il en estoit[2] digne de lire en la ruelle[3] au feurre emprez la cresche aux [19] veaulx, et soubz l'ombre d'ung ormel ou tilleul par[4] derriere les brebis, lors vint il[5] demourer ou palais royal en l'ostel de messire Arnoul de Grant Pont, lors[6] tresorier de la Saincte Chapelle royalle dudit palais[7] a Paris. Et en l'ostel dudit tresorier, ledit de Brie, comme pasteur voulant donner bon[8] exemple aux autres par bonne et vraye humilité, lava les escuelles par plusieurs fois, jasoit ce que des lors il eust acquis, comme dit est, toutes les facultez en sa science. Et continua depuis ou service dudit tresorier tout le residu du temps que ledit tresorier vesquit, c'est assavoir par quatorze ans ou environ.

Et aprés la mort dudit feu tresorier,[9] ledit[10] Jehan de Brie, joyeux[11] de l'abitacion des hotelz dudit[12] palais a Paris, ne se transporta pas loing et ala[13] demourer en l'ostel et habitacion ou service[14] de maistre Jehan de Hetomesnil,[*] conseillier du roy nostredit seigneur, maistre des requestes de son hostel et chanoine de ladicte Sainte Chapelle dudit palais royal,[15] avecques lequel de Hetomesnil[16*] il a depuis demouré et encore demouroit au temps de la confection de cest traictié.[17] [20] Si souffise ce que dit est de l'estat dudit de Brie, car par ce peult on entendre qu'il est expert et ydoine pour monstrer ce qui[*] s'ensuyt.

18.21 referez *B*] reserez *TV*
19.20 Hetomesnil] Hetomesuil *BTV*
19.23–24 Hetomesnil] Hetomesuil *TV*
20.03 qui] quil *BTV*

---

[1] maistre *B*
[2] et qu'il estoit *B*
[3] rue *B*
[4] par *om. B*
[5] il *om. B*
[6] lors] *om. B*, alors *T*
[7] dudit palais *om. B*
[8] bonne [*sic*] *T*
[9] la m. du t. *B*

[10] ledit *om. B*
[11] fut moult j. *T*
[12] du *B*
[13] et s'en alla *T*
[14] et habitation ou service *om. B*
[15] S. Ch. royalle *B*
[16] de H. *om. B*, Jehan de H. *T*
[17] cest petit t. *T*

present subject in any of their books, so it will indeed seem to be a new thing. Jean de Brie, for the public good, at the command of his sovereign lord and Christian prince, has taken upon himself the burden and presumption of doing this, for to that lord, in his highness and nobility, all secrets of knowledge should be interpreted, made manifest, reported and revealed.

Moreover, when de Brie had been granted license and mastery[‡] in this science of shepherdry so that he was worthy of teaching in Straw Lane near the calf crib and beneath the elm or linden tree's shadow behind the ewes, then he came to live at the royal palace in the household of Sir Arnoul de Grand Pont, then treasurer of the royal palace's Sainte Chapelle in Paris. In the treasurer's household de Brie, like a shepherd wishing to give a good example to others through good and true humility, washed the dishes on many occasions, although by then he had acquired, as has been said, all the entitlements of his knowledge. He continued in the service of the treasurer for the remainder of the latter's life, about fourteen years.

After the death of the treasurer, Jean de Brie, delighted with living in the household of that palace at Paris, did not move far. He went to live in the household and service of Master Jean de Hetomesnil, king's councilor, Master of Requests of his household and canon of the aforementioned Sainte Chapelle of the royal palace, with whom he has since stayed and was living still at the time of the composition of this treatise. Let this suffice for information about the status of de Brie, for from this it can be understood that he is expert and suitable to present what follows.

De l'utilité et pouffit de cest[1] traictié. ii[e]

Du prouffit et utilité de cest[2] traicitié, nous lisons que Dieu le tout puissant fist et crea les peres de[3] ce monde des cieulx et des elemens, et que il forma l'homme sur terre[4] et que entre les autres grans dons qu'il fist a l'homme par sa grace, il luy donna bestes nommees *oeilles* portans laine, et les soubmist et abandonna a l'homme pour ses alimens et nourritures[5] et pour autres necessitez[6] a son prouffit. Et de ce parle le roy et prophete[7] David en son psaultier, ou septiesme ver du huitiesme pseaulme. Dieu, ce dit il, Tu as toutes choses[8] soubmises[9] soubz les piedz de l'homme : oeilles, beufz et vaches et tous les bestiaux des champs. Assez est bon a croire et devons entendre que la vie qui fait remuer et vegeter l'esperit et le corps par iceluy nous est donnee des cieulx de lassus et par eulx est gouvernee. Et la nourriture et pasture nous est donnee des elemens, si comme nous le voyons, car nous usons des oyseaulx [21] et volatilles de l'air et des bestes,[10] aumailles, oeilles, et des fruictz, semences, plantes, herbes et racines de la terre, des poissons de la mer et des rivieres et eaues doulces. Le feu aussi y est convenable et necessaire pour chaleur, pour mouvement et conservacion de la generacion, pour recouvrer la corruption, pour cuire les viandes, pour ayder a la digestion et pour autres choses qui sont de sa proprieté.

Si[11] doit l'homme rendre graces a Dieu son createur de tous ses benefices, et mesmement des oeilles, qu'il a soubmis, comme dit est, a l'usage et prouffit de l'homme, dont tant pour le don de Dieu qui fait les gens et personnes de si grant honneur et de telle dignité que il[12] sont, comme pour le prouffit et utilité[13] des oeilles. Chascun pasteur, de quelconque dignité, auctorité ou preeminence qu'il[14] soit, est tenu de garder et defendre ses oeilles et bestes qui sont soubz sa cure et en sa subjection de tous ennemys, visibles et invisibles, et leur doit donner santé et faire secours contre tout ce qui[15] leur pourroit nuyre.

---

[1] ce *B*

[2] ce *BJ*

[3] les peres de *om. B*

[4] sur la t. *B*

[5] nourriture *B*

[6] aultres ses n. *B*

[7] le royal p. *B*

[8] t. tes choses *T*

[9] submises *T*

[10] et aussy des b. *T*

[11] Or *B*

[12] ilz *B*

[13] utille *T*

[14] qui *B*

[15] qu'il *B*

Chapter 2

Concerning the Worth and Profit of this Treatise

Concerning the profit and worth of this treatise, we read that God the all-powerful created the fathers of this world from the heavens and the elements and that He formed man on earth. Among the great gifts which by His grace He gave to man were animals called wool-bearing sheep, and He placed them under his dominion and gave them over to man for his nourishment and sustenance and other things necessary for his benefit. King David the Prophet speaks of this in his Book of Psalms, in the seventh verse of the eighth psalm.‡ "God," he said, "You have given dominion over all things to man: sheep, oxen, cows, and all the animals of the field." It is well and good to believe and we should understand that the life that stirs and quickens the spirit and body is a gift from the heavens above and is ruled by them. Food and sustenance[1] are given to us by the elements, as we see, for we use the birds and flying things in the air, the animals, oxen and sheep, the fruits, seeds, plants, grasses and roots of the earth, the fish in the sea, rivers, and fresh water. Fire is also proper and necessary for heat, for the stirring and maintaining of generation, to repairing the damage of decay, for cooking food, to aid digestion, and for all other things that belong to it.

So man should render thanks to God his Creator for all these gifts, likewise for the sheep, which He has placed, as was said, for man's use and profit, as much for God's gift to people of such great honor and dignity as they are as for the profit and usefulness of the sheep. Each herdsman, no matter what authority or preeminence he may have, is obligated to watch over and protect the sheep and animals who are under his care and dominion from all enemies, visible and invisible, to give them health and rescue them from all that might harm them.

---

[1] *pasture*: "pasture and also nourishment, feeding, sustenance" (Cotgrave).

La raison et la cause mouvant[1] de l'utilité et prouffit est tres clere et tres demonstrative et prouvable. [22] Premierement, de la laine et tonsure de l'oeille sont fais les draps, desquelz les princes, les roys et grans seigneurs et toutes les personnes* de l'umain gendre[2] sont vestuz et de quoy nostre humanité est couverte communement. Et en peult l'en ouvrer en plusieurs et diverses guises et manieres et luy donner diverses couleurs et tainctures pour draps de graine, que l'en nomme *escarlette*, pour faire les ouvrages que on dit *de haulte lice* de plusieurs ymages[3] et pourtraitures de bestes, de poissons, d'oyseaux, de flours,[4] de fueilles et autres belles et merveilleuses choses et plaisantes a veoir. Et pourroit on porter des draps de laine en telles parties de ce monde que on les venderoit[5]* plus chierement que draps de soie. Et aussi est et doit estre une brebis plus honnoree et chiere tenue pour le bien de sa laine que ung ver ou vermine dont vient la soie.

Les peaulx des oeilles, moutons, brebis et bestes a laine dont nous traictons sont prouffitables a faire parchemins pour faire livres et notes et plusieurs escriptures, et pour tanner et mesgissier et conrayer[6] en plusieurs et diverses manieres a faire grandes* lanieres et au[23]tres choses necessaires et prouffitables a plusieurs bons usages, dont les particularitez seroient trop longues a mettre en escript.

La chair du mouton et de l'oeille est bonne pour nourrir creature humaine, pour mengier avec la poree et pour faire plusieurs viandes en temps convenable. Les escoliers a Paris, a Orleans et ailleurs et plusieurs autres le sçavent bien, et en fait l'en service a table plus communement que de chars d'autres bestes. Les entrailles, que l'en appelle *trippes*, et la teste du mouton ou de brebis, que les gens de Picardie[7] nomment *rebbardeure* ou *demie rebbardeure* ; les piedz, le foye, le poulmon,[8] quant il n'est point blecié ne corrumpu de[9] dauves ou d'autres males herbes, et les autres choses de par dedens sont bonnes et prouffitables aux povres gens, car plusieurs en prendent[10] nourriture et recreacion a grant souffisance.

Le suif et la graisse est bon et prouffitable a faire chandelle[s] et oinctures et aucunefois* en met l'en es[11] oignemens* des cyrurgiens pour la bonté et saincteté de la beste. Les boyaux sont bons et prouffitables a faire plusieurs cordes grosses

---

22.03 personnes *B*] personnages *TV*

---

[1] mouvans *B*

[2] genre *B*

[3] que . . . ymages *om. B*

[4] fleurs *B*

[5] vendroit *B*

[6] courrayer *B*

[7] Picardee [*sic*] *B*

[8] paulmon *B*

[9] des *B*

[10] prennent *B*

[11] es *om. T*

The reason and primary cause of the utility and profit is very clear, demonstrable, and provable. First of all, clothes are made from the wool and shearing of the sheep, from which princes, kings, great lords, and all people of the human race are dressed and by which our human condition is commonly covered. It can be worked in many diverse ways and manners and given different colors and tints for cloth of grain, which some call scarlet,[‡] to make large and rich articles called tapestries with many depictions of animals, fish, birds, flowers, leaves, and other beautiful and wondrous things, delightful to see. These woolen goods could be carried to some parts of the world where they could be sold more dearly than silk. It is thus and should be that the ewe is more honored and valued for the bounty of its wool than a worm or bug from which comes silk.

The hides of the sheep, rams, ewes, and woolbearing animals that we are discussing are useful for making parchment for books and letters and various writings. They are also useful for tanning, dressing, and processing in many and diverse ways: to make wide straps and other necessary and beneficial things for many uses, whose details would be too long to list.

The flesh of the wether and of the ewe is good nourishment for the human creature, to eat with vegetables and to make many dishes at the proper time. Scholars in Paris[‡] and Orléans and elsewhere and many others are well acquainted with it and use it at table more commonly than the flesh of other animals. The entrails are called tripe and the head of the wether or ewe is named *rebbardeure* or *demi-rebbardeure* by the people in Picardy. The feet, the liver, the lungs (when not harmed or infected by buttercup[‡] or other bad plants) and the other internal parts are good and salutary for poor folk, for many take nourishment and comfort from them in great plenty.

The suet and grease[‡] are good and useful in making candles and ointments and sometimes are put in surgeons' ointments because of the goodness and holiness of the animal. The bowels are good and useful in making many thick and

et menues, les grosses [24] pour mettre en ars, en espringales et autres engins a geter, ou au mains pour mettre es instrumens de quoy l'en bat la laine pour faire menue, pour la draperie que l'en appelle *archonner*. Les menues cordes des boyaulx, bien lavez, sechiez, tors, rez, essuez et filez, sont pour la melodie des instrumens de musique : de vielles, de harpes, de rothes, de luthz, de quiternes, de rebebes,[1] de coros, de almaduries, de symphonies, de cytholes, et de autres instrumens que l'en fait sonner par dois et par cordes. Dont pour la difference des choses et pour la variacion des courages, et de la maniere de vivre qui a esté et est entre les brebis et les loups, bon seroit a esprouver cordes de boyaux desdictz loups pour mettre en aucuns bas instrumens avec cordes de boyaux de brebis ou de chieveres* pour sçavoir mont[2] se il se pourroient accorder ensemble. Et croit l'acteur[3] que non.

Le fiens des oeilles est moult prouffitable a fumer et amender les terres arables, et pour ce les sages laboureurs, depuis printemps[4] jusques en la fin d'autompne que il ne fait pas trop froid de nuyt, font tenir et gesir [25] leurs oeilles aux champs de jour et de nuyt[5] pour engresser les terres. Et sont en giron aussi comme en maniere de parc, et les maine et remue le pasteur successivement de[6] lieu en autre petit a petit. Et au lieu ou elles sont emparchees et pour la garde, une logette de fust sur quatre roelles en maniere de borde portable. Et en celle maisonnette gist le pasteur[7] de nuyt et se y peult retraire pour la pluye, et y a des

---

[1] rebecs *B*
[2] mont *om. B*
[3] l'auteur *B*
[4] d. le p. *BT*
[5] de j. et de n. *om. B*
[6] du *T*
[7] pastour *B*

slender cords, the large ones to put in bows, in machines of bombardment[1] and other similar instruments, and also to put in the implements with which wool is beaten to make it fine for drapery, which is called bowing.[2] The thin bowel cords, well washed, dried, twisted, flattened,[3] cleaned and drawn, are for the tunable sounds of musical instruments: vielles, harps, viols,[4] lutes, gitterns,[5] rebecs, drums,[6] *almaduries*, hurdy-gurdy,[7] citoles,[8] and other instruments made to sound with fingers and strings. So, because of the difference between things and the variation in nature and manner of living that has always existed between sheep and wolves, it would be good to try to put the bowel cords of wolves in some low instruments with the bowel cords of sheep or goats to know for certain whether they would harmonize together. The author believes they would not.

Sheep manure[‡] is very useful for fertilizing and improving arable land. Consequently, wise workers, from spring to the end of fall when it is not too cold at night, keep and bed down the ewes day and night in the fields to fertilize them. They are in a circle, as in a sheepfold,[9] and the shepherd leads and moves them successively from place to place, bit by bit. In the place where they are held there is a small wooden lodging on four wheels for the guardian, like a portable cabin. In this cabin the shepherd rests at night and can retreat there from the rain, and

---

[1] *espringalle*: "engine of war used to shoot pieces of iron and large arrows at walls of a beleaguered town" (Cotgrave).

[2] *arçon*: "outil pour battre la laine, utilisé surtout par les chapeliers" (Lachiver). [A tool used for working wool, especially used by hatmakers.]

[3] *rez: mettre rez pied rez terre*: "To rase, cast or beat down, lay flat unto, even with the ground" (Cotgrave).

[4] *rote*: "Instrument de musique à cordes frottées du genre de la vielle ou violon" (Godefroy). [Musical instrument with strings stroked, like a hurdy-gurdy or violin.]

[5] *Gitterne*: "A plucked lute of the Middle Ages, particularly the period 1200–1350, related to the fiddle. It evolved into the cittern in the 15th century. It was mistakenly called gittern by Galpin and is still referred to as such in many modern works." (*New Grove*, 9: 907–9).

[6] *choron*: "Instrument de musique à percussion et à baguettes, du genre tambour" (Godefroy). [Percussive musical instrument with drumsticks, like a drum.]

[7] *symphony, cifonie*: "Instrument de musique du genre de la vielle à roue" (Godefroy). [Musical instrument like a hurdy-gurdy.]

[8] *citole*: "Citole: A plucked lute of the Middle Ages, particularly the period 1200–1350, related to the fiddle. It evolved into the cittern in the fifteenth century. It was mistakenly called gittern by Galpin, and is still referred to as such in many modern works (*New Grove*, 5: 872–6) . . . The strings were made of sheep gut (according to a not wholly reliable source in *Le Bon berger*, written in 1379 but surviving in later adaptations)" (*New Grove*, 5: 873).

[9] *parc*: "sheepfold" (Cotgrave). "The open field system, by concentrating crops in either one or two big fields . . . made . . . the fallow available for browsing . . . In addition, it assured that the manure would not be wasted on wild pasture but deposited on next year's arable" (White, *Medieval Technology*, 55–56).

chiens qui font le guet pour les oeilles* contre leurs adversaires. Et aussi, comme il est dit ou livre Ezechiel,[1]* quelque part que les bestes aloient, les roes aloient pareillement[2] emprez[3] elles. Tout aussi[4] est il que, quant les oeilles se remuent et que le parc va ou est mené avant ou arriere ou[5] d'encoste,[6] la petite maison sur les roelles les suist et est menee aprés les bestes, et ainsi sont les terres engraissees et amendees du fient* des oeilles, qui est moult prouffitable chose. D'autre part la crote des brebis vault moult en medicines,[7] et est maintesfois donnee* aux malades et patiens en bruvages ou en autre maniere pour leur santé recouvrer. Le suyn de la[8] laine vault a laver et net[26]toyer draps et autres choses soulliees et aussi vault il a mettre aucunesfois sur playes, empostumes et ulceres, qui bien en sçait ouvrer.

Par ces raisons et autres assez meilleur[e]s* que Jehan de Brie ne fait pas mettre en escript, conclut il, et est assez souffissamment monstré, que les oeilles sont moult prouffitables. Et par consequens[9] le traictié et la doctrine en est bonne et prouffitable et le pasteur ou bergier est digne de grant honneur, si comme il apparestra[10]* cy aprés.

25.22–23 donnee *B*] donnees *TV*

---

[1] ou l. de E. *T*
[2] pareillement *om. B*
[3] aprés *B*
[4] ainsi *B*
[5] ou *om. B*
[6] de costé *B*
[7] medecine *B*
[8] la *om. B*
[9] consequent *B*, -quant *T*
[10] apparoistra *B*

dogs are there who stand guard for the ewes against their enemies. As is said in the Book of Ezekiel, wherever the animals go, the wheels go along with them.[‡] Likewise, when the ewes move about and go back to the sheepfold or are led back and forth or to the side, the little house on wheels follows them and is drawn after the animals. So in this way the fields are fertilized and improved with the dung of the sheep, which is very beneficial. On the other hand, the dung of ewes is very valuable as medicine and is often given to the ill and to patients in beverages or in another manner to help them recover their health. The wool's grease is valuable for washing and cleaning linens and other soiled things. Sometimes it is useful to put on wounds, abscesses, and ulcers, which is well known to work.

For these reasons and others even better, which Jean de Brie has not had written down,[‡] he concludes that it has been sufficiently demonstrated that sheep are very profitable. Consequently the treatise and the knowledge about them is good and useful and the herdsman or shepherd is worthy of great honor, as will appear hereafter.

De l'onneur et estat[1] du bergier. iiie.

Le mestier de la garde des oeilles est moult honnorable et de grant auctorité. Ce peult on prouver apertement par nature et[2] par la Saincte Escripture. Par nature on voit communement que toute humaine creature est inclinee naturellement a suyvir, amer et honnorer ce dont bien luy vient et prouffit, et specialement ce dont elle prent son vivre, ses alimens et sa soustenance corporelle. Et plusieurs personnes sans nombre prendent[3] leur vivre, nourriture et susten[27]tacion, pour la plus grant partie, du prouffit et emolument des oeilles.[4] Item : par la Saincte Escripture et par les figures des anciens est assez tesmoignié que l'en doit[5] moult honnorer l'estat des pasteurs et de la bergerie, car si comme on list en Genesis,[6] Abel fust le premier bergier et pasteur des oeilles et offrit a Dieu don acceptable. Et quant les gens commencerent a croistre et multiplier[7] sur terre,[8] leur premiere chevance et leur premier gouvernement dont ilz montoient a honneur, en[9] puissance et en estat de vivre si[10] furent de nourriture[11] des bestes. Les patriarches et aucuns roys anciennement furent bergiers et pasteurs et garderent les oeilles et bestes a laine[12] en leurs propres personnes. Des patriarches, n'est il[13] point de doubte qu'il[14] ne feussent bergiers, si comme Abraham, Ysaac et Jacob, et principalement Jacob, duquel yssirent les douze ligniees d'Ysrael, fust bergier par long temps et moult expert en la doctrine et science de garder oeilles.[15]

Celuy Jacob servit Laban son oncle et garda ses oeilles par sept ans[16] en esperance[17] d'avoir a femme Rachel, la[18] [28] fille dudit Laban. Et quant il faillit a son intencion et que l'autre fille nommee Lya luy fust donnee en lieu de Rachel, il fust bergier audit Laban par autres sept annees pour avoir ladicte Rachel. Et pour son loyer luy fust octroyé par ledit Laban qu'il aroit* toutes les oeilles et brebis

---

1 De l'onneur estal [*sic*] *T*
2 par nature et *om. B*
3 prennent *BT*
4 oeilles *followed by* Pourquoy *and what may be an end-of-line filler TV.*
5 l'en i doit *T*
6 Genese *B*
7 et a m. *T*
8 sur la t. *T*
9 en *om. B*
10 si *om. B*
11 fut de la n. *B*
12 laines *T*
13 il n'est *B*
14 ilz *BT*
15 g. moutons et oeilles *T*
16 par l'espace de sept ans *T*
17 esperant *T* (*om.* en)
18 la *om. T*

Chapter 3

Concerning the Honor and Profession of the Shepherd

The profession of the care of sheep is most honorable and of great importance. This can be manifestly proven through nature and by Holy Scripture. In nature it is commonly seen that all human creatures are naturally inclined to follow, love and honor that which is good for them, especially that from which they take their food, nourishment and bodily support. Numberless people take their living, food, and support, for the most part, from the profit and gain from sheep.

Item: From Holy Scripture and from ancient models there is sufficient witness that the status of shepherds and the sheepfold should be honored. As one reads in Genesis, Abel was the first shepherd and herdsman of sheep and offered an acceptable gift to God. When men began to grow and multiply upon the earth, their first wealth and first authority by which they rose to honor in power and position was in the raising of animals. The patriarchs and other ancient kings were shepherds and herdsmen who themselves watched over sheep and wool-bearing animals. As for the patriarchs, there is no doubt that they were shepherds, like Abraham, Isaac, and Jacob, especially Jacob from whom there came the twelve lines of Israel, and who was a shepherd for a long time and greatly expert in the learning and science of caring for sheep.

That Jacob served his uncle Laban and cared for his sheep for seven years in the hope of having Rachel, Laban's daughter, as his wife. When he was foiled in this plan and another daughter named Leah was given to him in lieu of Rachel, he remained a shepherd for Laban for another seven years in order to have Rachel. For his salary, Laban granted that he should have all the sheep and ewes

qui seroient tachiees, vairolees ou grivelees. Si applica ledit Jacob sa malice,[1] a ce que ou[2] mois de septembre, que[3] les moutons saillent et luisent[4] les brebis por-tieres, selon la condicion de leur nature, Jacob leur mettoit au devant choses de diverses couleurs opposites, si comme blanc et noir, pers et janne,[5] rouge et vert, ou semblables choses, et mesmement il peloit d'ung lez les verges et bastons des[6] saulx ou autres arbres, et a l'autre lez lessoit l'escorce pour donner ymaginacion auxdictes brebis ou* moutons en luisant et saillant,[7] affin que les portieres, en re-gardant la diversité, conceussent faons et aigneaux tachiez, vairolez, ou grivelez, de diverses couleurs, et que par ce il[8] demourassent au prouffit dudit Jacob, dont par sa cautelle il fust moult enrichi.

Juda, le filz dudit Jacob, duquel issirent les roys d'Ysrael, [29] fust bergier. Et est vray que quant il aloit faire tondre ses brebis en la saison, sa[9] femme Thamar estoit reposee ou[10] chemin en une logette et se estoit deguisee et descongneue. Juda ne sçavoit pas que ce fust Thamar sa femme,[11] toutesfois engendra il lors en elle deux enfans, Pharés et Zaran.[12] Et depuis qu'il sceust que il avoit esté deceu et qu'il avoit pechié par maniere de fornicacion, il se repentit et ne voulut* oncques puis retourner a ladicte Thamar. Ce fait est bien a noter pour les pasteurs, affin que ilz se gardent[13] de fornicacion.

Moÿses fust bergier et garda les brebis. Et aprés ce qu'il eut occis ung Egypcien et le cachié[14] ou[15] sablon, il s'en fouyst en l'isle de Eleopoleos et trouva lors Sephora, fille de Jetro le prestre de la loy,[16] laquelle avoit besoing d'ayde a abruver ses oeilles pour le chault et pour la presse des pasteurs qui estoient environ le puys. Et Moÿses luy ayda a abruver ses bestes et depuis la print a femme. Moÿses gardoit les oeilles quant il vit la flamme du buisson ardant, duquel il n'eust rien ars ne bruslé.

28.18 brebis ou moutons *T*] ou *om. BV*

---

[1] son engin *B*
[2] au *B*
[3] que *om. T*
[4] luitent *T*
[5] joulne *B*
[6] de *T*
[7] en luitant ou s. *T*
[8] ilz *T*
[9] une *B*
[10] au *B*
[11] sa belle fille *B*
[12] Zaram *B*
[13] que ilz gardoient *T*
[14] l'eut caché *B*, le cachia *T*
[15] au *B*
[16] de Madian *B*

that were spotted, mottled gray or brown speckled.[‡] Jacob planned his stratagem so that in the month of September, when the rams mount and breed the breeding ewes, according to the circumstances of their nature, he placed before them things of sundry opposite colors, such as white and black, blue and yellow, red and green,[‡] or something similar, and likewise he peeled one side of branches of willows or other trees and left the bark on the other side to give imagination to the rams or ewes in their mounting and breeding so that the breeding ewes in looking at this diversity would conceive spotted, gray, and speckled kids and lambs of various colors, and in this way would remain as Jacob's profit. By this sharp practice he was much enriched.

Judah, son of Jacob, from whom issued the kings of Israel, was a shepherd. It is true that when he went out to shear his sheep in season, his wife Tamar [‡] had placed herself on the way in a shelter and was disguised and unrecognizable. Judah did not know that it was Tamar his wife; in any case he begot on her two children, Pharez and Zarah. When he learned that he had been deceived and had sinned by fornication, he repented and never wished to go back to Tamar. This fact is well noted by shepherds so that they may keep themselves from fornication.

Moses was a shepherd and tended sheep. After he had killed an Egyptian and hidden him in the sand, he fled to the island of Eleopoleus and there he found Sephora, daughter of the priest of law, Jethro.[‡] She needed help watering her ewes because of the heat[‡] and because of the crowd of herdsmen around the well. Moses helped her water her animals and then took her as his wife. Moses was guarding his sheep when he saw the flame of the burning bush, which was neither scorched nor burned.

David gardoit les brebis quant il fust esleu pour aler combatre a Golias [30] de Jeth,[1] le fort geant, lequel il deconfist par la pierre qu'il getta de la fonde.[2] Et depuis fust David roy[3] d'Ysrael aprés Saül. Saül mesmes avoit gardé les bestes, les asnes[4] et les asnesses de son pere ainçois qu'il feust* roy. Cyrus fust bergier et garda les brebis ; les pastoureaulx en firent leur roy et venoient a luy aux jugemens. Et depuis fust il roy de Perse et de Mede, et destruit Babiloine la Grant et fist moult de grandes* proesses.[5]

Assez y pourroit on mettre et assigner des exemples. Et par les dessusdictz est assez prouvé, attendu que tant de vaillans hommes furent bergiers, que l'en doit bien faire et porter honneur aux loyaulx pasteurs et bergiers entrans par le droit huys en la bergerie.

---

[1] Jethe *B*

[2] fronde *T*

[3] fut roy David *T*

[4] et les asnes *B*

[5] de grandes veillances et p. *T*

David was watching his sheep when he was chosen to go forth to fight Goliath of Gath, the mighty giant, whom he slew with the stone that he threw from his sling. And then David was king of Israel after Saul. Saul himself had watched over the animals, asses and jennies, of his father, before he was king. Cyrus was a shepherd and watched over sheep; the herdsmen made him their king and came to him for decrees. Later he was king of the Persians and Medes and destroyed great Babylon and accomplished many wonderful feats.

Many examples can be cited and mentioned. Because of the above it is sufficiently proven that, since so many valiant men were shepherds, honor should be accorded and given to the loyal herdsmen and shepherds who enter the sheepfold by the right door.

Des reigles generaulx* de cest art. iiiiᵉ.

Quiconques se veult entremettre de l'art de bergerie, il doit, sans enfraindre, tenir, garder et maintenir solennelement les reigles qui cy aprés seront recitees generalement,[1] car elles sont convenables, necessaires et prouffitables.

Premierement, les aigneaux, qui sont jeunes et tendres, doivent estre traictiez amyablement et sans vio[31]lence, et ne les doit on pas ferir ne chastier de* verges, de bastons, de corgies, ne d'autres manieres de bastures qui les puissent blecier ou froisser, car ilz en descroistroient et seroient maigres et chetives. Mais par introduction et chastiement les doit on mener doulcement et amyablement.

Item : quant les aigneaux sont creuz et nourris, que il pevent souffrir discipline, ilz doivent estre menez et corrigez par la houlette de terre legiere, ne on ne leur doit faire moleste jusques a tant qu'il[2] ont esté tonduz la premiere fois. Et les doit on lesser* faire et demener a leur voulenté, et ainsi prendent[3] ilz amendement et acroissement, car par la legiere correction se tournent ilz[4] a obeissance et a aler par tout ou le bergier les veult mener et conduire.

Les bestes antenoises, portieres, brebis, moutons, chastris[5] et toutes autres doit on chastier et corriger[6] de* corgies de cuir, ou de cordelles menues, pour ce que aucunes en y a si pareceuses que de leur gré ne veulent yssir hors de l'estable, si advient[7] souvent qu'il en convient tirer aucunes hors par violence* au crochet[8] du bout[9] de la houlette pour yssir et aler devant. [32] Et l'en fiert et bat les autres des corgies pour les esmouvoir et haster a suivyr les autres, affin que tout le fouc se parte de l'estable et isse hors ensemble pour aler en pasturage, la ou le bergier les veult mener. Et ainsi par corgies et autres molestes convient il[10] corriger et contraindre aucuns qui ne veulent recevoir discipline ne eulx mettre a obeissance.

Item : quant les oeilles repairent de leurs pastis, mesmement ou temps d'esté depuis may jusques en septembre, le bergier ne les doit pas mettre ne les bouter[11]

31.01 chastier de verges *BT*] de *om. V*
31.20 de corgies *T*] des c. *BJV*
31.24 hors par v. *BJ*] hors par la laine *T*, hors de la laine par v. *V*

---

[1] seront generallement recitees *T*
[2] ilz *T*
[3] prennent *BT*
[4] ilz *om. B*
[5] chastrez *B*, chastrés *T*
[6] doivent estres [*sic*] chastiees et corrigees *T*
[7] advint *B*
[8] au crochet *om. T*
[9] ou du b. *T*
[10] il *om. B*
[11] ne les bouter *om. B*

Chapter 4

General Rules Concerning this Art

Whoever wishes to enter into the art of sheep husbandry must, without reservation, keep close and solemnly uphold the rules that are hereafter recounted altogether, for they are suitable, necessary and profitable.

First of all, the lambs, young and tender, should be treated kindly and without violence and should not be struck or corrected with switches, sticks or whips nor any other kind of beating that could hurt or bruise them, for they would fall off‡ and become thin and weak. Rather one should lead them gently and kindly by leadership and correction.‡

Item: When the lambs are grown and fleshed out so they can withstand discipline, they should be led and chastised with a light shower of dirt from the crook,[1]‡ nor should they be harried until they have been shorn for the first time, but should be allowed to move about at will. In this way they will accept correction and training, for by light correction they will turn to obedience and go wherever the shepherd wishes to lead them.

The yearling ewes,[2] pregnant ewes, ewes, rams, wethers and all others should be corrected and chastised with lashes of leather or narrow cords, because there are some who are so lazy that they will not go out of the stable on their own. It often happens that it is necessary to drag some out forcefully with the hook at the end of the crook so they will go out and move forward, to hit and strike others with whips to make them move and hurry to follow the others so that the whole flock will leave the stable and go out together into the pasture where the shepherd wishes to lead them. Thus it is necessary by whips and other irksome methods to correct and constrain those unwilling to accept discipline or submit to obedience.

Item: When the ewes come back from their pasture, especially in summertime from May to September, the shepherd should not put them or make them

---

[1] "houlette: long bâton dont une extrémité est large et aplatie. Il s'en sert pour jeter des mottes de terre devant la bête qui s'écarte, et l'incite ainsi à rejoindre le troupeau" (Lorcin, *France*, 38). [A long staff wide and flat at one end. It is used in throwing dirt clods ahead of the sheep who strays, thus urging her to return to the flock.]

[2] ". . . dans la basse latinité, la jeune brebis s'appelait encore *bidens*; et le mouton, *castrat*. Nous croyons que par hogatre, on designait surtout en Angleterre les jeunes moutons." (Delisle, *Etudes*, 240). [. . . in the late Latin era, the young ewe was still called *bidens* (has her two-year-old teeth); and the wether, *castrat*. We believe that by hoggit, were designated, above all in England, the young sheep.] A footnote to this goes further, giving the phrase: "inter gerces et hogastres." *Gerce: gerque*: "La brebis en Nomendie" (Lachiver). [The ewe in Normandy.]

doit umbrager et refroider soubz ung ourmel ou tilleul ou autre arbre spacieux, se aucuns en a prez des estables et herbergeries. Et si non, il y doit pourvoir par autre[1] voye et maniere convenable pour l'aysement des bestes pour remedier a leur chaleur.

Le bon remede contre la chaleur des bestes est de curer et nettoier les estables[2] et oster[3] le fiens,[4] pour refroidir[5] les bestes et les tenir freschement. Et se[6] ce estoit a la venue de prangiere vers midy ou heure de none, et le soleil gettoit ses rais [33] par l'uys de la bergerie, le pasteur doit clorre l'uys et doit pourvoir d'eaue fresche et froide pour espandre et getter a l'entree de l'uys et ailleurs par l'estable pour le lieu rafreschir[7] et refroidir, pour donner temperance contre la chaleur aux bestes oeilles,[8] qui de leur nature sont chauldes et seches en complexion, par quoy la chaleur est nuysant et contraire.

Et toutesfois soit tenu pour reigle que ou moys* de may[9] l'en ne doit pas curer les estables des bergeries, pour ce que les humeurs qui lors yssent de la terre plus habundamment que en autre saison se adherdent[10] aux parois et maisieres[11] des bergeries[12] et estables, et engendrent corruption au bercal par mauvaise feteur et odeur plus que en autre temps, car en temps d'yver la gelee et froidure degaste[13] telles humeurs et feteurs, et[14] ne pevent[15] tant nuyre comme en may.[16] Et la raison est que la terre oeuvre lors ses conduitz et gette ses[17] superfluitez de ses entrailles plus habundamment. Si est le meilleur et plus expedient de laisser le fiens[18] es estables aux oeilles oudit[19] mois de may que de l'oster, car l'umeur de la terre, qui engendre mauvais air [34] et punaisie es estables, n'a pas si grant vertu quant elle est couverte de fiens. Et la punaisie engendre plusieurs maladies

---

[1] autres *T*

[2] les bestes *T*

[3] hoster *T*

[4] fient *T*

[5] refrodir *T*

[6] se *om. T*

[7] refraischir *B*, refreschir *T*

[8] b. et ouailles *B*, b. oeillis *T*

[9] moy *T*

[10] se montent *B*

[11] maigieres *B*

[12] bergeris *B*

[13] gaste *T*

[14] et *om. T*

[15] ne p. pas *T*

[16] c. ou moys de may *T*

[17] les *B*

[18] fient *T*

[19] audict *BT*

go immediately into the fold. Rather, he should lead them the whole way at great leisure and should give them shade and let them cool off under an elm or linden or some other spacious tree, if there are any near the stable or sheepfold. If none exist, he should find another means and convenient way for the relief of his animals, to relieve their heat.

The good remedy for the animals' heat is to muck out and clean the stable and remove the manure, to cool the animals' heat and keep them refreshed. And if, with the approach of dinnertime toward noon, the sun should cast its rays in the door of the sheepfold, the shepherd should close the door and provide fresh cool water to scatter and throw in the door's entry and throughout the stable to refresh and cool it to give moderation of the heat to the ewes, who by nature have a warm and dry constitution, wherefore heat is harmful and adverse.

It should always be a fast rule that in the month of May the stables and sheepfolds should not be cleaned out because the dampness that comes forth from the earth more abundantly then than in any other season adheres to the walls and partitions of the folds and stables and breeds corruption in the fold from its dreadful miasma and stench. In winter the ice and cold dissipate such humors and miasmas and they are not as harmful as in May. The reason is that the earth then opens its passages and spews forth the excesses of its bowels more abundantly. Therefore it is better and more advisable to leave the manure in the ewes' stable in May than to remove it, since the earth's humor, which breeds bad air and stench in the stable, does not have as great strength when it is covered with manure. The fetid air causes many maladies and great grief

et grans inconveniens aux bestes oudit[1] mois, si y fait bon obvier par laisser ledit fiens, car la frescheur d'iceluy fiens n'est pas si male ne si[2] perilleuse comme l'umeur corrumpu de la terre des estables par les vapeurs qui lors yssent d'icelle terre, comme dit est.

Et[3] en tous autres mois, excepté ledit mois de may, l'en peult et doit curer les estables, et en oster le fiens en chascun mois par deux fois ou plus. Et qui plus le fait, mieulx vault, pour ce que plus[4] sont les bestes tenues et gouvernees nettement, et plus fructifient.

Item : le pasteur doit eschever et obvier de tout son pouoir que ses* bestes et oeilles ne soient moullees en nul temps, pour ce que la pluye est contraire et nuysible aux oeilles et les fait descroistre et empirer. Si s'en doit[5] garder songneusement que elles ne voisent* a la pluye et que elles ne soient moulliees,[6] excepté ou[7] mois de may, car en may est bon que les oeilles ayent de la pluye par avant que elles soient tondues, pour ce que la laine en est plus [35] nette et meilleur[e]* a tondre et mieulx vendable. Et[8] aussi la pluye qui chiet sur la laine avant la tonsure engendre aux oeilles le bon suyn, qui leur garde le corps et leur est moult prouffitable pour lors. Mais autant que ladicte pluye vault et prouffite aux oeilles par avant la tonsure, de tant plus assez leur est elle nuysant et dommagable aprés la tonsure et en toutes autres saisons.

En tous temps et en toutes saisons[9] doit le bergier conduire et raconduire son bestial* et oeilles a leur aisement[10] et prouffit, et les doit garder songneusement, choyer et defendre de toutes les choses qui leur pourroient porter dommage. Toutes ces reigles doit garder chascun bergier et aucunes autres qui sont bien necessaires et[11] convenables a ceste doctrine, et lesquelles seront baillees cy ensuyvant en especial.

34.17 ses *T*] ces *BJV*

---

[1] audict *B*, audit *T*
[2] si *om. B*
[3] Et aussi *T*
[4] vault car tant plus *T*
[5] Si les doit *T*
[6] moueillees *T*
[7] au *B*
[8] En *B*
[9] et en toutes saisons *om. B*
[10] aise *T*
[11] et *om. B*

to the animals in this month, so it is good to avoid that by leaving the manure, for the freshness of the manure is not so bad or dangerous as the corrupt dampness of the stable's earth because of the vapors that come from the earth, as has been said.

Item: In all other months, except this month of May, the stable can and should be kept clean and the manure removed each month two or more times. If done more, even better, for the more the animals are kept clean and in order, the more they prosper.

Item: The shepherd should avoid and prevent with all his power his animals becoming wet at any time, because rain is unfavorable and harmful to sheep and makes them weaken and fall off. Therefore he should watch carefully that they do not go out in the rain and that they are not wet except in the month of May. In May it is good for the ewes to have rain before they are shorn, because the wool is more clean, better to shear, and more marketable. Also the rain falling on the wool before shearing brings forth the ewes' good grease, which protects their body and is very beneficial to them. However, as much as the rain is valuable and helpful to the ewes before shearing, it is even more harmful and damaging after they are shorn and at all other times.

In all weathers and all seasons the shepherd should lead forth his animals and ewes and bring them back for their comfort and profit and keep watch over them carefully, preserving and defending them from all things that might harm them. All these rules should be observed by each shepherd, as well as others that are necessary and appropriate to this learning and those which will be presented separately hereafter.

De la maniere de congnoistre le temps par les oyseaux, et de sçavoir du beau temps ou de la pluye. v^e.

Necessairement appartient et convient que le bergier ait congnoissance du temps, et pour avoir de ce aucuns enseignemens,[1] il doit avoir consideracion a plusieurs choses.

[36] Des* estourneaux

En temps d'yver advient souvent que les estourneaux se assemblent a grans tourbes et volent ensemble, et aucunesfois se assieent sur ung ourmel[2] ou autre grant arbre. Si doit le bergier avoir[3] regart comment les estourneaux se partent de dessus l'ourmel,[4] car quant ilz se partent tous ensemble a une volee, ce signifie grant froidure. Et se ilz partent par petites volees, l'ung aprés l'autre, ce est signe de pluye.

Du heron

Quant le heron se lieve de sa pasture et il se escrie hault au lever, ce est signe de fort et dur temps. Se il vole contre le vent de bise, ce[5] signifie grant froidure. Se il vole contre le vent d'aval, que les bergiers appellent Plungel, ce signifie pluye. Se le heron a son retour de son vol se[6] rassiet prez du lieu dont il est[7] parti, ce est signifiance que le temps dessusdit est a advenir prouchainement. Se il vole et se rassiet loing de la ou il se leva, la mutacion dudit temps[8] sera differee[9] et ne advendra pas si tost.

De l'aronde

Quant l'aronde vole bien hault et par loysir a longs traictz, ce signifie pluye, et [37] quant elle vole bas et hastivement prez de terre, ce est signe de foison[10] pluye. Et quant elle est en l'air en son esbatement querant[11] les mouchetes, ce signifie beau temps.

36.01 Des *BJ*] De *TV*

---

[1] de ce enseignement *T*
[2] ormeil *T*
[3] d. avoir le b. *T*
[4] l'ormeil *T*
[5] se *T*
[6] vol et se r. *T*
[7] cest *T*
[8] est a advenir . . . dudit temps *om. T*
[9] sera admoderé et differé *T*
[10] s. foison de p. *B*
[11] en l'air soy esbatant q. *B*

Chapter 5

Concerning the Way of Telling the Weather by the Birds, and Knowing if it Will be Fine or Rainy Weather

It is necessarily part of the shepherd's job that he should know about the weather and in order to take instruction in this, he should pay attention to several things.

Concerning Starlings[‡]

It often happens in winter that starlings gather in great crowds and fly together and sometimes they sit on an elm or other tall tree. So the shepherd should pay attention to how the starlings take off from the elm tree, for when they leave all together in one flock, this means great cold; if they leave in small groups, one after the other, this is a sign of rain.

Concerning the Heron[‡]

When the heron rises from its foraging and cries out loudly on its ascent, this indicates rugged and harsh weather. If it flies into the north wind, this means great cold. If it flies into the southwest wind from the valley, which the shepherds call *Plongel*,[1] this means rain. If the heron on return from its flight settles again near the place from which it left, this indicates that the weather described above will soon arrive. If it flies and settles at some distance from where it took off, the change in the weather will be delayed and will not come as soon.

Concerning the Swallow[‡]

When the swallow flies really high and leisurely in long swoops, this means rain. When it flies low and fast near the ground, this means an abundance of rain. When it is in the air sporting about seeking little flies, this indicates fine weather.

---

[1] *Plongel: plonge; action de s'enfoncer dans l'eau, action d'engloutir* (Greimas). [Downpour, plunging in water, action of being swallowed up.]

Du huas

Le huat, que l'en appelle *escoufle*,* est ung oyseau qui a maniere et coustume de siffler et crier en l'air, et ce peult estre pour deux causes. L'une est quant il a faim et lors crie il et siffle plus aigrement. L'autre cause est a quoy le bergier doit avoir consideracion, qui[1] fait au significat du temps, car quant il crie plus basse-ment et molement, en disant "huy, huy, huy," il annonce la pluye.

De l'espec[2]

De l'oyseau que l'en nomme *espect*[3] ou *pymart*,[4] peult on faire semblable juge-ment comme il est dit de l'escoufle ou huas, car il crie et hennist forment quant il doit plouvoir.

De la verdiere

Toutesfois que la verdiere met a point ses plumes et les aplanoye de son bec, ce est vray signe de pluye. Ceste significacion est souvent esprouvee par les ber-giers qui ont regart audit oyseau. Et est appellee verdiere pour la couleur de ses plumes, dont les[5] [38] plusieurs sont de verte couleur.

Du butor

Ung autre oyseau y a que l'en nomme *butor*; aucuns l'appellent *bruitor*. Il a long bec et agu et habite es mares et es prez sur les rivieres, aussi[6] que fait le heron, et ne chante fors que en temps d'esté et est sa voix oÿe de bien loing. Quant il doit faire beau temps, il chante haultement et donne si grant son et tel bondissement de sa voix, que par nuyt on le pourroit oÿr de plus de demye lieue[7] loing. Et quant il doit plouvoir, il chante plus bas et plus lentement et ne rent pas si grant son.

De la pye

La pye, que aucuns nomment *agache*, est moult malicieuse et en pronosticacions est une droite sebille, mais chascun bergier n'entent pas son langage. Aucunesfois par sa criee annonce elle le beau temps et aucunesfois la pluye, et combien que elle soit assez tricheresse, toutesfois principalement quant elle brait et agache et crie souvent et[8] continuellement et se tient prez des hayes ou des[9] buissons en demenant sa noise, ce signifie qu'il y a loup ou renart ou aucune male beste assez prez.

---

[1] qu'il *T*

[2] l'espect *B*

[3] l'espec *B*, espec *T*

[4] pyvart *B*

[5] les *om. B*

[6] ainsi *B*

[7] lieu *B*

[8] et *om. T*

[9] des *om. B*

Concerning the Kite‡

The kite, the one called the red kite, is a bird that has the manner and habit of whistling and calling in the air, which can be from two causes: one is when it is hungry, and then it calls and whistles most sharply. The other cause is the one the shepherd should notice and that indicates the weather. When it cries lower and softer, saying "huy, huy, huy," it announces rain.

Concerning the Green Woodpecker‡

As to the bird called the green woodpecker, one can make a similar judgment as was made about the kite or eagle, for it calls out and bawls strongly when it is due to rain.

Concerning the Green Finch‡

Every time the green finch preens its feathers and smooths them with its beak, it is a true sign of rain. This significance is often proven by shepherds who watch this bird. It is called green finch because of the color of its feathers, many of which are of a green color.

Concerning the Bittern‡

There is another bird called a bittern; others call it the noisemaker. It has a long sharp beak and frequents marshes and meadows near rivers, as does the heron, and sings only in the summer, its voice heard at a great distance. When the weather is going to be fair, it sings loudly and gives such great sound and such projection to its voice that at night it can be heard for more than half a league. When it is going to rain, it sings more quietly and slowly and does not send forth such a great sound.

Concerning the Magpie‡

The magpie, which others call the pie, is very deceitful and is a genuine sibyl when it comes to prognostications, but not every shepherd understands its message. Sometimes its cry will announce good weather and sometimes rain. And while it may be mischievous, yet when it calls out loudly, sharply, frequently and continuously, and keeps near the hedges or bushes while making its racket, this means that there is a wolf or fox or other harmful animal nearby.

[39] De la corneille

La corneille annonce souvent la pluye par son cry, auquel cry le soutil bergier doit avoir regart, car il se differe en aucuns motz. Et aucunesfois au matin quant il doit plouvoir, elle prononce une maniere de cry et semble que elle die "glaras, glaras," et ce signifie pluye, mesmement quant il est prononcé par la corneille bise que l'en nomme *faissie*, et vient tousjours contre l'yver temps, quant les arondes se partent de ceste region. Et aussi s'en depart et s'en va mucier et repondre,[1] quant les arondes viennent en la nouvelle saison qui commence a l'entree d'avril.

Ces oyseaulx, et plusieurs autres qui volent en l'air, sçavent du temps par la divine pourveance. Et aussi voit on que les coulons s'en retournent moult radement[2] a leur coulombier. Et quant il viennent ainsi volant en grant haste, ce signifie tempeste ou grosse pluye a venir prouchainement. Si doit le bergier considerer diligemment les choses dessusdictes et assez d'autres, qu'il peult aprendre pour sçavoir de l'estat du temps pour le gouvernement de son bestial.

---

[1] respondre *B*
[2] roidement *B*

Concerning the Crow[‡]

The crow often announces rain with its cry, of which cry the clever shepherd should take notice, for it differs in some notes. Sometimes in the morning when it is going to rain, it emits a kind of cry and seems to say, "glaras, glaras," and this means rain, when it is pronounced by the blackish[1] crow, which is called *faissie,* and always comes toward winter, when the swallows leave this region. Also it leaves and conceals itself to lay its eggs again when the swallows come in the spring at the beginning of April.

These birds, and many others that fly in the air, know about the weather through divine providence. In addition, one may see doves returning most quickly to their cote. When they come flying thus in great haste, this signifies the near approach of a storm or heavy rain. Therefore, the shepherd should diligently consider the abovementioned things and many others so that he can learn to know the condition of the weather for the management of his animals.

---

[1] *bise*: "Browne, duskie, swart, blackish" (Cotgrave).

De congnoistre le temps par les bestes. vi[e] [1][40]

E ncore pour congnoistre le temps avec ce que dit est des oyseaux, convient il que le bergier sache de l'augur[2] des bestes par certains signes.
Pr[e]mierement du mouton

Chascun bergier ou pastoureau gardant fouc d'oeilles doit avoir ung mouton debonnaire et assoté et auquel il donne de son pain, lequel mouton par mignotise et pour estre mieulx congneu entre les autres porte une sonnette ou petite clochette de laton a son col, pourquoy en Brie il est appellé *le sonnaillier* et en aucuns autres pays est nommé *clocheman*.[3] Celuy mouton de sa nature congnoist partie de prenostique ou de augur du beau temps ou de la pluye, car quant il doit faire beau temps, il se lieve premier et vient premier a l'uys de l'estable pour yssir hors et aler en pasturage. Et[4] quant il doit plouvoir et faire lait temps, il se[5] tient par derriere les autres et monstre a sa contenance qu'il n'ait pas voulenté d'yssir. Et au soir quant il vient en l'estable et il doit faire froidure, il herice sa laine et se esqueult tellement que on l'entent bien au son de la petite clochette.

Aucuns dient que quant le chat lieve son visa[41]ge et lesche ses piedz de sa langue, se il met son pié par dessus l'oreille, ce signifie pluye. Mais de si orde beste ne doit on pas[6] parler en ceste partie, car par moult d'autres peult on avoir enseignement.

Les chevaux, les jumens, les asnes et asnesses, qui portent le charbon, le fruit et autres petites denrees aux povres gens, trepent et regibent quant les mouches ou les guepes les poingnent et piquent, et ceulx qui les mainent souloient dire que ce sont signes de pluye et de mutacion de temps.

Par meilleur[e]s* et[7] plus soutilles raisons peult le bergier congnoistre du temps, par ce que il convient que chascun jour en temps convenable il voist[8]* sur les champs mener ses oeilles en pasture. Et quant Phebus, qui par sa clarté enlumine tout le monde, se demonstre au matin es parties d'Orient, le bergier le voit tournier et aler tout le jour par son cercle, en faisant son mouvement en soy eslevant vers Midy, que aucuns appellent Auster, et puis descendre petit a petit jusques en Occident. Et en faisant tel chemin en nostre emyspere,[9] est mené en moult noble et moult riche char [42] attelé de quatre grans et puissans destriers de si tresgrant valeur que nulz hommes mortelz* ne les pourroit[10] extimer.

---

[1] vii *T*

[2] l'auguer *T*

[3] clocleman *BJ*

[4] Et *om. B*

[5] si [*sic*] *B*

[6] point *T*

[7] meilleurs et *repeated TV*

[8] voyse *BJT*

[9] hemysfere *B*

[10] pourroient *BJ*

Chapter 6

To Know About the Weather by the Animals

In addition to recognizing the weather by what was said about the birds, it is necessary for the shepherd to know the forewarnings by certain signs from animals.

First the sheep: Each shepherd or herdsman watching over a flock of sheep should have a good-hearted and devoted wether to whom he gives some of his bread. This wether, through gentle handling and to be more distinguishable from the others, carries round its neck a small bell of brass or some other metal. This is why in Brie he is called a *sonnaillier* and in other regions a *clocheman*.[1] This wether by nature recognizes predictions or signs of fair weather or rain: when it should be fine, he rises first and goes first to the stable door to go out to pasture. When it is going to rain and be foul, he keeps behind the others and shows by his demeanor that he has no wish to go outside. In the evening when he comes into the stable and it is going to be cold, he bristles his wool and shakes so that the sound of his bell can be clearly heard.

Some say that when the cat lifts its face and washes its feet with its tongue, if it puts its foot over its ear, this signifies rain.[‡] However there is no need to speak of such a nasty beast in this part, for there are many others from whom enlightenment can be had.

The horses, mares, jacks and jennies who carry the coal, fruit, and other small wares to poor folk, stamp and kick out when the flies or wasps sting and prick them,[‡] and those who lead them were wont to say that these are signs of rain and a change in the weather.

The shepherd can recognize the weather by much better and more subtle signs, for each day he must, at a suitable time, go out in the fields to lead his ewes to pasture. When Phoebus, who by his brilliance lights up the whole world, shows himself in the morning in the east, the shepherd sees him turn and go all day in his round, making his course in raising himself toward the south (which some call Auster)[2] and then dropping down little by little in the west. In making this course in our hemisphere, he is drawn in a most rich and most noble chariot by four great and powerful steeds of such great value that no mortal man could calculate

---

[1] The bellwether who helps lead the flock.

[2] *Auster*: "nom poétique du vent du Midi" (Lachiver). [Poetic name for wind from the south.]

L'ung de ces nobles chevaux qui mainent le soleil est nommé Eoüs, et vient devant droit a l'aube du jour jusques environ heure de tierce. Et pour ce que ces beaux chevaux se monstrent de plusieurs couleurs, le bergier doit considerer que se Eoüs appert vermeil et ardant au matin, ce signifie pluye et mutacion de temps. Et quant il se monstre plus blanc, ce est signe de beau jour. Et les pelerins qui cheminent en font feste quant il[1] le voient.

Aprés vient l'autre cheval, qui est nommé Ethoüs, lequel fait son service au soleil environ heure de midy. Et quant il se monstre de pale couleur, ce est bon signe de beau jour.

Et aprés midi sert[2] le tiers cheval attelé au noble char du soleil, lequel cheval est appellé Pyroüs. Et[3] en son venir voit on reflamboier[4] et estinceler les gros yeux reluisans de celuy Pyroüs, le puissant cheval,[5] tellement que veue de creature humaine ne le pourroit longuement regarder. Lors ne volent pas les chauves soris, car elles ne pourroient soustenir ne endu[43]rer si tresgrande[6] et noble lumiere qui si espant a l'advenement des rais du soleil qui ainsi fait son cours. Et quant ces deux chevaux sont trop chaux et ardans, c'est a dire Ethoüs[7] et Pyroüs, par leur puissance et chaleur il attraient les vapeurs de la terre et de l'eaue,[8] et les font monter en l'air. Et se ces[9] vapeurs ainsi eslevees ne sont degastees[10] par aucunes fumees, elles se assemblent et tournent en nuees qui se forment des parcelles d'icelles vapeurs, lesquelles[11] nuees de leur nature tendent a descendre et retourner ou centre. Et aucunesfois les dictes nuees sont muees en pluye, et[12] aucunesfois en vens, aucunesfois en naige et aucunesfois en gresil, selon la disposition des temps. Et ainsi peult veoir le bergier que par trop grant ferveur et chaleur des chevaux dessusditz vient la mutacion du temps.

Or disons du quatrieme cheval, que l'en appelle Phylogeüs, lequel fait son office en descendant ledit char du soleil. Celuy Phylogeüs tent voulentiers vers les eaues, car il sert contre le vespre. A luy et a celuy du matin doit le bergier prendre son augurement[13] a[14] congnoistre du temps. [44] Et la raison si[15] est que quant

---

[1] ilz *BJT*

[2] sort *BJ*

[3] Et *om. T*

[4] flamboyer *B*

[5] le puissant cheval *om. BJ*

[6] tresgrand *B*

[7] Eoüs *B*

[8] l'eur *T*

[9] ses *BJ*

[10] degastés *T*

[11] lesquelle *T*

[12] et *om. T*

[13] argument *T*

[14] a *om. B*

[15] si *om. B*

their worth. One of these noble steeds that draws the sun is named Eoüs and he comes just at dawn, near the hour of tierce.[1] Because these fine steeds appear in many colors, the shepherd should take note that if Eoüs appears red and fiery in the morning, this means rain and changing weather. If he appears more white, this is the sign of a fine day. The pilgrims who wend their way are joyful when they see it.

After him comes the second horse, named Ethoüs, who performs his duty for the sun near the hour of noon. When he appears with a pale color, that is the sign of a fine day.

After noon the third horse attached to the noble chariot of the sun does service: this horse is named Pyroüs. With his coming, the huge shining eyes of powerful Pyroüs rekindle and flash so that human creatures cannot look on him for long. It is then that the bats do not fly because they cannot bear or endure such a great and noble light that is thrown out by the coming of the sun's rays as it makes its course. When these two horses, Ethoüs and Pyroüs, are too hot and fiery, they draw vapors from the earth and from the water by their great power and heat and make them rise in the air. If these vapors are raised up and not dissipated by any evaporation, they gather and turn into clouds formed by the particles of these vapors. These clouds, according to their nature, tend to lower and return to the center. Sometimes these clouds are transformed into rain, sometimes to wind, sometimes into snow or hail, depending on the season. Thus the shepherd can see that by the too great warmth and heat of the horses there comes a change in the weather.

Now let us speak of the fourth horse, named Phylogeüs, who runs his course in the descent of the sun's chariot. This Phylogeüs leans willingly toward the waters, for he does his work at evening's approach. The shepherd should take his prognostication of the weather from him and from the morning horse, because when

---

[1] "The third hour of the canonical day, ending at 9 am" (*Oxford Universal Dictionary*).

le soleil[1] au matin est vermeil ou trop ardant, ce signifie pluye et lait temps. S'il est blanc, ce signifie beau temps, comme dit est. Au vespre, quant Phylogeüs se va abruver et maine le noble char du soleil en l'eaue, ou quant il est trop blanc ou trop[2] pale au couchier et est environné[3] de nuees[4] noires ou perses, tout ce signifie pluye par nuyt ou a l'endemain.[5] Et lors se[6] Phylogeüs[7] en Occident est assez vermeil et l'air purgié de nuees, ce signifie beau temps. Et le proverbe commun que l'en souloit dire vulgaument[8] et est tel:[9] Rouge vespree[10] et blanc matin font esjouyr le pelerin*—se concorde assez a l'exemple que le bergier doit prendre es chevaux dessusdictz. Et ceste doctrine est plus vraye et plus notable assez que celle des oyseaux ne des bestes.

Et se le bergier congnoissoit les corps du ciel et la cause des influences des signes et des planetes, ce luy feroit[11] grant avantage pour avoir congnoissance de ces choses, car par les corps du ciel est causee et faicte toute la mutacion des temps qui est faicte es elemens. Si s'en taira Jehan de Brie, et toutesfois est [45] il si sage que pour certain il congnoist bien le fouc* des estoilles.

45.02 fouc] four *BTV*

---

1 le conseil *T*
2 trop *om. B*
3 et en environné *T*
4 nues *T*
5 au lendemain *B*
6 ce *B*
7 Philogieus *T*
8 vulgairement *B*
9 ytel *T*
10 vespre *B*
11 seroit *BJ*

the morning sun is bright red or too fiery, that means rain and nasty weather. If it is pale, that means fine weather, as has already been mentioned. In the evening, when Phylogeüs goes to drink and draws the noble chariot of the sun into the water, or when he is too white and too pale at sunset and is surrounded by black and purple clouds, all this signifies rain by night or on the next day. If when Phylogeüs in the west is very red and the air swept clean of clouds, that means fine weather. The usual proverb as generally said: *Red at night, white in the morning, makes the pilgrim rejoice* agrees with the example that the shepherd should take from these horses. This rule is truer and much more noteworthy than those of the birds and animals.

If the shepherd were cognizant of the heavenly bodies and the causes of influences by signs and planets, there would be a great advantage in having knowledge of these things, for by the bodies in the sky is occasioned and brought about all the change of weather that is made in the elements.

Here Jean de Brie will leave off, but he is wise who for certain knows well the flock of the stars.

De la consideracion des vens et lesquelz sont proufitables. viie.

Des vens doit sçavoir le bergier pour deux causes. L'une si[1] est pour la[2] congnoissance du temps dont dessus est parlé, pour ce que aucuns vens sont plus enclins a la pluye que les autres. L'autre raison si[3] est pour ce que aucuns vens sont nuysans et dommagables aux oeilles, et les autres non.

Les vens, selon les charnieres et les quatre climas du monde, sont divisez[4] en quatre parties : en orient, en occident, en midy et en septentrion. Et pour ce que le soleil ne fait pas tousjours son orient en ung mesme lieu, ne aussi ne[5] fait il son occident, car en temps equinoctial, si comme en mars, que le soleil est ou[6] signe du[7] Mouton, et en septembre, que il est ou[8] signe de la Livre, que aucuns nomment Balance, le orient et l'occident du soleil sont directement[9] opposites en regart et a droite ligne. Et lors pourroit on faire les quatre parties egaulz[10]* l'une a l'autre et justement proporcionnees durant le temps [46] de l'equinoce.[11] Autre fois, en temps d'esté, quant le soleil est ou[12] signe de l'Escrevice, il fait son orient plus vers septentrion. Et aussi fait il son occident, et tournoie et gire plus grant partie de nostre emyspere et est lors appellé *orient solsticial*. Autre fois, en temps d'yver, fait son orient ou[13] signe de Capricorne et se trait plus vers midy et aussi tire plus son occident vers midy et lors tourne mains, car il ne gire ne va pas si hault ne[14] prent tant de la partie dudit emyspere[15] ou semispere et adonc est appellé *orient yvernage*.

Le vent qui vient vers nous du droit orient equinoctial[16] est appellé Subsolain—les Grejois l'appellent Aphelotes. De l'orient solsticial yst ung vent que les Latins ne sçavent nommer. Les Grejois l'appellent Eurus.[17] De l'orient d'yver

---

[1] si *om. B*
[2] la *om. T*
[3] si *om. B*
[4] diversés *T*
[5] ne *om. T*
[6] au *BT*
[7] de *B*
[8] au *T*
[9] droictement *T*
[10] egalles *BJ*
[11] l'equinoctial *B*
[12] au *T*
[13] au *BT*
[14] ne *om. T*
[15] hemysfere *B*
[16] aquinoctial *T*
[17] Eureus *T*

Chapter 7

Consideration of Winds and Which Are Beneficial

The shepherd should know about the winds[‡] for two reasons: one for knowledge of the weather as mentioned before, because some winds tend more toward rain than others; the other because some winds are more injurious and harmful to ewes and others not.

The winds, according to the earth's axis and its four regions, are divided into four parts: east, west, south, and north. Since the sun does not always rise in the same place, neither does it likewise set. At the equinox, in March when the sun is in the sign of the Ram and in September when it is in the sign of Libra, which some call the Scale, the rising and setting of the sun are in direct opposition and on a straight line. Then the four parts can be made equal, one to the other, and equally apportioned during the time of the equinox.

At other times, in summer when the sun is in the sign of the Crab, it rises more toward the north, likewise setting farther north, and turns and circles through the largest part of our hemisphere, and it is then called the solstitial sunrise. At other times, in winter, it rises in the sign of Capricorn and draws closer to the south and also sets more toward the south and then turns less, for it neither circles nor goes so high nor takes up so much of the hemisphere, and is then named the winter sunrise.

The wind that comes to us from the equinoctial true east is named Subsolain, which the Greeks call Aphelotes. From the solstitial east comes a wind for which the Romans have no name. The Greeks call it Eurus. From the

yst ung vent que les Latins appellent Vultur.[1] De devers l'occident equinoctial
yst ung vent nommé Fanonius,[2] que aucuns appellent Zephirus. De l'occident
solsticial vient ung vent qui est appellé Chorus. De l'occident d'yver yst ung
vent nommé Affricus, qui en son temps est moult forsené et puissant [47] et les
Grejois l'appellent Lybs. De devers l'aixeul de[3] midy vient ung vent nommé Euronochus.[4] Aprés, de la partie devers midy, vient Euroauster et puis ung autre
qui a nom Auster. Du costé de septentrion vient Aquilo, que aucuns nomment[5]
Galerne, et de la vient Nothus. Et de la en traiant[6] vers orient solsticial, vient
Boreas, ung vent plain de froidure. Avec ces vens en y a aucuns autres nommez
en la mapemonde.

Autrement, pour mieulx entendre, les peult[7] diviser en quatre parties et
en chascune partie trois vens, en equipollant[8] les oriens et les occidens, tant de
l'equinoce, comme de esté,[9] d'yver, et des autres saisons. Entre orient et midy
naissent trois vens : Eurus, Subsolanus et Vulturus. Entre midy et occident naissent trois autres : Euroauster, Auster et Euronochus.[10] Entre occident et[11] septentrion naissent trois autres vens : Affricus, Fanonius et Chorus. Entre septentrion
et orient naissent trois autres : Notus, Aquilo et Boreas. Les mariniers* et aucuns
autres devers la coste[12] de Normendie [48] en nomment[13] quatre vens principaulz,
c'est assavoir Nort, West,* Eth et Sut.[14] Les bergiers les appellent *vent d'amont,*
vent d'aval, vent de bise, vent de escorchevel, vent de France, vent de galerne, et ainsi
qu'il leur plaist. Et pour ce que question de langages est reputee de petit[15] pris
et de petite valeur, et que, par incidens, on pourroit yssir hors de sa[16] matiere de
la[17] bergerie, on lerra chascun nommer[18] les vens[19] par tel langage qu'il vouldra et
Jehan de Brie retournera a son droit et principal propos, et en procedant dira des
proprietez d'aucuns vens, ce qui en affiert a cest[20] present traictié, et lesquelz sont
prouffitables ou dommagables aux brebis.

47.24 mariniers *T*] manieres *BJV*

---

[1] Vulturus *B*

[2] Favonius *B*

[3] l'aixeul de *om. T*

[4] Euronothus *B*

[5] appellent *B*

[6] tirant *BT*

[7] on les peult *T*

[8] equipolent *T*

[9] de l'esté *T*

[10] Euronothus *B*

[11] et *repeated V*

[12] le costé *B*

[13] nommant *BT*

[14] Nort, Vuest, Oost et Suet *B*; Nort,
vuest, Eth et Sut *J*; Nort, vvest, Eth et Suth
T

[15] petite *B*

[16] sa *om. B*

[17] la *om. T*

[18] terminer *T*

[19] les ungs [*sic*] *BJ*

[20] ce *B*

south-east comes a wind the Romans name Vultur. From the equinoctial west comes a wind called Fanonius,[‡] which some call Zephirus. From the northwest there comes a wind named Chorus, and from the southwest a wind named Affricus, which is most wild and powerful in its season and which the Greeks call Lybs. From the inclination of the axis of the south comes a wind called Euronochus and later from the area toward the south comes Euroauster, then another named Auster.[‡] From the north side comes Aquilo,[‡] which others call Galerne, from there comes Nothus and from there, aiming toward the northeast, comes Boreas, a wind full of cold. Along with these winds, there are others mentioned in the World Map.[‡]

Another way to better understand is to divide them into four parts and in each one there are three winds, splitting the east and west equally as to the equinox, as in summer, winter and other seasons.[‡] Between the east and the south arise three winds: Eurus, Subsolanus, and Vulturus. Between the south and the west arise three others: Euroauster, Auster, and Euronochus. Between the west and the north arise three other winds: Affricus, Fanonius, and Chorus. Between the north and east arise three others: Notus, Aquilo, and Boreas.

Mariners and others[‡] toward the coast of Normandy speak of four principal winds, namely: North, West, East, and South. The shepherds call them the east wind,[1] the west wind,[2] the north wind, the calf-skinning wind, the wind of France, the northwest wind, and whatever they please. Since the question of word use is reputed to be of little value and incidentally could go far from the subject of sheep husbandry, let people call the winds by whatever names they like and Jean de Brie will return to his right course and principal concern and, continuing, will tell of the properties of each wind and those that apply to this present work and which are helpful or harmful to sheep.

---

[1] *"Vent d'amont*: "the East Wind. Also called Solaire" (Cotgrave).
[2] *"Vent d'aval*: A West-South-West Wind" (Cotgrave).

De la vie du bergier et des choses qui luy affierent. viii^e.

En ceste partie commence le droit art et maniere[1] de garder brebis.[2] Et pour ce que le bergier est plus digne que les brebis, et[3] on doit commencer au plus digne selon raison et le droit ordre de proceder, dirons de l'estat du bergier et de ses choses.

Le bergier doit estre de bonnes meurs et doit eschever la taverne et le bordeau[4] et tous lieux [49] deshonnestes et doit aussi eschever tous jeux excepté le jeu des merelles et du baston et ne doit point jouer aux dez,[5] mais doit mener son jeu des merelles a traire subtilement contre son compaignon.

Item : le bergier doit estre de bonne vie, sobre, chaste et debonnaire, tout aussi comme Saint Pol[6] en[7] escript a Tyton[8] en ses epistoles.[9] Et doit estre loyal et diligent sur la cure des oeilles et brebis a luy commises, affin qu'il en puist[10] faire bonne garde et prouffitable.

Le bergier doit avoir chausses de blanchet gros, ou de camelin,[11] et soulliers bobelinez et taconnez de fort cuir et, en yver temps, par dessus ses chausses doit avoir vuagues[12] de cuir des buhos[13] d'ung[s]* vieux houseaux pour la pluye. Il doit estre garny de tacons et de semelles de fort cuir bien pourpointes de gros fil de chanvre bien cyré de cire blanche, poix rasiné[14] et[15] de suif pour plus durer. Et doit sçavoir asseoir ses tacons ou semeles en ses bobelins par dessoubz le buisson quant besoing en est.

La chemise et les braies du bergier doivent estre de grosse toile et forte, que l'en appelle *chanevas*. Et la brayete doit [50] estre de fil tissu de deux dois de large, a deux boucles rondes de fer. La façon de la chemise doit estre fendue par devant a deux pointes, et les deux pans de devant doivent estre amples et longs en

---

[1] matiere *T*

[2] g. les b. *B*

[3] et *om. T*

[4] le bordeaux *B*

[5] detz *T*

[6] Saincte Paul [*sic*] *B*, Sainct Paul *J*

[7] en *om. BJ*

[8] a Tite et a Timothee *B*, a Tite *J*, ad Tyton *T*

[9] epistres *BJ*

[10] peust *T*

[11] camali *T*

[12] en yver doit avair [*sic*] par d. ses chosses vagues *T*

[13] des buhos *om. T*

[14] raisiné *T*

[15] ou *T*

Chapter 8

About the Shepherd's Life and the Things that Concern Him

In this section begins the true art and method of keeping sheep. Because the shepherd is more worthy than the sheep, and one should begin with the most worthy according to reason and correct order of procedure, we will speak of the shepherd and of his affairs.

The shepherd should be of good morals, should avoid the tavern, bawdy house and all dishonest places, and should also shun all games except the game of *merelles*[1] and of staffs,[2] and should not play at dice.[‡] However, he should play his game of *merelles* to draw craftily against his partner.

The shepherd should lead a good life, sober, chaste and good-hearted, just as Saint Paul writes to Titus in his epistles.[3] He should be loyal and diligent in the care of the sheep and ewes committed to him in order to keep a good and profitable watch over them.

The shepherd should have trousers of heavy white wool or *camelin*[4] and shoes patched and reinforced with strong leather.[‡] For the rain in winter, over his trousers he should have gaiters of leather from old boots. He should be equipped with patches and strong leather soles, well sewn with heavy hemp string that is well waxed with white wax, pitch and tallow to last longer. He should know how to seat the heels or soles of his boots under a bush should the need arise.

The shirt and the breeches of the shepherd should be of heavy and strong cloth called canvas. The codpiece[5] should be of string, woven two fingers wide with two round iron buckles. The shirt should be split in front with two long points,

---

[1] *merele*: "sorte de jeu qu'on jouait avec des disques, semblable à nos dames, qui étaient faits de carton de cire, de plomb, ou de cuivre" (Godefroy). [Sort of game that one played with discs, like our checkers, which were made from waxed cardboard, lead or copper.]

[2] *Bâton*: *baston*: "staffe, bat, cudgell, trunchion" (Cotgrave).

[3] Titus 1:7–8.

[4] *camelin*: "étoffe de poil de chèvre, mélange de laine et de soie" (Godefroy). [Fabric of goat hair, mixed with wool and silk.]

[5] *brayette*: *braguette*: "sorte de poche attachée en haut des chausses" (Greimas and Keane). [A kind of pocket attached at the top of the pants.] *braguette*: "a codpiece" (Cotgrave).

maniere[1] d'ung pennoncel* agu, affin qu'il y puist mettre[2] et enveloper son argent et nouer le pan au droit neu. Et sur la chemise doit avoir ung coteron de blanchet[3] ou de gris camelin sans mances, lequel coteron doit estre doublé par devant depuis les espaules jusques a la çainture pour garder sa[4] fourcele et son estomac des vens et tempestes, et pour champaier plus seurement[5] aprés ses brebis, car elles sont de telle nature que voulentiers vont contre vent.[6] Et pour ce doit estre ledit coteron doublé par devant. Et sur le[7] coteron doit avoir une cote de blanchet ou de camelin gris a deux pointes, l'une par devant, l'autre par derriere, et a mances, et si large et ample qu'il y puist[8] entrer aisement sans boutons, car il ne luy affiert pas a avoir boutonneures[9] laches ou autres empeschemens qui le puissent nuyre au vestir, mais y doit entrer de plain comme en ung sac ou en la tunique Aaron.*

[51] Et par dessus la cote doit avoir ung sourplis de fort tresliz[10] a mances a quatre noyaux ou boutons, de la façon mesmes de la cote.* C'est[11] sourplis garde le bergier de la pluye, et aucunesfois convient il que il le despoulle pour enveloper l'aigneau quant il est faonné aux champs. Par dessus son sourplis doit avoir une grosse çainture de corde menue et forte, faicte par maniere de tresce en trois cordons, a une boucle[12] de fer ronde. Et a celle çainture doit pendre et avoir plusieurs choses.

Premierement, et pour honneur, y[13] doit pendre[14] la boiste a l'ongnement en ung estuy de cuir. Et est bien a noter que le bon bergier ne doit non plus[15] estre trouvé sans la boiste a l'ongnement que le notaire doit estre sans escriptoire, car ce est le plus notable et necessaire de ses instrumens et outilz. Avec ce doit il avoir ung canyvet ou coutel agu pour picoter et oster la roingne* de la brebis,[16] affin que

---

51.05 cote *T*] coste *BJV*

---

[1] en la m. *B*
[2] qu'il lui peust m. *T*
[3] blanc *T*
[4] la *T*
[5] seulement *B*
[6] c. le vent *T*
[7] ledit *T*
[8] qui lui p. *T*
[9] boutonneurs *BT*
[10] treillis *T*
[11] Ce *B*
[12] boulle *B*
[13] il *T*
[14] prendre *BT*
[15] nomplus *T*
[16] des brebis *B*

and the two panels in front should be ample and long in the manner of a narrow pennant so that he can place and wrap up his money there and tie the tip of the shirt-tail with a square knot. Over his shirt he should have a sleeveless vest of white wool or gray camelin.[‡] This vest should be doubled in front from his shoulders to his belt to protect his breastbone and stomach from winds and storms, in order to follow more confidently after his ewes in the fields, for they are of such a nature that they go willingly against the wind, which is why the vest should be doubled in front. Over the vest he should have a coat of white woolen cloth or gray camelin with two points, one before and the other behind, and with sleeves so large and wide that he can get into it easily without buttoning. It is not suitable for him to have loose buttons or any other impediment that can hinder dressing, but rather he should get into it smoothly, as in a sack or Aaron's tunic.[‡]

Over the coat he should have a sleeved surcoat of stout knitting with four hooks or buttons, in the same fashion as the coat. This surcoat protects the shepherd from the rain, and sometimes it is necessary to take it off to wrap up a lamb when it is born in the field. Over his surcoat he should have a wide belt of narrow, strong cord made by plaiting of three strands, with a round iron buckle. From this belt he should hang several things.[‡]

First, in place of honor, he should hang the ointment case in its leather container. It is well to note that the good shepherd is no more found without his ointment case than the notary without a writing table, for it is the most important and necessary of his instruments and tools. Along with this, he should have a pocket knife or a sharp knife to pick out and remove the mange[1‡] from the ewes

---

[1] *Roingne: gale*: Mange (*Harrap's*). Scabies, or gale, is caused by mites, occurs worldwide, and can be cured by the use of sulphur (*Newsom's*, 201).

l'ongnement y puist[1] mieulx entrer et que la brebis soit plus tost guerie.[2] Aussi convient il que il porte ung[s]* cyseaux pour couper et aonnier[3] la laine de la[4] brebis par dessus la rongne.

[52] Le bergier doit porter alesne a coudre soulliers, bobelins, semeles et tacons, laquelle alesne doit estre en ung instrument de fust pour bouter le fer de l'alesne[5] jusques au millieu du mance, et par dessoubz le doit attachier d'ung noyau ou d'ung anneau de cuir pour mieulx[6] fermer.

Item : a celle çainture doit porter ung aguillier[7] a mettre ses aguilles quarrees et[8] rondes, lequel aguiller[9] est de l'oz de la cuisse d'une oue, menu et longuet,[10] ou de l'oz d'ung pié d'aignelet, et doit[11] estre mis et attachié avecques le pendant de l'alesne. Encore doit le bergier avoir[12] boisset ou coutel a forte alemele a trenchier son pain, amancié[13] de deux pieces plates de tylleul ou d'autre tendre bois, et le mance doit estre lyé tout au long d'une menue cordelete de fil bien ciree* pour le mieulx tenir et pour estre plus fort. Et la gayne du coutel doit estre d'une vielle savate de l'empigne d'ung soulier vieux de vache, bien cousue, et faicte par le bergier a la mesure ou quantité dudit coutel. Celle gayne doit estre pendue a la çainture d'une cordele de gros fil de chanvre ou d'une vielle laniere renouee. Aprés doit pendre a la [53] çainture ung guyteau ou fourreau de vieux cuir mesgissié ou du cuir de la peau d'une anguille pour mettre les flaiaux du* bergier, lequel fourreau doit estre de la quantité des flaiaux.[14] Et par dessus toutes ces choses devant dictes le bergier doit porter et çaindre sa panetiere pour mettre le pain pour luy et pour[15] son chien. La panetiere doit estre de cordele trelliee et nouee au droit neu, en maniere de la harace au potier de terre. Et celle panetiere doit estre attachiee au senestre costé du bergier, car il ne doit point empescher son dextre costé, affin

---

52.17 ciree *T*] curee *BJV*
53.03 les flaiaux du bergier *BJ*] les f. ℂ Et du b. *TV*

---

[1] puisse *B*
[2] guarie *B*
[3] onnier *T*
[4] la *om. B*
[5] de la lance [*sic*] *T*
[6] pour le m. *T*
[7] aguilletier *T*
[8] ou *T*
[9] agailler *B*, aguilletier *T*
[10] menu et longuet *om. T*
[11] doit *om. B*
[12] doit a. le b. *T*
[13] amanché *BJ*, enmanché *T*
[14] flaioux *T*
[15] pour *om. B*

so that the ointment can reach them better and the ewe may sooner be cured. He also must carry scissors in order to cut and level the wool on top of the mange.

The shepherd should carry an awl to sew shoes, patches, soles and leather strips,[‡] and this awl should be in a wooden receptacle for thrusting the iron of the awl into the middle of the sleeve, and moreover it should be attached by a hook or leather ring for better closure.

On this belt he should carry a needle case in which to put his square and round needles. This case is from the thigh bone of a ewe, slender and long, or from the bone of a lamb's foot, and should be placed with and attached to the awl's holder.

In addition, the shepherd should have a knife[1] with a corded haft and a strong blade to slice his bread, hafted with two flat pieces of linden or some other soft wood, the haft being wound its whole length with a narrow cord of well-waxed string for a better grasp and to be stronger. The sheath of the knife should be of an old cowhide shoe upper, well sewn and made by the shepherd to the size or dimension of the knife. This sheath should be hung from the belt by a heavy hemp string or by an old knotted thong. Next to be hung from the belt is a sheath[2] or scabbard of old dressed leather or of eelskin leather, in which to put his flails, and each scabbard should be equal to the number of flails.

In addition to all these things already mentioned, the shepherd should take along and gird on a scrip[3] in which to put bread for himself and his dog.[‡] The scrip should be of trellis-woven cord and knotted with square knots like a large pottery basket. This scrip should be attached to the shepherd's left side, since he should not hinder his right side so that he may be able more quickly

---

[1] *boisset*: "Au xive siècle, couteau à manche cordelé" (Lachiver citing J. de Brie, *Le bon berger,* 73). [In the fourteenth century, a knife with a corded haft.]

[2] *guyteau*: "Au xive siècle, gaine de couteau" (Lachiver citing *Le bon berger*). [In the fourteenth century, a knife's sheath.]

[3] No modern equivalent seems adequate to translate the word *panetiere*, so we use the English term in use at that time for a satchel or bag in which to carry one's provisions.

que plus prestement il puist[1] tondre, recoper, oindre, seigner ou besongner sur
ses[2] brebis se mestier est. A la panetiere doit estre attachiee une cordele de une
toise et demie de long, que l'en appelle *la laisse du chien*, et doit estre redoublee
jusques au point de la panetiere et ou[3] meillieu doit avoir ung cuiret avec ung
petit bignet de bois pour attachier le chien et pour le destachier et envoyer tost[4]
et delivrement contre* les loups ou autres males bestes qui vouldroient meffaire
aux brebis.

Le chien du bergier doit estre ung grant [54] mastin fort et quarré, a[5] grosse
teste, et doit avoir entour le col ung colier armé de crampons de fer aguz ou de
cloux longs* et aguz boutez parmy le fort colier de cuir a plates testes, et aucuns
en y a qui ont coliers de platines[6] de fer fermans a charnieres[7] pour resister aux
loups sur les champs ou aux larrons, se aucuns en venoient par nuyt aux herbergeries, ou la ou les brebis sont emparchiees. Et aussi, pour l'armeure du colier, le
mastin est plus hardy et plus animé et ne seroit pas si tost[8] estranglé des loups,
car il en a plus grant defense contre eulx. Cest[9] mastin suyt le bergier et luy tient
bonne compaignie quant il menge son pain, quoy qu'il soit de la defense, car tel
est amy a la despense qui ne l'est pas a la defense. Quant le bergier a ung bon
mastin loyal et hardy, il est tres prouffitable a la garde des brebis.

Le bergier est aussi noblement paré de sa houlette, selon son estat de
bergerie,[10] comme seroit ung evesque ou ung abbé de sa croce, ou comme ung
bon homme d'armes est bien acesiné et asseuré[11] quant il a ung bon glaive pour la
guerre — combien que l'en ne [55] doit pas faire comparaison de telles choses, car
elles ne sont pas pareilles de trop loing. Et jasoit ce[12] que la croce du prelat soit de
plus grant dignité et de plus grant honneur que le glaive ne que la houlette, et que
il ait difference, considerees les choses a considerer selon l'estat des personnes,
neantmains il y a bonne et ydoine convenience,[13] car selon Dieu, qui est le plus
grant, il se doit humilier, et soy faire comme le plus petit quant est[14] a humilité

54.03 longs *BJ*] longues *V*, songues [*sic*] *T*

---

[1] puisse *B*
[2] les *BT*
[3] au *B*
[4] toust *T*
[5] et *T*
[6] plataines *BJ*
[7] charniers *B*
[8] toust *T*
[9] Ce *B*
[10] berger *B*
[11] esseuré *T*
[12] ce *om. B*
[13] convenance *T*
[14] q. il est *T*

to shear, trim, anoint, bleed, or tend to his ewes as needed. A nine-foot-long cord, called a leash, must be attached to the scrip. It should be doubled back to the tip of the sack and in the middle have a bit of leather with a small wooden pin to fasten the dog and to unleash him, sending him quickly and with dispatch after the wolves and other evil animals wishing to harm the ewes.

The shepherd's dog should be a large mastiff, strong and broad-shouldered, with a big head, and he should have around his neck a collar armed with studs of sharp iron or of long sharp nails with flat heads.[‡] Some have collars with thin hinged plates of iron to withstand wolves in the field or thieves if some should come in the night to the sheepfold where the ewes are penned. In addition, because of the collar's armor, the mastiff is more courageous and emboldened and will not be strangled by wolves, for with it he has greater protection against them. This mastiff follows the shepherd and is good company when he eats his bread even though the dog is on guard duty, for someone may be a friend at the spending who is not one when defending is to be done.[‡] When the shepherd has a good mastiff, loyal and brave, it is very beneficial for the tending of sheep.

The shepherd is as nobly equipped with his shepherd's crook, according to his status as a shepherd, as is a bishop[‡] or abbé with his crozier, or the good man-at-arms is well prepared and confident when he has a good lance for war—although comparison should not be made between such things, for they are not alike to a great extent. Although the prelate's crozier may be of greater dignity and honor than the lance or the shepherd's crook, and there is a difference taking into account things relating to people's status, nevertheless there exists a good and proper connection. According to God, he who is grandest should humble himself and make himself as the least in humility and, according to

et[1] selon la doctrine de l'Evangile non pas par tout.[2] Et ces trois choses—la croce, le glaive, et la houlette—representent trois estas de cest monde.[3] La croce est tenue de nous enseigner et corriger espirituelement[4] sans lance et sans espee, et de prier et supplier humblement a[5] Dieu pour nous, c'est a dire pour le glaive et pour la houlette. Le glaive doit defendre, par sa puissance temporelle et corporelle, la croce et la houlette de tous les adversaires qui contre raison les vouldroient inquieter et molester indeuement. La houlette, qui en ceste partie peult et doit estre comparee[6] a la beche dont l'en feust et laboure la terre, doit curer au prouffit [56] de la croce et du glaive a ce qu'il leur puist livrer et administer alimens et nourriture du prouffit de son labeur et de sa garde. Ainsi peult apparoir qu'il y a convenience et qu'il conviennent l'ung avec l'autre pour soustenir le bien publique, chascun en son degré. Pour ce est la houlette convenable au bergier aussi comme la croce au prelat, et le glaive ou l'espee a l'omme d'armes, c'est a dire a la seigneurie temporelle qui est en puissance de espee. Et se[7] ces[8] trois veulent faire chascun son devoir, tout est bon et en tous estas, car aux champs, a la ville et* au monstier[9] se entre aident de[10] leur mestier.

La houlette est ferree[11] d'ung long fer concave en aguisant et la bouterole ou l'en met et fiche le mance doit estre long et ront, bien clere et burnie de terre legiere, ou elle est souvent boutee pour chastier les brebis et aigneaux. La hante de la houlette doit estre de nefflier ou d'autre bois dur et ferme.[12] Au premier bout de la hante ou baston doit estre le fer dessusdit, concave et ung peu courbé pour coper et houler la terre legiere sur les brebis, car de houler est elle dicte *houlette*. A l'autre bout de dessoubz [57] doit estre ung crochet de fust de la nature et essence du bois du mance mesmes, qui tel le[13] peult trouver, et si non si soit fait le crochet par addicion d'ung trou ou d'une cheville de estrange bois. Par ce crochet du bout de la houlette sont prises, tenues et acrochiees les brebis et les aigneaux pour visiter s'il y a rongne, pour oindre, pour seigner et mettre a obeissance et pour y

56.13 a la ville et au moustier] et *om.* BTV

---

[1] et *om.* B
[2] non . . . tout *om.* B
[3] e. en ce m. B
[4] spirituellement B
[5] a *om.* T
[6] comparé T
[7] si B
[8] ses B
[9] moustier T
[10] a T
[11] ferré T
[12] ou d'autre bois du ferme [*sic*] T
[13] telle B

the teaching of the Gospel, not in all places. And these three things, the crozier, the sword, and the shepherd's crook, represent the three estates of this world. The crozier should teach us and correct us spiritually without lance and without sword, to pray and beseech God humbly for us, that is to say, for the lance and the shepherd's crook. Through its temporal and corporal power, the lance should defend the crozier and crook from all adversaries who against reason unduly wish to upset and harass them. The shepherd's crook, which in this frame of reference can be compared to the spade by which the earth is broken open,[1] should work for the profit of the crozier and the lance, so that it might furnish and dispense the produce and food from the profit of its labor and caretaking. Thus it can be seen that there is a connection and that it behooves one with the other to maintain the public good, each in his station. This is why the shepherd's crook is appropriate to the shepherd, as is the crozier to the prelate and the lance to the man-at-arms, that is, the earthly lordship that is in the power of the sword. If these three each are willing to do their duty, all is well in all estates for, from countryside to town to church, they help each other, according to their calling.

The shepherd's crook is tipped with a long concave tapering iron piece and the sheath where one sets and thrusts the shaft should be long and round, quite clear and well polished with dust, where it is often thrust in order to chastise the ewes and lambs. The shaft of the crook should be of medlar[2] or some other firm and hard wood. At the main end of the shaft or staff there should be the afore-mentioned iron, concave and a bit curved for flinging and throwing dust on the ewes, which is why it is called a *houlette*. At the other end there should be a wooden hook of the nature and kind of wood as the staff itself, if it can be found. If not, the hook should be made by the addition of a hole or a pin from a different wood. The ewes and lambs are caught by this hook at the end of the crook, held and brought under control to see if they have mange, to apply ointment, bleed, subdue,

---

[1] *feust*: interpreted as the third-person present singular indicative of *foer* (variant form *foir*), Modern French *fouir*, "to dig (with a spade)".
[2] *Nefflier*: Medlar, *Mespilus germanica* L. (Coombes).

pourveoir de remede. Avec la houlette convient il que le bergier ait baston et que il ait corgies de trois lanieres de[1] cuir ou de trois cordeles menues pour corriger et chastier ses brebis en temps deu, car grans biens et grans[2] prouffis viennent de la[3] bonne correction.

Il affiert au bergier que il soit affublé d'ung grant chapeau de feutre, ront et bien large. Et par devant sur le chief doit estre redoublé de plaine paume ou plus. Le redoublement est necessaire pour deux choses : l'une pour defendre le bergier de la pluye et mal temps quant il va contre vent aprés ses[4] brebis ; l'autre pour le prouffit de son maistre de qui sont les[5] bestes, car toutesfois qu'il convient que le bergier face oincture sur ses[6] brebis quant au[58]cunes en y a de rongneuses[7] aux champs et il fait tonsure[8] de ses cyseaux pour descouvrir[9] la laine, pour attaindre la rongne, il met les recoupes de la[10] laine et les tonsures[11] ou ploy et redouble de son chapeau et les doit porter et rendre a son maistre a l'ostel, car il est tenu et abstraint a faire[12] et[13] garder le profit* de son maistre en faisant son office de bergier. D'autre part ledit chapeau est moult prouffitable et ydoine au bergier, tant pour obvier a la[14] pluye, vens et tempestes des temps, comme pour la garde de son chief, et est droit estat de pasteur de porter grant chapeau et ront.

Mais il y a difference entre les chapeaux des prelas et les chapeaux des bergiers, en ce que les chapeaux des prelas sont de bievre et[15] plus chiere chose que n'est que feutre,[16] et aussi ne sont ilz point reploiez ne redoublez par devant. Et peult estre[17] que ce est pour ce que ilz ne veulent pas reporter aucun prouffit a leur maistre qui les a commis au gouvernement ou ilz sont, car les prelas tondent et prendent voulentiers et retiennent tout le prouffit pour eulx mesmes.[18] Et se aucuns en y a qui en reportent aucun prouf[59]fit a leur maistre, ce est pour estre promeuz en plus hault degré par le moyen de symonie, si comme l'en dist.

---

[1] du *B*

[2] grand *B*

[3] la *om. T*

[4] ces *T*

[5] ses *T*

[6] les *T*

[7] rougneuses *T*

[8] tonseure *T*

[9] escouvrir *T*

[10] la om. *T*

[11] tonseures *T*

[12] tenu de faire *B*

[13] et om. *T*

[14] la om. *T*

[15] bievre et om. *B*

[16] n'est le f. *B*, n'est que feure *T*

[17] Et peult estre . . . si comme l'en dist om. *B*

[18] mesme *T*

and to provide a remedy for them. Along with the crook, the shepherd must have a staff and flays with three narrow leather thongs or three narrow straps to correct and chastise his ewes when needed, for great good and profit come from good correction.

It is appropriate for the shepherd to be outfitted with a large felt hat, round and wide. On the front of his head it should be folded over to the width of a full palm or more. The fold is necessary for two reasons: one is to protect the shepherd from the rain and bad weather when he goes against the wind after his ewes; the other for the profit of his master whose sheep they are. Sometimes it is necessary for the shepherd to put ointment on his ewes in the field when some have mange and he shears them with scissors to open up the wool to get to the mange. He puts the clippings and shearings in the fold of his hat and must carry and turn them over to his master at his lodging, for he is required and obliged to make and preserve the profit of his master in performing the office of shepherd. Besides, the hat is most beneficial and fitting to the shepherd, as much for warding off the rain, wind and stormy weather as for the protection of his head, and it is the true estate of the shepherd to wear a large and round hat.

But there is a difference between the hats of prelates and those of shepherds. The hats of prelates are of beaver, a more costly thing than felt, and so are not folded or doubled back in front. This could be because they do not wish to carry back any profit to their master who has given to them the dominion of where they are, for prelates shear and take at will and keep all the profit for themselves and if there are any who carry back any profit to their master, it is in order to be promoted to the highest degree through simony, as it is said.‡

En yver temps affiert au bergier que il ait moufles pour garder ses mains de la froidure, lesquelles moufles il ne doit pas acheter mais les doit faire de sa science ou a l'aguille,[1] en lachant[2] de fil de laine filé de main de bergerette, ainsi comme l'en fait les aumuces, ou il les doit faire de plusieurs pieces de draps et de plusieurs couleurs que le bergier quiert a son avantage. Et quant elles sont eschequetees, elles en sont assez plus jolies. Et quant il ne fait pas trop froit ou quant il convient que le bergier face besongne[3] de ses mains, il doit pendre[4] ses moufles a une billette a sa çainture dessus devisee.

Des instrumens doit avoir le bergier avec ses flaiaux[5] pour soy esbatre en melodie, c'est assavoir fretel,[6] estyve, douçaine, musette d'Alemaigne ou autre musette que l'en nomme *chevrette*, chascun selon son engin et subtilité. Et puis que le bergier est ainsi armé de toutes les pieces[7] dessusdictes afferans[8] a son mestier, il peult champaier seurement, la houlette en la main, en gardant ses brebis.

---

[1] la guille *T*

[2] larchant *T*

[3] Et quanl [sic] il ne fait pas de b. *T*

[4] prendre *T*

[5] fleaulx *T*

[6] frentel *B*

[7] chosses [*sic*] *T*

[8] affierans *B*

In winter the shepherd should have mittens to keep his hands from the cold. He shouldn't buy these mittens but should skillfully make them, whether with a needle knitting a thread spun by the hand of a shepherdess as amices[1] are made, or he should make them of several pieces of cloth, of many colors, which the shepherd seeks out to his advantage. When they are checkered, they are even prettier. When it is not too cold or the shepherd needs to use his hands, his mittens should hang from a small peg on his belt mentioned above.

The shepherd should keep some instruments along with his flails to divert himself with melody, for instance, a whistle, panpipe, oboe, German bagpipe, or another bagpipe called a *chevrette*,[2] each person according to his talent and ability. Since the shepherd is thus armed with all the items aforementioned belonging to his job, he can go confidently into the field, shepherd's crook in hand, watching over his ewes.

---

[1] *amice*: A cap, a hood, or hooded cape, later a badge, made of, or lined with, grey fur worn by the clergy (*Oxford Universal Dictionary*).

[2] *chevrette*: "espèce de musette sans soufflet" (Godefroy). [A kind of bagpipe without a bellows.] See T. McGee, "Musical Instruments," *ODMA* 3:1183–85.

[60] [Du mois de janvier. ixe][1]

O r dirons proprement de[2] la garde des brebis et par ordre en chascune saison, en commençant au mois de janvier pour ce que janvier est le premier mois et l'entree de l'an selon le kalendrier.[3]*

Ou mois de janvier sont les brebis portieres moult griefves et pesantes des aigneaux et faons qui sont en leurs ventres. Et aucunes aignelent et faonnent oudit mois quant elles ont esté luites et saillies en aoust, car aussi comme des fruictz, les unes sont plus hastives que les autres. Et encontre ce, la pourveance divine y a mis bon et convenable remede, car oudit[4] mois les loups suyvent les louves et vont aprés elles pour faire leur cohit, et par ce se oublient en ce mois et ainsi ne font point de dommage aux brebis, car se ne fust l'empeschement qu'il ont lors de poursuyr leur chaleur et de[5] continuer avec les louves, ilz effondreroient les ventres des brebis pour avoir les aigneaux. Mais Dieu ne le veult pas, qui ainsi y a pourveu par sa grace.

Ou[6] mois de janvier se doit le bergier lever moult matin, et si tost qu'il voit le jour se doit desjeuner et mengier du [61] pain et du potage qui est demouré et gardé du soir du jour de devant, et bien matin doit mener ses bestes aux champs se il n'y a empeschement de pluye ou de blanche gelee. Oudit mois de janvier les brebis portieres qui ont esté saillies du septembre precedent approuchent[7] le temps de faonner sur le fevrier, et pour ce doit on eschever de les mener aux champs a la blanche gelee pour le peril et inconveniens[8] qui en ensuit, pour ce que la blance* gelee fait mourir les aigneaux es ventres des meres et fait les brebis abortir,[9] et les petis aignelez ainsi mors sont nommez *avortons*.

Et se le bergier est jeune et ne soit pas encore instruit souffisamment en ceste science, il se doit adviser que il face a l'exemple et a la semblance des autres bergiers de la ville ou il demeure ou des autres villes voisines, avec lesquelz il doit converser et de eulx aprendre l'art et usage, car en aprenant devient on maistre.

---

[1] Du moys de janvier | Chapitre xi [*sic*] *B*; *no chapter title or number JTV*
[2] que *T*
[3] kalendier [*sic*] *BJ*
[4] audit *BT*
[5] de *om. T*
[6] Au *B*
[7] p. et a. *B*
[8] inconvenient *B*
[9] avorter *T*

Chapter 9

Now we will appropriately discuss the care of sheep and in each season in order, starting with January since it is the first month and the beginning of the year according to the calendar. In January the bred ewes are very heavy and weighed down with the lambs that are in their bellies. Some lamb in this month when they have been covered and bred in August, for just like some fruits, there are those that are more precocious than others. To counter this, Divine Providence has provided a good and suitable remedy: in this month the wolves[‡] follow the she-wolves and go after them to breed, thus forgetting themselves in this month and therefore they do no harm to the ewes. Were it not for this hindrance at this time, of following their rut in keeping after the she-wolves, they would rip open the bellies of the ewes for the lambs. But God, not wishing this, has provided against it thus by His grace.

In the month of January the shepherd must rise early and, as soon as he sees daylight, must breakfast, eating bread and soup left over from the day before. He must lead his ewes into the fields early if there is no hindrance from rain or hoar frost.[‡] In January the ewes who were covered in the preceding September approach their time to lamb in February and, because of this, leading them into fields with frost must be avoided for the danger and the disadvantages therefrom: frost makes lambs die in their mother's bellies and makes the ewes abort, the little lambs thus killed being called stillborn.

If the shepherd is young and not yet sufficiently learned in this art, he should be advised to follow the example of the other shepherds of the town where he lives, or other neighboring towns, with whom he should converse, and learn from them the art and custom, for in learning he becomes a master.

Du mois de fevrier. x^e.

Ou^1 mois de fevrier doit le bergier lever bien matin devant le jour pour affour-
rager ses bestes portieres de feurre de [62] blé bien matin^2 pour les recon-
forter. Et pour ce que en fevrier communement fait* noire gelee, le pasteur doit
mettre ses bestes aux champs bien matin, car la noire gelee essuie l'erbe et adoncques les bestes paissent voulentiers, et l'erbe ainsi essuee leur est moult prouffitable. Et s'il advenoit que par jour survenist rousee ou pluye ou desgel dont les
herbes fussent moulliees, le bergier doit donner a ses brebis au soir du fourrage
de favatz de feves, et non pas^3 de celuy de pois, car le fourrage de feves est sec et
celuy des pois est moiste.

Et^4 oudit^5 mois de fevrier le bergier ne doit point porter de houlette, ne^6 il
n'en est besoing, pour ce que les brebis portieres sont griefves et prestes a faonner.
Si ne doit pas getter terre sur les brebis ne les batre de corgies, qu'il ne les froisse
ou blesse, et de son pouoir* doit garder qu'il ne nuyse aux bestes ne aux faons,
et^7 en lieu de houlette doit avoir et porter ung crochet de coudre pour prendre
ses bestes par le pié s'il en y a aucunes qu'il vueille oindre ou luy^8 faire quelque
chose necessaire au mestier. Et pour chasser ses brebis doit^9 porter une vergette^10
de saulx deliee a trois cyons, dont il les fiert^11 [63] en lieu de corgies, pour mains
blecier et pour l'aisement des brebis.^12 Et^13 oudit^14 mois le bergier ne se doit point
seoir ne il ne doit^15 point esloigner de ses bestes, mais doit estre curieux emmy^16 ses
bestes et avoir l'oeil a^17 elles moult^18 ententivement, affin que se aucune faonnoit

---

62.02–03 communement fait *T*] faict com. *B*, souloient faire com. *V*

---

1 Au *B*
2 bien matin *om. B*
3 nompas *T*
4 Et *om. B*
5 Audict *B*, audit *T*
6 car *B*
7 et *om. B*
8 luy *om. T*
9 Et pour les chasser doit *T*
10 verge *T*
11 deliée. . . fiert *om. T*
12 pour moins blecer les brebis *B*
13 Et *om. B*
14 Audict *B*, audit *T*
15 il ne doit *om. BJ*
16 de *BJ*
17 sur *BJ*
18 moult *om. T*

Chapter 10

Concerning the Month of February

In February the shepherd must rise early, before daybreak, to feed his pregnant ewes with wheat straw to assuage their hunger. Because in February there is often black frost,[‡] the shepherd should put his animals on the fields early, for the black frost dries the grass and therefore the animals graze willingly, the grass thus dried out being highly beneficial to them. If it should happen that the day turns out to be dewy or rainy or thaws so that the grass is damp, at night the shepherd should give his ewes forage of dry bean stems and not those of peas, for bean forage is a dry feed and that of peas is moist.

In February the shepherd should not carry a shepherd's crook nor does he have any need of one because the bred ewes are heavy and ready to lamb. Nor should he throw dirt on the ewes or hit them with lashes, lest he harm or wound them, and should do his utmost to take care not to hurt either the animals or the lambs. In place of the shepherd's crook, he should own and carry a crook of hazelnut in order to catch the animals by the foot if there are any to whom he might want to apply ointment or do anything else that might be needed. To herd his ewes, he should carry a flexible wand of willow split in three shoots with which he hits them, instead of lashes, in order to hurt them less and for their comfort.

This month the shepherd should not sit down at all or get far away from his beasts, but should be most mindful of his animals and watch over them most

ou aigneloit[1] aux champs, qu'il y puist[2] secourir et aider incontinent si comme il affiert, car par la coulpe et defaux[3] des[4] mauvais et nices bergiers, plusieurs aignelez faonnez aux champs ont esté mengez des corbeaux, des huas et des corneilles, ou[5] dommage du maistre.

Au soir, quant le bergier repaire[6] du pasturage, il doit ramener ses bestes le petit pas tout doulcement sans traveiller, et les doit establer spacieusement, car oudit[7] mois de fevrier est moult prouffitable chose quant celui bestial est au large. Et quant le bergier veult aler couchier, il doit visiter ses brebis et les faire lever, car le trop gesir en ce temps leur pourroit nuyre pour les faons qui sont en leurs ventres. Et doit estre si tres[8] curieux que il ne doit dormir seurement se il ne sent son fouc en bon estat et convenable. Et en ce temps doit laisser les huis et fenestres des establers ouvertes quant le vent de bise vente,[9] pour y recevoir le dit vent [64] de bise, car il vault et prouffite aux brebis en ce temps. Et se autres vens ventoient, le bergier doit estouper les fenestres et clorre les huys des* bergeries, pour ce que lors nul autre vent n'y prouffite que celuy de bise.

Si tost comme la brebis a aigné ou faonné,[10] le bergier doit estre tout prest pour presenter l'aigneau devant sa mere, affin que par elle soit nettoyé et conreé, selon l'introduction de nature. Et quant l'aigneau est nettoyé, on doit prendre la brebis[11] et la couchier sur le dextre costé emprez l'aigneau,[12] si que il puist[13] prendre le piz, qui est la mamelle de sa mere, et sucgier du lait pour sa nourriture. Et lors le bergier doit plumer et oster de la laine du piz de la mere au lez[14] par devers le ventre. Et ne doit pas plumer par derriere, pour ce que la gelee et la froidure dudit mois de fevrier feroit grant mal a la brebis.

Et avec ce, le[15] bergier doit prendre le piz de la brebis et espraindre par ses dois deux ou trois goutes du premier lait de chascune broce[16] de la mamelle et

64.04 les huys des bergeries *BT*] les h. de b. *V*

---

[1] aignelet *T*
[2] qu'il lui peust *T*
[3] default *BJ*
[4] de *T*
[5] au *T*
[6] revient *B*
[7] audit *B*
[8] tres *om. T*
[9] vient *T*
[10] comme la b. aignele ou faonne *B*
[11] le b. [*sic*] *B*
[12] son aigneau *T*
[13] puisse *T*
[14] au lez *om. T*
[15] le *om. T*
[16] brosse *T*

attentively so that if one should lamb in the field, he could run to her and help immediately as is appropriate. By the misdeed and failure of false and stupid shepherds, many lambs dropped in the field have been eaten by ravens, kites and crows, to the master's loss.

In the evening, when the shepherd returns from the pasture, he should lead his animals back at a slow pace, most gently without worrying them, and should stable them roomily, for in February it is most beneficial for these animals to have enough space. When the shepherd wants to go to bed, he must visit his ewes and make them get up: lying too long at this time can be harmful for the lambs that are in their bellies. Also he should be very careful not to sleep too soundly if he does not feel that his flock is in good and proper order. At this time he should leave the doors and windows of the fold open when the north wind blows in order to let in that wind, for it is valuable and beneficial to the ewes at this time. If other winds should blow, the shepherd must stop up the windows and close the doors of the fold, for no other wind is good for them except the north wind.

As soon as the ewes lamb, the shepherd must be ready to present the lamb to its mother so that she can clean and stimulate it,[1]‡ according to nature's way. When the lamb is tidied up, he must take the ewe‡ and lay her on her right side next to the lamb so that it can take the teat, which is the udder of its mother, and drink some milk for nourishment. Then the shepherd must strip and remove some wool from the mother's udder on the side toward the belly. He should not remove it from her backside because the freezing and cold of February cause great trouble to ewes.

This done, the shepherd should take the teat and, with his fingers, express two or three drops of the first milk from each side of the udder,‡ letting

---

[1] *conreé: conroyer:* "to settle together by a thorough working" (Cotgrave).

laisser couler* sur terre ainçois que l'aignelet en gouste, car ces[1] premieres goutes de lait sont nommees *bet* et ne sont pas saines. [65] Et se[2] l'aignelet en[3] goustoit,* il pourroit encourir une maladie que l'en apelle *l'affilee*, de laquelle les aigneaux se meurent et perissent souventesfois. Et de celle[4] maladie et d'autres sera dit es chapitres des maladies et des cures et remedes. Et pendant ce que on veult guerir l'aignel* du mal de l'affilee, l'en ne doit pas tirer ne traire le lait du piz a la mere de l'aigneau, mais s'en doit on cesser[5] par deux jours du mains, affin que le lait de la brebis descroisse, car par la grant habondance du[6] lait en la nouvelleté, aprés ce que la brebis a faonné, vient le bet en la mamelle de la beste, lequel bet est de grosse nature et de grosses[7] humeurs, et pour ce est perilleux a l'aignelet et a sa nourriture. Et quant le lait de la brebis est ainsi purgié par deux jours et est plus valable, l'en doit prendre l'aignelet et remettre[8] a sa propre mere, et lors doit il[9] demourer et gesir avec la mere par quinze jours et quinze nuys continuelement et non plus,[10] sans oster ne separer d'avec la mere. Et est a noter que se l'aigneau demouroit avec sa mere plus de quinze jours sans oster et il mouroit en celle demeure, ce seroit la coulpe dudit [66] bergier et seroit tenu au rendre et restituer a son maistre, car chascun bergier doit sçavoir que la longue demeure de plus de quinze jours avec la mere souloit* engendrer communement aux aigneaux une maladie que l'en appelle *le pousset*,* dont les aigneaux meurent souvent. Et n'y a que peu ou neant de remede contre celle maladie du pousset. Et pour y obvier le bergier doit oster les aigneaux d'avec les meres quant il[11] y ont esté par quinze jours, comme dit est, et les doit establer et mettre en ung toict ou estable tout par eulz. Et chascun matin les doit laisser alaicter leurs meres[12] ainçois qu'ilz voisent* aux champs. Et quant les brebis repairent[13] des champs au soir, le bergier les doit laisser reposer ainçois qu'il leur baille leurs aigneaux pour alaicter, pour ce que quant

64.23 couler *B* (couller *T*)] couleur *V*
65.01 en goustoit *BJT*] en goustant *V*
66.04 souloit] souloient *BJTV*

---

[1] ses *T*
[2] Car si *BJ*
[3] le *BJ*
[4] ceste *T*
[5] s'en doit garder *B*
[6] du *repeated V*
[7] et aussi de grosses *T*
[8] et le remettre *T*
[9] et lors il doit *T*
[10] nomplus *T*
[11] ilz *T*
[12] laisser a laicter leurs m. *B*, l. alaicter a leurs m. *T*
[13] reviennent *BJ*

it run on the ground before letting the lamb taste it, for the first drops of milk are called colostrum[1] and are not healthy.[‡] If the lamb ingests it, it could get a malady called scours[2‡] from which lambs often die. This malady and others will be told about in the chapters of maladies, cures and remedies. When one wishes to cure the lamb of scours, one should not draw the milk from the teat of the lamb's mother but should stop milking her for two days or more so that the milk of the ewe may decrease. The colostrum, which comes in the great abundance of milk in the freshening of the ewe's udder after she has lambed, is of a thick nature and heavy humors, and therefore is dangerous to the lamb and its nourishment. When the ewe's milk has been clarified over two days and is more worthwhile, one should take the lamb and put it back with its own mother, after which it should stay with its mother constantly for fifteen days and nights and no more, without being taken away or separated from its mother. It should be noted that if the lamb should stay with its mother more than fifteen days without being re-moved and should die during this stay, it would be the fault of the shepherd and he would be required to pay back and make restitution to his master. Each shep-herd should know that the long stay of more than fifteen days with the mother can often engender among lambs a malady called pneumonia,[3] from which lambs often die, and for which there is little or no remedy. To avoid this, the shepherd should remove the lambs from their mothers when they have been there fifteen days, as was mentioned, and should put them under a roof or in a fold all by themselves. Each morning he must let them go nurse before their mothers go to the fields and, when the ewes come back from the fields in the evening, the shepherd should let them rest before he allows their lambs to nurse: when the

---

[1] *béton*: "au XVIe siècle, le colostrum, premier lait d'une nouvelle accouchée" (Lachi-ver). [In the 16th century, colostrum, first milk from a new mother.]

[2] *Affilee*: Scours; Hemorrhagic enterotoxemia: "an acute, highly fatal disease of young lambs caused by the bacterial organism *Clostridium perfringens* Type C."

[3] *Pousset*: maladie des moutons; *Pousser*: être essoufflé (Godefroy) [to be win-ded.] Most probably pneumonia, to which young lambs are very susceptible.

les brebis sont traveillees leur lait est chault et batant, et n'est pas bien attrem-
pé pour les aigneaux, car aucunesfois pour alaicter les meres lassees vient aux
aigneaux une maladie que l'en appelle *le bouchet*,[1] de laquelle yceulx aigneaux
meurent souvent.

Aprés ce que[2] les aigneaux sont separez et [67] ostez d'avec leurs meres quant
ilz y ont esté la premiere quinzaine et que ilz sont mis et establez[3] tout par eulz,
en autre quinzaine ensuivant ilz ne doivent menger autre chose que du lait de
leurs meres seulement. Et ainsi que dit est doivent estre gouvernez et gardez par
ung mois entier sans ce que il menguent* que pur lait. Du seurplus de la garde et
de la* nourriture des aigneaux sera dit es mois ensuyvans.

67.08 de la nourriture] la *om. BV,* de la *om. T*

---

[1] rouchet *T*

[2] Et aprés que *B*

[3] mis es estables *T*

ewes are hot and weary, their milk is hot and not clear and not well moderated for the lambs. Sometimes a malady called sore mouth[1‡] comes to lambs from nursing tired dams, from which lambs frequently die.

After the first fifteen days, when the lambs have been segregated and removed from their mothers and have been put in a fold all by themselves, for another fifteen days following they should not have anything else to eat other than their mother's milk. As noted, they should be tended and watched over for a whole month without eating anything except pure milk. The rest about the caring and feeding of lambs will be told in the months that follow.

---

[1] *bouchet*: "Maladie signalée par Jean de Brie au xive siècle et qui atteint les moutons" (Lachiver). [Illness pointed out by Jean de Brie in the 14th century and which attacks sheep.] *bouchiere*: "éruption de boutons autour de la bouche" (Godefroy). [Eruption of pustules around the mouth.] *bouchet*: Sore mouth. Contagious pustular dermatitis.

Du[1] mois de mars. xie.

Ou[2] mois de mars le bergier doit avoir grant consideracion et[3] aviser en quelz pastis il maine ses brebis, pour ce que lors la terre gette ses vapeurs, et les grosses herbes commencent a croistre et yssir de terre, mesmement une male herbe que l'en nomme *bouveraude*.* Et est de mauvaise digestion et moult nuysant[4] aux brebis ou guoitron[5] de leur gorge, car si tost come les brebis ont gouté[6] de la bouveraude, il convient que le bergier soit tout prest pour elles ayder et secourir[7] et incontinent leur fault du sel en la bouche pour donner occasion de boire, pour digerer et avaler l'amertume de la bouveraude.

Le bon pasteur se doit garder souverainement[8] de conduire ses bestes en pasture oudit[9] mois [68] de mars en lieux marescageux,* bas et moistes, car lors naist et croist[10] es palus une herbe tres perilleuse a une petite fueillette[11] ronde et bien verte que l'en appelle *dauve*, laquelle* les brebis convoitent[12] moult a mengier, mais elle leur est trop nuysant et dommageuse,[13] car si tot* que les brebis en ont gousté et l'ont avale[e]* en leurs entrailles, la dauve est de telle nature que elle demeure et se adhert[14] au foye de la brebis ou autre oeille. Et celle male herbe ne remonte plus ne revient a runge a la gorge de la beste si comme font autres herbes, mais de celle dauve par sa corruption sur le foye sont engendrez une maniere de vers, qui par pourriture ont vie et menguent et corrumpent tout le foye de la beste, dont elle est mise a mort par l'infection de ladicte male herbe nommee *dauve*. Et aprés ce que la brebis l'a receu[e]* et menge[e],* on s'en peult apparcevoir a ce que elle boit plus souvent et plus habondamment que quant elle est saine. Et se peult celle maladie des dauves tapir et latiter es brebis ung an ou plus, mais en la fin convient il que elles en meurent, car la dauve destruit le foye et le [69] foye est ung des trois membres principaulz ou la vie gist, aprés le cueur et le cerveau, et par ce la brebis endauvee ne peult vivre. Si doit bien doncques le bergier eschever que il ne conduise ses brebis prez des lieux et marescages, esquelz croist et regne ladicte dauve par tout le temps d'esté.

68.01 marescageux *B*] marescages *TV*

---

[1] Au *T*

[2] Au *B*

[3] et *om. B*

[4] nuisante *T*

[5] gueteron *T*

[6] mengé *T*

[7] pour les a. et s. *B*, pour les s. *T*

[8] souverainement *om. T*

[9] audict *B*

[10] croist et naist *T*

[11] fueille *T*

[12] couvoitent *T*

[13] dommageable *T*

[14] adhere *T*

Chapter 11

Concerning the Month of March

In March the shepherd must use great caution and consider carefully the pastures into which he may lead his ewes, because at that time the earth throws forth its vapors and baneful plants begin to shoot up and spring from the earth, especially an evil plant called gorse.[1‡] It is poorly digested and is very harmful to ewes in their throat's gullet. As soon as the ewes have tasted gorse, the shepherd should very quickly give them aid: they need salt in their mouths immediately to make them drink in order to digest and cut the bitterness of the gorse.

Above all, in March the good shepherd will avoid leading his animals into pasture in low marshy and moist places, for then in the swamps is born and thrives a very dangerous plant with a small and quite round green leaf that is called ranunculus, or buttercup,[‡] which the ewes are most eager to eat, but which is very harmful and detrimental to them. As soon as the ewes have tasted it and swallowed it down to their entrails, the buttercup is so constituted that it remains there and adheres to the liver of the ewe or other sheep. This wicked plant never comes back to the cud of the animal as other plants do, but from this buttercup, by its spoiling of the liver, is born a kind of worm[2‡] that has life through contamination, and eats and corrupts the whole liver of the animal. Therefore she is brought to death by the infection of the aforesaid evil plant named buttercup. After the ewe has gotten and eaten it, it is noticeable that she drinks more often and more deeply than when she is well. It is possible that this malady from buttercup can lie hidden and lurk in the ewe for a year or more, but in the end she must die, for buttercup destroys the liver and the liver is one of the three principal members where life lies, after the heart and the brain. Because the ewe having eaten buttercup cannot live, it behooves the shepherd to avoid leading his ewes into swampy areas where the buttercup grows and flourishes all summer long.

---

[1] *Bouveraude*: Gorse. In its natural state gorse provides food for sheep. *Ulex gallii* L.

[2] *Manière de vers*: Kind of worm, in this case liver fluke: *Fasciola hepatica*.

Et quant au[1] gouvernement et garde des aigneaux oudit[2] mois de mars, quant les aigneaux ont ung mois passé qu'il[3] commencent* a croistre et leurs membres se fourment, le bergier leur doit lors[4] donner du fourrage pour leur nourriture, c'est assavoir, du foing et de l'avaine et a la fois[5] de la vesche deliee, non pas de la plus grosse, et ung pou fois aprés autre.[6] Et doit on bien aviser que on ne leur donne trop de vesche, car elle est trop forte. Et au commencement leur doit on donner de l'avaine meslee avecques bran, que aucuns nomment *gruis* ou *tierceul*. Et doit le bergier eschever que il ne donne aux aigneaux trop a boire en leur estable, car planté boire leur nuyroit. Et qui leur veult donner a boire pour en avoir esbatement mette de l'eaue clere en ung bacin ou chauderon ou autre beau vaisseau bien cler [70] et bien escuré, car les aigneaux se mirent voulentiers ou vaisseau cler et y prendent[7] grant plaisance. En tous ces* poins doit le bergier estre curieux. Et quant a la garde et gouvernement des aigneaux et antenois, doit garder bien et diligemment la doctrine dessusdicte, especialement que bouveraude ne dauves ne leur puissent nuyre.

Et en oultre, oudit[8] mois de mars le bergier doit eschever curieusement que ses[9] aigneaux il ne mette soubz la repercussion du soleil, car en ce mois de mars le soleil est ou[10] signe du Mouton, qui est fort et vertueux. Et lors le soleil par sa grant vertu penetre et perce de ses rais jusques au cerveau des aigneaux et leur engendre une merveilleuse maladie[11] que l'en appelle *evertin*,* qui les fait tournaier, dont ilz sont tous escervelez et en affolent et meurent par maintes fois.

Item : oudit[12] mois de mars le bergier ne doit donner a boire a ses brebis ou aigneaux se[13] n'est en cas de grant necessité, si comme contre l'erbe bouveraude ou pour trop grant chaleur de soleil, et se besoing en est leur doit faire boire eaue courant, s'il estoit en lieu ou il en peult[14] recouvrer. [71] La cause pourqouy

---

69.10 commencent *BJ*] commence *TV*
70.03 ces] ses *BTV*

---

[1] au *om. B*, ou *T*
[2] audit *B*
[3] ilz *BJ*
[4] lors *om. B*
[5] et aulcunesfois *B*
[6] ung pou aprés de l'autre *B*, ung pou de fois aprés autre *T*
[7] prennent *B*
[8] audict *B*, audit *T*
[9] ces *B*
[10] au *B*
[11] meladie *T*
[12] audict *B*
[13] ce *B*
[14] peust *B*

As for the management and care of lambs in March, when the lambs are a month old and they begin to grow and their limbs begin to take shape, the shepherd should give them some fodder for their nourishment, for example, some hay‡ and oats, and sometimes slender vetch, not the coarsest, and once in a while. He should take great care not to give them too much vetch, for it is very strong.‡ In the beginning, he should give them oats mixed with wheat bran, which some call oat groats or bran. The shepherd should avoid giving the lambs too much to drink in their fold, for too much to drink is harmful to them. Whoever wishes to give them something to drink in a way to provide amusement should put clear water in a basin or large bowl or other handsome vessel that is very clear and well scoured, for the lambs willingly look at themselves in a clear basin and take great pleasure in doing so. The shepherd must be conscientious about all these points. Regarding the care and management of lambs and yearlings, he should observe the above rules well and diligently, especially so that the gorse and buttercup may not harm them.

In addition, in March the shepherd should assiduously avoid putting his lambs under the beating of the sun, for in March the sun is in the sign of the Ram and is strong and powerful. When the sun, with its great strength, penetrates and pierces the brain of the lambs with its rays, it brings on them a strange malady called staggers,[1]‡ which makes them reel about, from which they are brain-damaged and crazed and from which they frequently die.

In March the shepherd should not give drink to his ewes or lambs except in case of great necessity, as to counter the gorse or too great warmth of sun. If need be, he should make them drink from running water if he is in a place where

---

[1] *Avertin*: "Maladie des moutons, vulg. appelée tournis."

on doit faire abstenir les[1] brebis de boire ou[2] mois de mars est pour ce que lors les eaues ne sont pas bien saines pour les mutacions de l'air et du temps qui est tourné en ver, que l'en dit *printemps*, et pour ce que la terre est lors eslargie et peureuse et gette lors ses vapeurs et superfluitez, comme dit est. Et par ce en celuy mois le boire n'est pas prouffitable au bestial,[3] mais est bon de mener en pasture par ses gaschieres aux herbes tendres et nouvelles pour seder et appaisier leur soif et pour obvier aux bruvages des flotz, des mares et des eaues, qui lors sont plus perilleuses que en autres saisons.

---

[1] ses *T*
[2] au *B*
[3] bestail *T*

he can find it. The reason for making the ewes abstain from drinking in March is that the water is not really healthy because of changes in the air and in the season, which is turning into spring and because the earth is opened up then and throws off its vapors and excesses, so it is said. Therefore in this month drinking is not helpful to animals, but it is good to lead them to pasture in the waste areas having tender and new plants to settle and appease their thirst and to prevent drinking from flood waters, ponds, and other waters, which are then more dangerous than in other seasons.

Du mois d'avril. xiie.

Ou[1] mois d'avril le bergier se doit lever fort matin pour visiter ses brebis et pour ouvrir les[2] huys et fenestres des estables pour leur donner l'air du matin, car il leur fait grant bien. Et doit le bergier veoir aux champs* pour sçavoir de la qualité du temps. Et se il fait bon pasturer, il doit incontinent mettre hors ses [72] brebis et les mener champaier. Et qui frequente les champs, il doit bien aviser selon les vens et les nuees, car il y a aucuns vens, lesquelz chassent les nuees[3] et les bruynes devant la face du soleil, par quoy l'air devient pur et serain et fait beau temps. Et aucuns autres acueuvrent l'er* de[4] nuees et amainent la pluye, et mesmement ung des vens que l'en appelle Plongel, qui vient de devers Occident, car il fait le temps pluyeux de son soufflement. Si voit on tout communement que oudit[5] mois d'avril souloit* venter et souffler ung vent que l'en nomme Galerne,[6] qui vient de devers septentrion, entre occident et bise, plus souvent que nul des autres, lequel vent de Galerne les bergiers mauldissent,[7] et le pays dont il vient.

Le bergier par generale doctrine doit avoir consideracion aux temps et aux vens, tant ou[8] mois d'avril comme es autres mois de l'an. Et doit eschever le bergier que il ne maine ne conduise ses brebis en pasture contre le vent de Solerre, que aucuns appellent Nort, qui vient de devers midy,* lequel est nuysant et dommagable aux brebis, car il les souloit* enfler de son espe[73]rit et de son soufflement. Si le doit le bergier eschever en tant que il peult, car il advient souvent que quant les bestes en sont enflees, il y convient mettre remede par seignee[9] ou autrement, si comme cy aprés en sera dit plus a plain des cures et des seignees.[10]

72.12 souloit] souloient *BJTV*
72.25 souloit] souloient *TV,* fait *BJ*

---

[1] Au *B*
[2] ses *T*
[3] nues *T*
[4] des *T*
[5] audict *B,* audit *T*
[6] calerne *T*
[7] les b. le m. *B*
[8] au *B*
[9] seignees *T*
[10] de c. et de s. *T*

Chapter 12

Concerning the Month of April

In April the shepherd must get up very early to visit his ewes and to open the doors and windows of the fold to give them the morning air, which does them great good. The shepherd should look at the fields in order to know the nature of the weather.[‡] If it is good for pasturing, he should immediately put his ewes out and lead them to pasture. Whoever frequents the fields should pay close attention to the winds and clouds. There are some winds that chase away the clouds and the mists from the face of the sun, whereby the air becomes pure and calm and the weather is fine. There are others that fill the air with clouds and bring rain, especially one of the winds called *Plongel*, which comes from the west, making rainy weather with its blowing. Usually in April one sees a wind called *Galerne* that blows and whistles, coming from the direction of the north, between west and north more often than any other, which wind the shepherds curse, both it and the country from which it comes.

As a general rule, the shepherd should pay attention to the weather and winds in April as much as in the other months of the year. He should avoid leading his ewes into the pasture against the wind named *Solerre*,[1] which some call the North wind,[‡] which comes from the South and is harmful and disadvantageous to the ewes, since they are wont to bloat from its force and its blowing. The shepherd must avoid this as much as he can, for it often happens that when the animals are bloated, it requires a remedy by bloodletting[2‡] or by other means, of which more will be said later more fully in the section concerning cures and bloodletting.

---

[1] *Solerre*: "the East wind," according to Cotgrave, echoed by Greimas and Godefroy.

[2] *La seignee*, "Phlebotomie, bloud-letting" (Cotgrave).

Du moys de may. xiii^e.

Ou^1 mois de may est le temps doulz et serain et ne fait pas encore trop chault. Et est tout flori sur terre, car elle a lors vestu sa belle robe qui est aorne[e]* de plusieurs beles^2 florettes de diverses couleurs es bois et es prez et sont lors les pasturages tous plains de belles herbes et tendres.^3 Ou^4 mois de may a l'en coustume a^5 tondre la laine des moutons, des brebis portieres, des antenoises et des aigneaux, car lors est la laine meure. Et aussi plus convenable et trop plus prouffitable chose^6 est de^7 despoullier lors et tondre les brebis que en nul autre temps, tant pour la chaleur attrempee du temps comme pour l'aisement de la pasture. De la maniere de tondre les bestes dessusdictes et comment on les doit prendre souef et lyer les piedz d'une laniere ou d'une cordele de laine molle pour [74] mains blecier et du surplus de faire la tonsure, que l'en doit faire le plus proffitablement que l'en peult,^8 ne sera^9 peu ou neant parlé en cest traictié, pour ce que la tonsure n'est pas de la propre essence du droit art du mestier de la^10 bergerie. Car combien que ce soit des dependences, toutesfois les bergiers n'ont pas coustume de tondre leurs brebis. Et pour ce s'en passe ledit Jehan de Brie.

Oudit^11 mois de may doit le bergier* mener ses bestes tart aux champs et aussi doit il revenir tot* a l'ostel : tart pour ce que les rousees de may nuysent au bestial a laine, car avec la rousee se mesle aucunesfois broullias ou mielaz, qui moult empirent les herbes et les fueilles. Et sur les fueilles des roinses le peult on congnoistre et apparcevoir plus tost^12 que ailleurs. Et les brebis de leur nature menguent voulentiers les fueilles des roinses quant elles y pevent advenir. Et aucunesfois pour celle^13 convoitise y laissent de leur laine et^14 de leur despoulle en alant trop prez des roinses poignans. Cestuy meffait doit on pardonner aux brebis par l'exemple des hommes, considD que les hommes, qui* sont discretz

74.10 bergier *T* (berger *BJ*)] berbier *V*
74.25 qui sont discretz] qui *om. BTV*

---

^1 Au *B*
^2 belle *T*
^3 tendre *T*
^4 Au *B*
^5 de *B*
^6 choses *T*
^7 de *om. T*
^8 que n'en p. *T*
^9 ne n'en s. *B*
^10 la om. *T*
^11 Au dit *B*
^12 plustost *B*, plus toust [*sic*] *T*
^13 celles *T*
^14 de leur laine et *om. B*

Chapter 13

Concerning the Month of May

In May the weather is fair and calm and not yet too hot. Everything on earth is in full flower, for then she has put on her beautiful gown, adorned with many lovely little flowers of diverse colors, in woods and meadows—it is then that the pastures are filled with beautiful, tender plants. In May it is the custom to shear the wool from the rams,[‡] ewes, yearlings, and lambs, since the wool is ready then. It is also more appropriate and greatly profitable to shear the sheep then than at any other time, as much for the season's moderate heat as for ease in pasturing. Regarding the manner of shearing the aforesaid beasts and taking them gently and tying their feet with a thong or a cord of soft wool in order to hurt them less, and the rest about shearing, which should be done as profitably as one can, little or nothing more will be said in this treatise because shearing is not rightly a part of the true art of shepherdry; for however much it may interrelate, nonetheless it is not the custom for shepherds to shear their sheep. And therefore Jean de Brie will move on.

In May the shepherd should lead his animals late to the fields and should also return early to the fold, late because the dews of May are harmful to wool-bearing animals: with the dew is sometimes mixed ground mist or fine rain,[1] which is very damaging to grasses and leaves. It can be seen and recognized on the leaves of blackberries[2‡] sooner than elsewhere. By their nature ewes readily eat the leaves of blackberries when they can come upon them. Sometimes because of their greediness they leave their wool and their hide there from going too near the thorny briers.[‡] This misdeed should be pardoned in the ewes, given the example of men, considering that men, who are prudent and reasoning,

---

[1] *miélat*: "En Picardie, petite pluie fine et douce, funeste aux blés et aux avoines" (Lachiver). [In Picardy, a small fine rain, disastrous for wheat and oats.]

[2] *ronce*: "Ronce arbrisseau, Mûrier des haies, *Rubus fruticosus*" (Belon, 537). [Shrubby blackberry, hedgerow blackberry.]

[75] et raisonnables, laissent[1] bien et engaigent[2] leurs despoulles en la taverne ou en autres lieux pour leur fole voulenté acomplir. Si[3] n'est pas grant merveille des brebis, qui sont brutes et non raisonnables, se elles perdent de leur laine pour acomplir leur desir et leur appetit. Et pour y obvier doit aler le bergier tart, que les rousees ne nuysent aux bestes a laine. Et d'autre part le tost repairer leur est bon pour eschever la force de l'ardeur du soleil quant il est en sa ferveur et chaleur vers heure de midi.

Et oudit[4] mois de may le bergier doit clorre et fermer les huys et fenestres de ses estables par jour. Et par nuyt les doit laisser ouvertes pour recevoir l'air de la nuyt et le temps serain es estables pour le bien, attrempance et aisement des brebis. Et ne doit on point nettoyer les estables pour les causes et raisons dessus-dictes. Encore doit on bien noter que qui veult faire tondre les jeunes aigneaux de la premiere tonsure, on ne les doit point laver, posé qu'il feussent crotez, car qui les laveroit pour nettoyer leur laine quant on les vouldroit laver,* il feroit son grant dommage et est bien esprouvé par ce que quant on les lave et nettoye en l'eaue, [76] ilz se esbahissent et tressaillent, et aucunes* que l'eaue leur entre es oreilles et en deviennent lours et estahieux tellement qu'il en sont tous affolez et ont les veues torves et ne sont pas prouffitables a garder. Et pour ce est il bon et expedient de tondre les aigneaux sans laver. Des moutons et des brebis n'est il pas a faire pareillement, car on ne les[5] doit pas tondre sans laver.

Quant les aigneaux sont tondus et despoulliez de leur premiere toison, le bergier doit estre curieux* de mener son tropeau d'aigneaux incontinent aprés leur tonsure parmy ung chemin sec et poudreux, affin que la poudre qu'il esmou-vent de leurs piedz se preigne* sur eulz et qu'il en soient empoudrez par deux jours ou trois. Et la raison si[6] est pour ce que la poudre leur fait cotele sur leur char et les garantist et defent de rongne ou de clavel, qui est une moult mauvai-se maladie et nuysant aux brebis et aigneaux,[7] si comme cy dessoubz[8] sera dit. Et s'il advenoit que sans moyen aprés la[9] tonsure fist temps pluyeux,[10] par quoy les aigneaux ne peussent* eulx empoudrer ou chemin pour l'empeschement de

75.23 laver *BJ*] *om. TV*
76.15 preigne] prengnent *BJV*, prengnes *T*

---

[1] laissant *B*
[2] et engaigent *om. B*
[3] Se *BJ*
[4] audit *B*
[5] le *BJ*
[6] si *om. B*
[7] et aux a. *T*
[8] cy aprés *B*
[9] la *om. T*
[10] plurieux *T*

leave and pledge their own hides in the tavern and other places in order to accomplish their foolish desire. Therefore it is no great marvel that ewes, which are dumb animals and unreasoning, should lose some of their wool in order to satisfy their desire and appetite. To prevent that, the shepherd should go out late, so that the dews do not harm the woolbearers. In addition, coming back early is good to avoid the force of the sun's burning when it is hot and strong near the noon hour.

In May the shepherd should close the doors and windows of his fold during the day. At night he should leave them open to let in the night air and the mild weather for the welfare, moderation and contentment of the ewes. Nor should he clean the fold for the causes and reasons mentioned above. Also it should be noted that whoever wishes to give the young lambs their first shearing should not wash them, supposing that they are dirty, for whoever washes them to clean the wool will cause great harm: it is well known that when one washes and cleans them in water, they are terrified and jump about. Some who get water in their ears become so dull and dazed that they are completely stupefied: they have a lowering look and are not worth keeping. For this reason, it is good and well-advised to shear lambs without washing. With rams and ewes it is not the same, for they should not be shorn without being washed.

When the lambs are shorn and stripped of their first fleece, the shepherd should be careful to lead his flock of lambs immediately after their shearing along a dry and dusty road so that the dust they stir up with their feet will cling to them and they will be dusted for two or three days. The reason is that the powder makes a jacket on their flesh, shielding and protecting them against mange or sheep pox, which is a very bad malady and harmful to ewes and lambs, as will be said below. If it comes about that immediately after shearing the weather is rainy and the lambs cannot dust themselves on the road (being prevented

la[1] pluye, si com[77]me il eschiet aucunesfois, lors doit on tenir lesditz aigneaux es estables, mais le bergier contre l'empeschement y doit pourveoir et doit prendre de la cendre et autre poudre sachee[2] bien delieement.[3] Et ycelle poudre doit getter sur ses aigneaux pour les empoudrer et pour yceulx garder et garantir, si comme dit est, car celle poudre leur fait une maniere de cotele sur leur petite laine, laquelle leur est moult prouffitable et les defent et garde de rongne et de clavel et si les garantist de la pluye. Et n'est pas doubte que a la mesure[4] que la laine leur croist et revient, elle deboute celle poudre et emporte avec soy amont et la char[5] des aigneaux demeure nette et pure soubz la laine, et en la fin se purge la laine par son suyn et chasse la poudre hors. Et[6] ainsi les aigneaux demeurent sains[7] et netz moyennant ladicte poudre. Et[8] pareillement est la poudre convenable, necessaire et prouffitable aux moutons, aux brebis et aux bestes antenoises. Et les doit on semblablement empoudrer aprés leur tonsure incontinent et sans moyen pour ycelles* garantir et defendre des maladies dessusdictes et pour [78] garder la char[9] soubz la laine.

77.24 ycelles (icelles *T*)] icelle *BJ*, ycelle *V*

---

[1] la *om. T*
[2] sacee *T*
[3] delicement *B*, deliement *T*
[4] a mesure *B*
[5] chair *BT*
[6] Et *om. BJ*
[7] sainctz *T*
[8] Et *om. BJ*
[9] g. la chair *BJ*, g. de la chair *T*

by rain, as sometimes occurs), then the lambs must be kept in the fold. However the shepherd should provide against this difficulty and should take ashes or other dry fine filtered powder and throw this powder on his lambs to dust them and in this way shield and protect them, as was said. This powder makes a kind of jacket on their short wool, which is very good for them and wards off and guards against mange and pox, protecting them from the rain. It is unquestioned that as the wool grows and comes back, it sloughs this powder, and brings it up along with it, and the skin of the lambs remains clean and unsullied under the wool, in the end the wool cleansing itself with its grease and expelling the dust. Thus the lambs remain healthy and clean because of the powder. The powder is likewise suitable, necessary and helpful to the male sheep, ewes, and yearlings. They should likewise be dusted immediately after shearing to protect them against the above-mentioned maladies and to protect the flesh under the wool.

Du mois de juing.* xiiii^e.

Ou^1 mois de juing doit le bergier aviser curieusement en quelles parties il maine ses brebis en pasture, pour ce que en ce mois de juing croist une herbe aux champs que l'en appelle *poucel*. Celle herbe est de deux manieres. L'une a la fueille cretelee et la tige verte et est bonne. L'autre a la fueille ronde et la tige vermeille et pelue et est si mauvaise que quant la brebis en mengue elle pert son runge et devient malade.

En ce mois de juing se doit le bergier lever au point du jour pour faire traire le lait de ses bestes et puis les doit mener aux champs bien matin, car lors y fait il bon. Et au retourner des champs les doit garder de trop grant chaleur, car la chaleur du soleil nuyst a la char^2 d'icelle[s]* brebis pour la povreté de leur laine. Et la chaleur des bestes peult le bergier assez apparcevoir a son mouton sonnaillier, car combien que par raison il soit le plus gras, dont il n'est pas si tost feru ne sourpris du soleil. Toutesfois le sonnaillier se arre[79]ste tout coy^3 quant il a grant chault et trippe des piedz et remue sa queue, et ce sont les signes de sa^4 chaleur, et aussi est il environné des mouches quant il est arresté. Si y doit pourveoir le bergier et faire umbraier ses bestes et mener paisiblement es estables.

Et n'est force se^5 les brebis ne menguent que ung petit^6 ou^7 mois de juing, car la graisse de ce mois ne leur est pas^8 prouffitable. En ce mois doit le bergier mener ses bestes hors des friches et des chemins herbeux^9 et les doit tenir es gaschieres et es haultz lieux en planté de chardons, car la pasture des chardons leur est bonne. Et quant elles menguent voulentiers les tendres chardons, ce est vray signe que elles sont saines. Et se elles n'en veulent menger, ce est signe que elles sont usees,^10 malsaines, et ne sont pas dignes de nourrir. Si doit considerer le bergier et en aviser son maistre pour son prouffit.

---

^1 Au *B*

^2 chair *BJT*

^3 quoy [*sic*] *T*

^4 la *T*

^5 que *BJ*

^6 les b. mengent beaucoup *B*, les b. menge [*sic*] b. *J*

^7 au *B*

^8 pas *om. BJ*

^9 herbus [*sic*] *T*

^10 usees *om. T*

Chapter 14

Concerning the Month of June

In June the shepherd should think carefully about where he takes his ewes to pasture, because in this month a plant called poppy[1][‡] grows in the fields. This plant is of two kinds: one has a notched leaf and green stem and is good; the other has a round leaf and red hairy stem and is so harmful that when the ewes eat it, they lose their cud and become ill.[‡]

In June the shepherd should rise at dawn to have the ewes milked,[‡] and then should lead them very early into the fields, for the weather is fine then. When coming back from the fields, he should protect them from getting too hot, because the heat of the sun hurts the ewes' flesh when their wool is lacking. The shepherd can judge how hot his animals are by his bellwether. Since it is reasonable that he is the fattest, therefore he may not be affected or overcome by the sun as soon. However, when he is hot, the bellwether may come to a standstill, completely quiet, stamp his feet and shake his tail as signs of heat. He is also surrounded by flies when he stops. So the shepherd should be foresighted and give his animals shade and lead them quietly to the fold.

It is all right if the ewes eat only a little in June, as the fat they put on in this month is not useful to them. In this month the shepherd should lead his animals past the fallow areas and grassy lanes and keep them in wastelands and in high places with plenty of teasels,[2][‡] for the grazing of teasel is good for them: when they willingly eat the tender teasel, it is a true sign that they are healthy. If they are not willing to eat them, it is a sign that they are worn out, unwell, and not worth feeding. The shepherd should take note of this and so advise his master for his benefit.

---

[1] *Poucel. Papaver rhoeas* L. Poppies.

[2] *Chardon*: Teasel.

Et a heure de prangiere[1] oudit[2] mois[3] ne doit pas le[4] bergier mener ses brebis aprés disner contre soleil,[5] mais doit[6] tourner le dos au soleil et les conduire[7]
es valees ou les herbes sont plus moistes. Et n'est pas doubte[8] [80] que les brebis
voient mieulx l'erbe verdoier quant elles ont les doz tournez au soleil que se le ray
du soleil luisoit parmy leurs[9] yeulx. Et est assavoir que lors[10] une herbe nommee
chaillie leur est moult prouffitable et nourrissant et leur fait avoir bon ventre, car
se les brebis estoient enflees ou maumises d'aucune male herbe, la chailliee les[11]
guerist et leur est vraye medicine. Et soit adoncques le bergier sage et discret en
ramenant ses brebis.

---

[1] prangier [*sic*] *T*
[2] audit *B*
[3] oudit mois *om. T*
[4] ledit *T*
[5] c. le s. *T*
[6] mais il doibt *T*
[7] et c. ses brebis *T*
[8] n'est point a doubter *T*
[9] les *B*
[10] lors *om. T*
[11] l'en *T*

In this month, in their time of rest and cud chewing,[1] the shepherd should not lead his ewes into the sun after lunch, but should turn his back to it and lead them into valleys where the plants are more moist. There is no doubt that the ewes see better the greenness of the grass when they have their backs to the sun than if the sun's rays are shining into their eyes. You should know that then there is a plant named camomile[2‡] that is very helpful and nourishing to them and is good for digestion: if the ewes are bloated or upset from some bad plant, camomile is real medicine and cures them. Therefore the shepherd should be smart and careful when bringing back his ewes.

---

[1] *prangière*: prangeler: "cud chewing time in the afternoon" (Cotgrave). "heure de repos des moutons, après midi, dans les plus longs jours de l'année" (Lachiver). [Rest hour for sheep, after lunch, during the longest days of the year.]

[2] *chaillie*: Camomile. *Chaillie: camomile romaine* (Lachiver). *Chaillie: herbe aux cailles*: "plantaine, Weybred" (Cotgrave).

Du mois de juillet. xve.

Ou¹ mois de juillet doit le bergier lever matin, aussi comme au mois de juing. Et jasoit ce² que oudit³ mois de juing soit dit et conseillié que le bergier doit mener ses brebis es gaschieres et es haultz lieux, toutesfois en ce mois de juillet se doit garder d'une herbe que l'en appelle *sauvres*, a une petite fueillette janne, laquelle herbe de sauvres est tant nuysant⁴ au bestial que se les brebis la menguent ainçois que la fleur y soit, elles en sont enflees et de la malice de l'erbe sont en peril de mort. Quant les brebis ont trop chault, assez est dit ou⁵ chapitre des reigles generaulx,* en quelle maniere [81] on les doit refroider et umbrayer.⁶

---

¹ Au *B*
² ce *om. B*
³ audit *BT*
⁴ nuysent [*sic*] *B*
⁵ au *B*
⁶ umbrager *BJ*

Chapter 15

Concerning the Month of July

In the month of July the shepherd should rise early, just as in June. Even though it was mentioned and advised in the month of June that the shepherd should lead his ewes into marshy areas and high places, however in this month of July he should watch out for a plant that is called mustard,[1] which has a very small yellow leaf. This plant is so harmful to animals that if the ewes eat it before it flowers, they are bloated and from the treachery of this plant are in peril of death. When the ewes are too hot, enough was said in the chapter of general rules about how they should be cooled and given shade.

---

[1] *Sauvres*: *Sanve*: Charlock (Heath) or Mustard. *Sanve*: *Sinapsis arvensis* L.

Du mois d'aoust. xvi^e.

En aoust doit le bergier* lever matin comme dessus, et soy desjeuner d'une soupe en eaue ou de[1] lait cler. Et ne doit porter pain en sa panetiere fors pour son chien. Et ne doit point porter de houlette ne d'autre baston fors que une verge de coudre en sa main par maniere de esbatement.

En aoust le bergier ne doit pas mener ses bestes en friches, en gaschieres ne en pasturages ou il ait verdure, mais les doit mener et tenir es chaumes et esteules ou les blez et avaines ont esté soyez. Et yllec doivent prendre les brebis leur pasture et non ailleurs, au mains selon la coustume de France et de Brie, laquelle est telle que chascun[2] bergier peult mettre ses brebis es chaumes aux champs[3] tout aussi tost que les guerbes[4] en sont ostees. Et devant disner les doit ramener assez tost es estables et les laisser reposer et attendre jusques a haulte prangiere,[5] et après disner doit aller tart aux champs et y doit tenir ses brebis jusques a une lieue[6] de nuyt.

Ou[7] mois d'aoust et[8] ou[9] mois ensuivant, peult on[10] faire et[11] laisser gesir [82] les brebis hors des estables et emmy la court ou ailleurs, mais que ce soit en lieux seurs. En aoust le bergier doit garder ses brebis que elles ne soient enflees de menger trop de espis, car mort s'en pourroit ensuyr,[12] qui n'y pourvoiroit de remede.

81.03 bergier *T* (berger *BJ*)] berbier *V*

---

[1] du *B*

[2] chascuns *B*

[3] aux champs *om. T*

[4] herbes *B*, gerbes *T*

[5] a h. heure *T*

[6] a une heure *T*

[7] Au *B*

[8] et *om. B*

[9] au *B*

[10] on peult *T*

[11] faire et *om. T*

[12] ensuyvir *T*

Chapter 16

Concerning the Month of August

In August the shepherd should rise early as before and should breakfast of soup[1] with water or whey[2] and should not carry bread in his scrip except for his dog. Nor should he carry a crook or any staff other than a hazelnut switch in his hand for amusement.

In August the shepherd should not lead his animals into wastes, plowed but unplanted lands, or pastures where there might be new growth, but lead and hold them in the stubble‡ where wheat and oats have been harvested.[3] The ewes should take their grazing there and not elsewhere, at least according to the custom of France and Brie, which is that each shepherd can put his ewes in the stubble of the fields as soon as the grain has been taken off. Before lunch time[4] he should lead them back to the fold rather early and allow them to rest for a long time, and after lunch should go late into the fields and keep his ewes there until an hour[5] before night.

In the month of August and in the following month the ewes may be allowed to lie outside the fold and inside the courtyard or elsewhere, provided it is in a safe place. In August the shepherd should take care that his ewes are not bloated from eating too many ears of grain,‡ for death can come from it if no remedy is provided.

---

[1] *soupe*: "sorte d'aliment fait de potage et de tranches de pain, ou même de pâtes, de riz, etc. et qui se sert avant tout autre mets" (Lachiver). [A kind of food made of soup and slices of bread, or even noodles, rice, etc., which is served before all other dishes.]

[2] *lait cler*: whey (Harrap).

[3] *soier*: "reap, cut down" (Cotgrave).

[4] *disner*: "Le repas, qui se prenait jadis à midi ou un peu avant" (Lachiver). [The meal formerly taken at noon or a little before.]

[5] *Une lieue* (var. *heure*) *de nuyt*: *Lieue*, a measure of distance, was also used as a measure of time. Cf. Greimas and Keane, *Dictionnaire*, s. v.: "L'espace d'une lieue de terre, c'est-à-dire une heure de temps." It recurs in Chapter 18, 84.11–12.

Du mois de septembre. xvii.*

Ou[1] mois de septembre doit le bergier mener ses brebis matin aux champs, et
pour pasturage les doit conduire devant disner es terres et chaumes ou il a eu[2]
blez, et aprés disner es lieux ou il a eu[3] avaines, pour asoupplir contre le vespre, et
doit eschever terres maigres et pierreuses, car lors y croist une herbe que l'en nomme *mugue[4] sauvage*, que les brebis menguent voulentiers, mais elle leur est nuysant[5]
et mal prouffitable. Et est ainsi comme semblable a la treffle en fueille et verdeur,
mais elle est plus haulte, et a une fleur janne par rinsiaux, et sur celle herbe et ses
rinsiaux descent une maniere de bylos, lesquelz descendent de l'air semblables a fil
de coton qui se adherdent[6] a celle herbe de mugue et y demeurent, et en eulx se
[83] nourrissent areignes, vermines et ordures envenimees. Et pour convoitoise de
l'erbe, les brebis la menguent avec l'ordure et en enquerrent[7] une* grant maladie
que l'en appelle *yrengnier*, qui tient en la teste, et dont* la brebis est enflee et enve-
nimee en peril de mort, et mourroit de celle maladie se l'en n'y mettoit remede.

En celuy mois de septembre, par commune ordonnance de nature, les brebis portieres sont luites[8] et saillies des moutons masles pour propaginer et continuer l'espece
des bestes a laine par generacion, selon la bonne disposition du Souverain Pasteur,
createur et conditeur[9] de toutes choses immorteles, morteles, raisonnables, brutes,
animees,[10] et sans ame. Si advient a la fois que aucunes brebis portieres sont luites[11] et
saillies en aoust et aussi sont elles plus hastives de faonner devant fevrier. Oudit[12] mois
de septembre le bergier doit estre diligent de la garde[13] de ses moutons saillans qui luisent[14] les portieres femelles. Et ce mois durant doit faire gesir les[15] moutons et portieres
emmy la court ou en autres lieux seurs hors des estables et les visiter souvent.

83.04 une *B*] en une *TV*
83.05 dont *BT*] donc *V*

---

[1] Au *B*
[2] il y a eu *BJT*
[3] il y a eu *BJT*
[4] muguet *BJ*
[5] nuisante *T*
[6] adherent *T*
[7] enquierent *B*
[8] luitez *BJ*, luittees *T*
[9] conducteur *T*
[10] animés *T*
[11] luitez *BJ*, luitees *T*
[12] Audit *B*
[13] de la garder [*sic*] *T*
[14] luittent *T*
[15] ses *T*

Chapter 17

Concerning the Month of September

In the month of September the shepherd should lead his ewes into the fields early and for grazing should guide them before the lunch hour into the stubble fields where there has been wheat, then after dinner into places where there have been oats, to calm them toward evening. He should avoid barren and rocky lands, because a plant grows there called love-in-a-mist,[1‡] which the ewes eat readily but which is very harmful and unprofitable to them. It is rather like clover[2] in leaf and greenness, but is taller and has a yellow flower on stalks; from this plant and its stalks comes down a kind of ball, which descends in the air like a cotton string and sticks to this trailing clover plant and remains there, and on which spiders, vermin and poisonous things feed themselves. Because of their avid desire for the plant, the ewes eat it along with the filth[‡] and get a severe ailment called cobweb disease[3‡] that takes hold in the head, so the ewe is bloated and poisoned, in danger of death. She will die of this malady unless given a remedy.

In this month of September, by the general rule of nature, the breeding ewes are covered and bred by the rams to propagate and continue the species of woolbearing animals by breeding, according to the good design of the Sovereign Shepherd, Creator and Guiding Spirit of all things immortal and mortal, reasoning and not, with and without souls. Yet sometimes it happens that some of the ewes are bred in August and thus they lamb sooner than February.

In this month of September the shepherd should be diligent in the care of his breeding rams who cover the breeding ewes. All during this month he should make his rams and ewes lie down in the courtyard or other safe places outside the fold and should visit them often.

---

[1] *Muguet sauvage*: lily of the valley.

[2] Most likely *trefle couché*, *Trifolium arvense* L. (Větvička 44).

[3] *yrengnier*: "araignier: Spiderie, of or like a spider or cobweb" (Cotgrave).

[84] De octobre. xviiie.

En octobre mette le bergier ses brebis matin aux champs pour pasturer,[1] eu regart[2] a la qualité du temps, comme dit est dessus. Et au matin les doit tenir et conduire es nouvelles gaschieres, car les nouvelles herbetes et chardons qui croissent es nouvelles gaschieres leur sont moult prouffitables. Et aprés disner les doit mener es[3] chaumes et es esteules, comme en aoust, et les tenir es chaumes jusques a une lieue[4] de nuyt ou environ. Et pour ce que en ce temps les bestes ne sont pas encore refroidies* et tiennent encore grant partie* de leur chaleur pour le cohit naturel, et que les chars[5] des bestes portieres ou moutons ne sont pas lors bien convenables[6] a menger, la seignee[7] oudit[8] mois est defendue et toute medicine a faire a tout bergin, tant aux moutons comme chastris,[9] portieres, brebis, antenoises et aigneaux—excepté que se aucune en estoit decouragee de menger ou malade par aucun accident, l'en luy doit donner a mengier des fueilles de choulz pour son appetit recouvrer.

---

[1] pasture *BJ*

[2] et eu r. *B*, au r. *T*

[3] aux *T*

[4] heure *T*

[5] chairs *T*

[6] convenable *T*

[7] seignie *T*

[8] audit *BT*

[9] chastrés *T*

Chapter 18

Concerning October

In October the shepherd should put his ewes out early to pasture, depending upon the kind of weather, as was said before. In the morning he should hold‡ and lead them into newly turned unsown areas because the fresh little plants and teasels‡ that grow in newly turned fields are very beneficial to them. After lunch he should lead them into the stubble and threshed fields as in August, and keep them in the stubble until an hour‡ or so before nightfall. Since at this time the animals are not yet cooled and still retain their heat for natural coition, and since the flesh of the breeding ewes or rams is not suitable to eat, bloodletting in this month is forbidden‡ and any doctoring to be done for the whole flock, rams as well as wethers, breeding ewes, (other) ewes, yearling ewes, and lambs. However, if any ewe is off its feed or sick from an accident, it should be given cabbage leaves to eat in order to restore its appetite.

De novembre. xix^e. [1][85]

En novembre le bergier doit mener et conduire ses[2] brebis es chaumes et esteules comme dessus, pour pasturer le regain des herbes qui sont regaynees,
car la doulceur d'icelles leur sont* moult nourrisans* et prouffitables. Et[3] en ce
mois de novembre est defendue la seignee et medicine,* tout aussi comme en octobre. Et se les moutons sont descouragez en ce mois, le bergier leur doit donner
a menger du sel ung peu. Et pour ce que en l'yver pleust plus souvent que en autre temps, quant il a pleu et que le bergier maine ses brebis en pasturage prez des
bois, il doit estouper et emplir les sonnettes de ses[4] bestes tellement qu'elles ne
puissent sonner ne faire noise, car les loups ne pevent bonnement endurer la pluye
pour les degoustz des ruisseaux et des fueilles du bois qui* leur chiet* es oreilles et
leur font mal. Et pour ce yssent hors des bois aprés la[5] pluye et se tapissent pour
agayter les brebis quant ilz les sentent au vent, ou quant ilz oyent les sonnettes.
Si les doit le bergier estouper pour oster la noise et doit lors champaier loing des
bois et contre vent et estre curieux sur son bestail [86] pour obvier aux perilz et
dommages.

85.18 qui] quil *BTV* | chiet] cheit *TV*, chet *B*

---

[1] Du mois de novembre *B*
[2] ces *T*
[3] Et *om. BJ*
[4] ces *T*
[5] la *om. BJ*

Chapter 19

Concerning November

In November the shepherd should lead forth his ewes and guide them into stubble and grainfields as above, to feed upon the leftover plants from haying that have grown back, for their tenderness is very nourishing and beneficial. In November bloodletting is forbidden and all medication too, as in October. If the rams are off their feed in this month, the shepherd should give them a little salt to eat. Because it rains more often in winter than at any other time, when it has rained and the shepherd leads his ewes out to pasture near the woods, he should stop up and plug the little bells of his animals so that they can not make any noise. Wolves‡ cannot easily endure the rain because of the streams and drops of water from the leaves of trees that fall into their ears and are painful to them. Because they come out of the woods after the rain and lurk about to ambush the ewes when they scent them on the wind or when they hear the little bells, the shepherd should stop up the bells to take away their sound‡ and should find pasture far from the woods and up-wind and be heedful of his flock to prevent danger and harm.

Du mois de decembre. xx.*

En decembre doit on aler tart aux champs en pasturage. Et lors les brebis menguent voulentiers une herbe que on appelle *hyebles*, mesmement celles qui sont grosses et empraintes et veulent avoir nouvelles pastures et sont ja saoulees des regains des herbes et des chaumes. Et quant elles ont gousté des hyebles, il n'a gueres de dangier en la garde. En celuy mois de decembre ne viennent point les bestes au disner a meridienne et les doit on tenir et garder aux champs jusques a soleil couchant. Et est moult a noter que tout aussi[1] que par rigle* generale est defendu a nettoyer et curer les estables des brebis ou mois de may, tout aussi[2] est commandé que ou mois de decembre les estables soient curees[3] et nettoyees, et n'y doit on laisser nul fiens, mais est bon de les curer souvent, pour ce que les fiens en decembre sont moult nuysans au bestail.

De la maladie que on dist l'affilee.[4] xxi.

L'affilee est une maladie qui vient communement aux aigneaux et la prendent[5] [87] quant il[6] goustent du lait de brebis, laquelle a de nouveau faonné, lequel lait l'en apelle *bet* et est le premier lait de la mamele ou du pis* de la brebis aprés[7] ce que elle a faonné de nouveau, si comme de ce est faicte mencion cy dessus ou[8] chapitre du mois de fevrier. Celle maladie affilee est moult perilleuse.

---

[1]   ainsi *BJ*

[2]   ainsi *BJ*

[3]   curés *T*

[4]   *Preceding the title to Chapter 21, BJ add the heading* Des maladies qui viennent aux (au *B*) brebis, aigniaux et aultres bestes a laine.

[5]   prennent *BT*

[6]   ilz *BJ*

[7]   auprés *B*

[8]   au *BT*

Chapter 20

Concerning the Month of December

In December one should go late to the fields to graze. Then the ewes willingly eat a plant called dwarf elder,[1] even those ewes that are heavy with lambs desire new pastures and are tired of the regrowth of grasses and grain fields. When the ewes have tasted dwarf elder, there is no difficulty in watching over them. In this month of December, the animals do not come in at the noon dinner hour and should be kept in the fields until sunset. It is important to note that, just as by general rule it is forbidden to clean and clear out the ewes' fold in the month of May, yet it is ordered that in the month of December the fold should be cleared out and cleaned and no manure should be left. Indeed it is good to clean it often, since manure in December is very harmful to animals.

Chapter 21

Concerning the Malady called Scours[‡]

Scours is a malady that comes commonly to lambs and takes hold when they ingest the milk of a ewe who has newly lambed. This milk is called colostrum and is the first milk from the teat of the ewe just after giving birth. As was mentioned before in the chapter on February, this malady of scours is very dangerous.

---

[1] *hièble*: "variété de sureau *(caprifoliacées)* à tige herbacée, à baies noires" (*Nouveau Petit Robert*). [A kind of elder with herbaceous stems, with black berries.] "Ground elder. Dwarf elder, danewort, weedwort" (Cotgrave). *Sambucus nigra* L. (Coombes).

Du poucet.* xxii.

Une autre maladie y a que les aigneaux preignent* quant ilz sont plus de quinze jours continuels* avec les meres depuis qu'ilz sont nez, laquelle maladie
est appellee *poucet*. De celle maladie et dont elle est causee est dit assez souffisamment ou[1] chapitre du mois de fevrier et ceste maladie du poucet est moult perilleuse, car contre elle a bien peu de remede.

Du Bouchet. xxiii.

La maladie du bouchet est semblablement contenue oudit[2] chapitre de fevrier
et dit le maistre que ceste maladie du bouchet est engendree aux aigneaux*
quant ilz alaictent leurs meres quant elles viennent des champs ainçois que elles
soient bien disposees[3] et refroidees. Et de celle maladie meurent les aigneaux
souvent se l'en n'y mettoit remede.

[88] Du clavel. xxv.*

Une maladie que on appelle *le clavel*, laquelle vient aux brebis, aigneaux et
autres bestes portans laine par trop boire et par autres excés de mauvaise
garde.

De la rongne. xxvi.

La rongne est une autre maladie, qui leur vient es dos, par pluye, par morfon-
dures[4] ou autres, a l'ayde de froidure.

87.11 continuels] continuez *BJ*, continues *TV*

---

[1] au *B*
[2] audit *B*
[3] disposés *T*
[4] morfontures *BJ*

Chapter 22

Concerning Pneumonia[‡]

Another malady, which lambs get when they have stayed continuously with their mothers after their birth for more than fifteen days, is called pneumonia. About this malady and its causes, enough has been said in the chapter on February. This malady of pneumonia is very dangerous and there is little remedy for it.

Chapter 23

Concerning Sore Mouth[‡]

The malady of sore mouth is likewise contained in February's chapter and the master shepherd says that this malady of sore mouth is brought about on the lambs when they nurse their mothers when the ewes come from the fields, before they are settled and cooled down. Lambs often die of this malady if no remedy is provided.

Chapter 25[1]

Concerning Sheep Pox[‡]

A malady called sheep pox[2] comes to ewes, lambs, and other woolbearing animals from drinking too much and from other intemperances of poor tending.

Chapter 26

Concerning Mange[‡]

Mange is another malady that comes to them on their backs from rain, catching cold, or other causes, with the help of cold weather.

---

[1] Note skip in chapter numbers.

[2] *clavel, claveau*: "C'est la variole ovine qu'on appelle aussi *clavelée, clavelade*" (Lachiver). [It is the sheep pox, which people also call *clavelée* or *clavelade*.]

Du poacre. xxvii.

La maladie du poacre vient aux brebis et bestial[1] de accident de pasturer es rousees es terres sablonneuses.[2] Et est le poacre une maladie et maniere de rongne, qui prent et tient es museaux des brebis. Et est assez pire et plus nuysant que la rongne du dos.

De bouverande.* xxviii.

De la maladie qui vient aux brebis d'une herbe qui est appellee *bouverande* est assez touchié ou[3] chapitre du mois de mars, comment la mauvaise herbe de bouverande prent les brebis par le guoiteron* de la gorge, et comment les bestes en sont en grant peril.

De la dauve.[4]* xxix.

[89]

Une maladie que l'en appelle *dauve* vient aux brebis de menger une herbe qui semblablement est nomme[e]* *dauve*. De laquelle herbe de dauve, et aussi de la maladie qui en est engendree, est dit plus a plain cy dessus ou[5] chapitre dudit mois de mars.

De l'avertin. xxx

Une maladie vient aux aigneaux, laquelle est nommee *avertin*, et leur est engendree de la force et repercusion du soleil qui les fiert es testes. Et leur fait par sa chaleur esmouvoir leur cerveau, dont ilz affolent et meurent et tournaient souventesfois, comme dit est oudit[6] mois de mars.

89.11 qui *BJT*] quil *V*

---

[1] et le bestail *T*
[2] en terre sablonneuse *T*
[3] au *B*
[4] douve *T*
[5] au *B*
[6] audict *B*

Chapter 27

Concerning Oral Lesions[‡]

The malady of oral lesions[1] comes to ewes and animals by misadventure from pasturing on damp and sandy ground. Oral lesions are a malady in the nature of mange, which takes hold on the ewes' muzzles. They are worse and more harmful than mange on the back.

Chapter 28

Concerning Swollen Throat[2]

The malady that comes to ewes from a plant called gorse has been touched upon sufficiently in March's chapter, how the harmful plant of gorse seizes the ewes in the windpipe of the throat and because of it the animals are in great danger.

Chapter 29

Concerning Liver Fluke[‡]

A malady called liver fluke comes to the ewes from eating a plant that is called buttercup. This plant, and also the malady generated by it, was clearly discussed in the chapter on March.

Chapter 30

Concerning Staggers[‡]

A malady called staggers that affects lambs is brought to them by the force and strength of the sun that strikes them on the head. The heat disorders their brains, whereby they become crazed, go round and round, and die, as is mentioned in the month of March.

---

[1] *pouacre*: "a filthie scabbinesse on the nose, or about the muzzle, of sheep"; *poacre*: "a kind of scab about the nose, or muzzle of a sheepe, gotten by 'feeding too early in the dewie fallowes'" (Cotgrave).

[2] *Guoiteron de la gorge*: Swollen throat. An affliction caused when the sheep eat gorse. See also 67.16.

De l'enfleure xxxi

De l'enfleure y a deux causes ou plusieurs, dont l'une est engendree ou[1] mois de juillet, quant les brebis menguent une herbe que l'en appelle *feuvrel*, a la petite fleur janne, ainçois que ladicte herbe soit fleurie. L'autre cause est quant elles mengent trop espiz ou[2] mois d'aoust et* en sont enflees.

Le runge. xxxii

Une autre maladie que l'en appelle le *rungot*[3] *perdu*. Et leur vient quant [90] elle[s] menguent d'une herbe qui est appellee *poucet** et celle herbe oste* aux bestes le gout de menger.

De l'yrengnier. xxxiii.

La maladie que l'on* dit *l'yrengnier* est[4] engendree aux brebis ou[5] mois de septembre, quant elles mengent l'erbe que l'en appelle *muguet** *sauvage*, sur laquelle herbe descendent* yraignes et vermines, qui* moult les empire.[6]

Autre chapitre des remedes.[7] xxxiiii.

Des remedes et cures de ces* maladies, prendrons du remede contre l'affilee,* qui est tel : quant l'aigneau est malade de l'affilee,* on luy doit faire alaicter une autre mere que la sienne pour deux ou trois jours et il garira.

89.22 et en sont enflees] et *om. BTV*
90.02–03 celle herbe oste] cest le test *BJTV*
90.10 descendent *B*] descent *TV* | qui] que *BJTV*
90.15 ces maladies] ses m. *BJTV*
90.17 qui] quil *BJTV*

---

[1] au *B*
[2] au *T*
[3] runge *BJ*
[4] est *om. T*
[5] au *B*
[6] empirent *B*
[7] Aultre [*sic*] remedes *B*

Chapter 31

Concerning Bloat

Bloating has two or more causes, one of which comes about in July when the ewes eat a small yellow-flowered plant called wood sorrel[1] before it has bloomed; the other cause is when they have eaten too many grain spears in August and become bloated.

Chapter 32

Concerning Lost Cud[‡]

Another malady is called lost cud or lost rumination. It comes to them when they have eaten a plant called poppy[‡] and this takes away the animal's desire for eating.

Chapter 33

Concerning Cobweb Disease[‡]

The disease called cobweb disease is engendered in the ewes in September when they eat the plant called lily of the valley, from which plant descend cobwebs and vermin, and which greatly weakens them.

Chapter 34

Other Chapter of Remedies[‡]

From the remedies and cures of these illnesses, we will take up the remedy for scours. When a lamb is sick with scours,[‡] have it nurse another mother than its own for two or three days and it will be cured.

---

[1] *fevrel*: plant with acid leaves and small yellow flower. *Oxalis acetosella* L. (Větvička, 122). wood sorrel, Europe (Coombes).

Remede du poucet. xxxv.

C ontre le poucet il y a peu de remede fors que de oster les aigneaux d'avec
[91] leurs meres quant ilz y ont esté quinze jours, si comme il est* dit ou[1]
chapitre de fevrier.

Remede du bouchet. xxxvi.

C ontre la maladie du bouchet a tel remede : on doit prendre ung baston de
sceur vert, de demy pié de long, et le fendre au bout en crois[2] et mettre icel-
luy en la gueulle de l'aigneau, et quant le baston a touchié la maladie en la gueulle
de l'aigneau, on le doit mettre en lieu ou il puisse* bien tost seicher, et lors qu'il
seiche, l'aigneau treuve bien tost garison.

Remede du clavel. xxxvii.

L e remede contre le clavel, tant pour aigneaux que pour autres bestes a laine,
est tel : le bergier doit cueillir la veille de la nativité Saint Jehan Baptiste une
herbe, laquelle est appellee *tume*, autrement *juscarime* ou *hennebonne*, et est assez
commune* ; on en* trouve en plusieurs lieux ou en plusieurs places. Icelle herbe
est de telle vertu[3] que ou elle est mise et[4] reposee secretement aux estables, affin qu'on ne la voye, et en reve[92]rence et honneur de monseigneur Saint Jehan
Baptiste, et ne doit pas chascun veoir ne sçavoir le secret et les grans biens qui*
sont en l'estat de bergerie.

91.02 si comme il est dit] est *om. TV,* si c. il dict *B*
91.22 commune *BJ*] comme *TV*
91.22 on en trouve *T*] on la t. *BJ,* on a t. *V*
92.03 qui] que *BJTV*

---

[1] au *B*
[2] en trois *T*
[3] nature *BJ*
[4] et *B*] *om. TV*

Chapter 35
Remedy for Pneumonia[‡]

For pneumonia, there is very little remedy outside of removing the lambs from their mothers when they are fifteen days old, as was said in February's chapter.

Chapter 36
Remedy for Sore Mouth[‡]

For the malady of sore mouth, the remedy is to take a stick of green elder half a foot long and split it at the end in a cross. Put this into the throat of the lamb, and when the stick has touched the malady in the lamb's throat, it must be put in a place where it can soon dry. When it dries, the lamb will soon be cured.

Chapter 37
Remedy for Sheep Pox[‡]

The remedy for sheep pox, for lambs and for other woolbearing animals, is such: on the eve of the nativity of St. John the Baptist,[‡] the shepherd must gather a plant called henbane,[1‡] which is very common and found in many places. This plant has such power that it is put and laid secretly in the stable so that no one may see it, and in reverence and honor of my lord Saint John the Baptist, nor should everyone see or know the secret and great virtues that belong to the occupation of sheep husbandry.

---

[1] *Tume*, or *juscarime* or *hennebonne*: henbane: *Hyoscyamus niger* L. (Větvička, 94).

Remede de la rongne. xxxviii

Contre la rongne ou[1] dos des moutons ou autres bestes a laine, on doit faire oignemens de viel oingt de porc, de vifz argent et d'alun de glace et de copperose, de vert de gris, et mesle[r]* tout ensemble avec ung peu de farine de semence de nesle, ou de cendre commune, et confire avec le viel oingt. Et de cest[2] oignement doit on oindre la rongne, si gariront les bestes. Et aux aigneaux convient ouvrer plus doulcement, pour ce qu'ilz sont plus tendres. Prenez viel oingt, vert de gris et cendres de serment de vignes. Et qui n'a serment, preigne* des genefvres et soit tout broyé ensemble pour oindre les aigneaux, si gariront. Et n'y convient mettre vifz argent ne alun de glace ne copperose, car[3] ilz sont trop fors corrosifz et pourroient faire mourir les aigneaulx.* Et se aucun povre mesnagier ne pouoit* finer des choses dessusdictes, doit prendre* des genefvres vers et coppe[r]* [93] mesmement par tronçons[4] et les faire bouillir en laissive cendre de* dauves et puis broyez les tronçons et les faire bouillir de rechief tant qu'ilz soient bien amolis et qu'ilz ayent attraict la substance et la force de la cendre et vault a faire oincture a garir et curer ladicte rongne, tant a bestes surannees que aigneaux.

92.17 qui] quil *BJTV*
92.18 preigne *BJ*] praignent *TV*
93.02 cendre de dauves] de *om. BJTV*

---

[1] au *B*
[2] ces *T*
[3] et *T*
[4] trançons *T*

Chapter 38

Remedy for Mange‡

For mange on the backs of sheep or other woolbearing animals, ointments should be made of old lard, quicksilver, rock alum,‡ copperas,‡ and verdigris, mixing everything together with a bit of flour from the seeds of a medlar tree or plain ashes and steeping it in old lard. With this ointment salve the mange and the animals will be cured. For the lambs, it is necessary to work more gently because they are more tender: take old lard, verdigris and ashes of grape twigs. If grape twigs cannot be had, take junipers and mash them together to salve the lambs and they will be cured. It is not appropriate to put quicksilver or rock alum or copperas in it because they are too corrosive and could kill the lambs. If some unfortunate husbandman cannot obtain the abovementioned things, he should take green junipers and cut them evenly in slices and boil them in ashy lye of buttercup,‡ and then mash the slices and boil them again so they are well softened and might draw the substance and strength from the ashes. It is worthwhile to make ointments to heal and cure mange, for older animals as well as for lambs.

Remede du poacre. xxxix*

Pour garir le poacre, prenez copperose, alun de glace et souffre vifz,[1] et broyés* tout ensemble et faictes boullir[2] en huille de chennevays,[3] et le mettez tout chault sur la beste poacreuse au soir quant elle reviendra des champs, car qui le mettroit au matin ne prouffiteroit neant,[4] pour ce que l'ongnement se degasteroit et chariroit en paissant. Et qui ne pourroit avoir les choses dessusdictes contre le poacre, preigne ung viel essieul[5] de charrier oinct de viel oingt et le face ardoir par le bout ; de la poudre mettez[6] sur la rongne et sur les museaux. Et n'est pas seullement que pour tappir ladicte maladie a certain temps, car la poudre de l'essieul[7] ne fait pas plaine ne parfaicte cure, mais le fait tappir ainsi comme l'en pourroit faire [94] de gouterose ou d'autre maladie contagieuse a certain temps sans curer a plain. Si est le plus expedient de oindre ses bestes pouacreuses quant la maladie est tarie, ainçois que leur pouacre* renouvelle. Et est ceste* maladie es[8] brebis ainsi que la pierre seroit aux hommes et ainsi incurable. Et toutesfois les bestes a laine en sont[9] aucunesfois curees et garies par l'ongnement dessusdict.

Contre bouverande,[10] si comme est[11] dit ou[12] mois de mars et tout comme[13] les brebis ont gousté de la bouverande, il convient que le bergier y secoure incontinent et leur mette du sel en la gueulle pour faire boire et avaler l'amertume de la male herbe. Aussi est bon remede de getter a[14] la beste de la terre et* de la tampiere[15] par dessus le doz ou de l'eaue pour la faire escourre et mouvoir, car quant elle se escoust après le goust de celle male herbe, il s'ensuyt santé.

93.14 qui *T*] quil *BJV*
94.18 et de la tampiere *BJ*] et *om. TV*

---

[1] vif *BJT*
[2] bouillie *B*
[3] cheneveys *BJ*, chennevys *T*
[4] rien *T*
[5] essueul *T*
[6] mette *T*
[7] l'essueil *T*
[8] en *T*
[9] en on si [*sic*] *T*
[10] Pour la b. *T*
[11] c. il est *T*
[12] au *B*
[13] m. aussi tost c. *T*
[14] a *om. BJ*
[15] taupiere *T*

Chapter 39
Remedy for Oral Lesions

To cure oral lesions, take copperas, rock alum and sulphur, mash them all together and boil them in hemp oil, put it, still hot, on the scabrous animal in the evening when it comes back from the field. If it is put on in the morning, it will do no good because the ointment will be wasted and will spoil while (the animal) is pasturing. Whoever might be unable to procure the above-mentioned things against scabies, should take an old oxcart axle greased with old lard, burn it at the end and put the powder on the lesions and on the muzzles. This is not only for covering the malady at certain times, for the axle-grease powder does not make a full or perfect cure, but protects them as well as one can against a reddish and pimply condition[‡] or other contagious maladies at certain times, without completely curing them. Thus it is most expedient to salve the scabrous animals when the disease is dried up before their scabies recurs. This malady is to sheep what kidney stones are to men and thus incurable. However, woolbearing animals are sometimes cured by the previously mentioned ointment.

For Swollen Throat[1‡]

For swollen throat, as was mentioned in the month of March: just as soon as the ewes have tasted gorse, it is necessary for the shepherd to help them immediately and put salt in their throats to make them drink and swallow the bitterness of the evil plant. It is also good to throw dirt and pebbles[2] or water on the animal's back to make it shake and move about, for when it shakes itself after having tasted this evil plant, health follows.

---

[1] Chapters are unnumbered henceforth in Vostre.
[2] *tampiere*: gravel, pebble; *Kies, kiesel* (Tobler-Lommatzch).

C ontre[1] la maladie de la dauve, combien que la brebis endauvee puisse vivre
par aucun temps, est malsaine. Toutesfois il n'y a peu ou neant de remede, et
[95] ce qu'il en peult estre, querés* le ou[2] chapitre en fevrier.

C ontre[3] la maladie d'avertin, qui vient aux aigneaux de force de soleil, le remede est tel : l'en doit prendre la fueille de l'orvalle, laquelle est nommee
toutebonne, et faire jus de la fueille et getter dedens l'oreille de l'aigneau pacient.[4]
Et qui ne peult avoir de la fueille, si preigne[5] de la graine d'icelle herbe, broyee et
destrampee[6] en vin aigre, et[7] soit getté en l'oreille de l'aigneau, si garira.

95.03 avertin, qui *BT*] a. quil *JV*
95.08 Et qui ne peult *T*] Et quil ne p. *BV*

---

[1] Pour *T*
[2] au *B*
[3] Pour *T*
[4] pacient *om. T*
[5] prene *T*
[6] et broyé et destrempé *T*
[7] ce *T*

Against the malady of liver fluke,[‡] although the ewe afflicted with liver fluke can live some time, she is in ill health. There is little or nothing in the way of remedy, and for what can be done, look in February's chapter.

For the malady of staggers,[‡] which comes to lambs from the force of the sun, the remedy is such: one should take a leaf of sage (clary),[1‡] which is called all-good,[2] and squeeze the leaf for its juice and throw it into the ear of the ailing lamb. If the leaf cannot be had, take the mashed seed of this plant, distempered in vinegar, and it may be thrown into the ear of the lamb and it will be cured.

---

[1] *Orvalle*: Clary, *Salvia sclarea* L.

[2] *Toutebonne*. "La sauge sclarée, dite aussi *orvale*" (Lachiver). [Clary, *Salvia sclarea*, also called orvale.]

Contre l'enfleure, qui vient de feuvrel quant la brebis la mengue ainçois que la fleur* y soit, le remede si* est tel : qu'il convient seigner la beste du chief de la vaine* sur l'oeil. Et quant le premier sang est cheu[1]* sur terre, on doit prendre de l'autre sang de la beste a l'oreille, du couteau, et en donner par trois fois a la beste. Et si tost qu'elle lesche son sang, elle tourne a garison. Et si* par adventure[2] elle seignoit trop, on luy doit mettre de la cendre sur la teste pour soy escourre, car a se escourre le sang cesse et prent autre chemin. Et quant l'enfleure vient de menger trop d'espis en aoust, [96] quant on apparçoit que les bestes sont enflees, on ne les doit pas mettre en l'eaue jusques au ventre, affin qu'elles se attrempent et que le lait se puisse nourrir ou[3] ventre de la beste pour le faire mouvoir et escourre ; en ce faisant elle fait tourner sa viande en son ventre. Et pour la faire plus tost escourre, on luy doit getter de l'eaue sur le dos. Et quant elle se escoust, c'est signe de garison. Et ce fait, doit le bergier eschever que la beste ne boive jusques au jour[4] et demy aprés ensuyvant, mais luy soit donné d'une fueille de blette[5] ou d'autre chose pour perdre la[6] soif, jusques a ce que la beste soit remise a santé et a son goust[7] de menger.

Contre le runge perdu, qui vient aux brebis quant elles mengent d'une herbe laquelle on appelle *poucet*, le remede est tel : que le bergier, si tost qu'il apparçoit que la brebis a perdu son runge, et le scet par ce qu'elle rent[8] eaue verte par la gueulle, lors si* la loeiste est male,[9] il doit ouvrir a la pointe d'ung coustel la gueulle soubz la langue, et d'une autre beste femelle en la gueulle de la loeste sur la langue. Et luy doit mener les machoires tant qu'il la voye menger et ronger. [97] Et si la beste qui a perdu son ronge* est femelle, on luy doit donner du ronge d'ung mouton chastris ou* masle. Faire comme dessus, si trouvera garison.

95.13 l'enfleure, qui *BJT*] l'enfleure quil *V*
95.15 la fleur] l'enfleure *BJTV* | si *BJ*] sil *V, om. T*
95.16 vaine] veue *BJTV*
96.20 si la loeiste *BJ*] sil la l. *TV*

---

[1] cheut *BJT*
[2] si d'aventure *T*
[3] au *B*
[4] a jour *BJ*
[5] bette *T*
[6] sa *T*
[7] et au g. *T*
[8] par ce quel la tent [*sic*] *T*
[9] malade *BJ*

F or bloat,‡ which comes from ewes eating horse beans[1]‡ before they bloom, there is a remedy that requires bleeding the animal from the top of the vein over the eye. When the first blood has fallen on the ground, with a knife take other blood from the animal's ear and give it three times to the animal. As soon as she licks her blood, she will start to heal. If by chance she bleeds too much, put some ashes on her head to make her shake, for from shaking the bleeding will stop and take another route. When bloating comes from eating too much grain in August, when one sees that the animals are bloated, they should not be put in water up to their bellies so that they cool off and the milk can nourish in the belly of the animal, to make it move and shake and in doing this she turns the food in her stomach. To make her shake sooner, throw some water on her back. When she shakes herself, that is a sign of healing. This done, the shepherd must prevent the animal from drinking until a day and a half later, but should give her beet leaves or something else to assuage her thirst until the animal is brought back to health and to her desire to eat.

F or lost cud‡ or lost rumination, which happens to ewes when they eat a plant called poppy,‡ the remedy is for the shepherd, as soon as he notices that the ewe has lost her cud (and he knows this because she runs green water from her throat), if the uvula is sick, he must open the mouth under the tongue with the point of a knife and place from another female animal's mouth some of the uvula on the tongue. And he must work her jaws until he sees her eat and chew her cud. If the animal who lost her cud is female, give her the cud of a wether or ram. Do as above and she will be cured.

---

[1] *Feuvrel*: Horse beans: *Vicia faba* L.

Contre[1] la maladie que l'en appelle *yrengnier*,[2] laquelle les bestes preignent[3] en mengeant* le muguet sauvage, le remede si[4] est tel : que le bergier doit visiter ses brebis curieusement, et quant aucune est enflee de ceste maladie, il luy doit premierement fendre les oreilles, et se par les oreilles sault le venin janne ou autre, il doit sçavoir que la beste est en peril de mort et luy doit fendre et trencher le cuir du museau et du visaige* au plain, mesmement d'ung canivet et hors des vaines en plusieurs lieux, car par les jarsures sault hors le venin de ladicte couleur janne. Et pour garison, le pasteur doit prendre d'une herbe appellee *roynette*, qui croist es gaschieres et a une petite fleurette ronde. Et doit froter l'erbe[5] entre ses mains et aprés[6] froter le museau de la beste. Et s'il ne peult promptement finer de l'erbe de ladicte roynette, preigne de la fueille de poreaulx et en face [98] jus, et ce jus soit mis sur le museau de la beste es lieux blecez,* si trouvera garison. Et quant les bestes sont ainsi malades et desgoutees,[7] le bergier leur doit donner a menger des miettes de pain meslees avec sel. Et ainsi doit faire et les garder par l'espace de trois jours pour leur donner goust de menger. Et pour donner goust, boute une herbe dicte *vervaine*, qui donne planté de lait aux femelles, mais pour ce qu'il est froit, il n'est pas expedient que les moutons en mengent ne usent ou[8] mois de septembre quant ilz sont en estat ou saison de saillir et luyter les brebis portieres.

En plusieurs manieres se fait la seignee des brebis. On les seigne du chief de la vaine sur l'oeil, d'ung canivet, et doit l'en oster ung peu de la laine pour veoir la vaine. Aucuns apprentis et non expers en l'art de seigner les seignent en[9] la queue et les[10] coppent les oreilles pour faire seigner, mais ceste oeuvre est defendue, car les brebis sans oreilles sont diffamees et ceulx qui en sont maistres ne les[11] leur coppent point.
[99] Des autres enseignemens pour enfleures et du museau est dit cy dessus et souffit pour briefveté sans en faire difficulté.

97.06–07 en mengeant *T*] et mengent *BJV*

---

[1] Pour *T*
[2] yrengnie *BJ*
[3] prenent *T*
[4] si *om. BJ*
[5] f. herbe *B*
[6] et puis a. *T*
[7] degoustees *T*
[8] au *B*
[9] a *T*
[10] leur *BJ, om. T*
[11] les *om. BJ*

For the disease called cobweb disease,[‡] which the animals get from eating *muguet*,[‡] the remedy is for the shepherd to visit his sheep conscientiously and when one is swollen with this malady, he should first slit the ears, and if from the ears springs a yellow or other venom, he knows that the animal is in peril of death. He should split and cut the leather of the muzzle and face immediately, even with a penknife, and the outside of the veins in several places. Yellow venom spurts from these cuts. For a cure, the shepherd should take a plant called queen of the meadows,[1] which grows in waste areas and has a small round flower. He should rub it between his hands and then rub the muzzle of the animal. If he cannot obtain the plant quickly, he should take a leek leaf, make juice of it, and put it on the wounded places of the animal's muzzle and she will recover. When animals are thus ill and off their feed, the shepherd should give them bread crumbs mixed with salt. He should do this and tend them for three days to give them a desire to eat. To give them an appetite, put in front of them a plant called vervain,[2] which gives plenty of milk to females; however, because it is cold,[‡] it is not expedient for male sheep to eat or consume in the month of September when they are in condition or season for breeding and covering breeding ewes.

Bloodletting[‡] is effected in many ways with ewes. The head is bled by a vein over the eye with a knife.[3‡] A bit of wool should be removed in order to see the vein. Some apprentices, inexperienced in the art of bloodletting, bleed them at the tail and cut their ears to make them bleed. However, this practice is forbidden, for ewes without ears are disfigured and those who are master shepherds do not cut them. Other instructions concerning bloat and about the muzzle were mentioned above and suffice for brevity without causing any hardship.

---

[1] *roynette*: "Queen of the Meadows: Maidsweet, Meadow-sweet, Queen of the Meadows, an herbe" (Cotgrave). *Filipendula ulmaria* L. (Coombes).

[2] *Verbena officinalis* L.

[3] *canif*: penknife: "petit canif, petit couteau; Dans l'Aube, lancette du berger" (Lachiver). [small penknife, small knife; In the area of Aube, the shepherd's lancet.] *canivet: canif*, lancette (Greimas).

La maniere[1] de chatrer et amender les aigneaux:
Se les aigneaux sont nez[2] en janvier, on les doit amender en mars ensuyvant.
Et y a deux jours environ la feste de la nativité Nostre Dame de mars, si[3] soit au
mardi ou jeudi[4] ou au samedi en toutes saisons. Et aux femelles est expedient de
rongner les queues de trois dois de long et non plus ne mains. De la maniere de
amender les moutons, l'en leur coppe plain doy de la boursette[5] aux genitoires.
Et doit lors le bergier estre sans peché et est bon de soy confesser, et ne doit ce
jour menger des[6] aux, pour avoir meilleure alaine. Et en la playe de l'aigneau doit
mettre de la cendre deliee et garde le berger ses aigneaux de boire et les doit visiter parmy la fenestre, qu'il ne les face lever ou efforcer. Et au soir les doit faire
alaicter en lieu estroit, qu'ilz ne fuient et que les playes ne se euvrent. Et regarder
aux piedz de ceulx qui sont chastrés pour moult veoir se[7] [100] ilz ont gros pieds
et cours : c'est bon signe. Et est a noter que mieulx est qu'ilz soient chastrés par
temps pluvieux que par[8] temps sec.

Du chien du bergier[9]

Du chien du bergier convient[10] a l'introduction le duire de aler arrester les
brebis et que le bergier entame l'oreille d'une brebis et[11] en face saillir le
sang et le face sentir a son chien par deux fois ou trois, et jamais ne prendra la
brebis que par l'oreille. Et affin que le chien suyve voulentiers le bergier, il luy
doit oindre et froter les joues de la croute de lart et les deux pieds de devant et le
mener souvent jusques a ce qu'il soit bien duit. Et quant le chien se couche[12] aux
champs, le bergier luy doit croiser les piedz, et se il ne se duit quant il luy aura
fait par deux ou trois fois, si luy donne congié,* car il n'est pas digne d'estre avec
les bergiers et brebis.

Et priez Dieu pour le bon bergier Jehan de Brie.

100.20 congié *T* (congé *BJ*)] congier *V*

---

[1] premiere [*sic*] *T*
[2] nees *T*
[3] si *om. BJ*
[4] ou au jeudi *BJ*
[5] bousette *T*
[6] m. que des *T*
[7] se *om. T*
[8] par *om. BJ*
[9] Du c. et du b. *BJ*
[10] et convent *T*
[11] et *om. BJ*
[12] sera couché *T*

The manner of castrating and altering lambs: if the lambs are born in January, they should be altered in the following March. There are two days for it near the Feast of Our Lady's Birth,‡ be it on a Tuesday or Thursday or Saturday whatever the weather. It is expedient to crop the tails of the females to three finger breadths and no more.‡ The way to alter lambs is to cut a full finger's breadth of the genital sack. The shepherd then must be without sin, have gone to confession, and should not have eaten garlic in order to have better breath. In the lambs' wound he should place fine[1] ashes. He should keep his lambs from drinking and should visit them often via the window so that he does not make them get up or make an effort. In the evening he should make them go to drink their milk in a confined space so they will not move about quickly and open their wounds. He should look at the feet of those who were castrated to see if they have swollen and short feet, and that is a good sign. It should be noted that it is better to castrate in rainy weather rather than in dry.

Concerning the Shepherd's Dog

With the shepherd's dog, at the beginning it is necessary to instruct it to go stop the ewes. The shepherd should cut open the ear of one ewe and make the blood run from it to let his dog smell it two or three times and then it will never grab a ewe except by the ear. So that the dog will willingly follow the shepherd, he should oil and rub his jaws and two forefeet with bacon rind and handle it often until it may become well trained. When the dog lies down in the field, the shepherd should cross his feet for him. If he has not learned to do it himself when it has been done two or three times for him, then he should be sent on his way, for he is not worthy of being with the shepherd and the sheep.

And pray to God for the good shepherd Jean de Brie.

---

[1] *delier*: "to make slender, small, fine, extenuate" (Cotgrave).

[101] Le simple bergier Jehan de Brie*
Ne parle que a la bonne foy.
A tous subtilz pastoureaux prie
Qu'ilz reçoivent en gré sa loy.
Vivant sans soucy, sans esmoy,   5
A esté en ville et villaige,
Mais[1] il composa soubz ung moy[2]
L'art des bergiers[3] en son usaige.*

De[4] premier eut beaucop* de paine
Et en aprés eut de grans biens.   10
Nonobstant la vie mondaine*
Il desprisoit sur toutes riens,
Monstrant les inconveniens
Qui peult* venir aux pastoureaux
Et comme par plusieurs moyens   15
Doivent supporter leurs aigneaux.

Les pasteurs portans crosse et mytre
Voullans a cecy regarder
Pourront apprendre maint chapitre
Pour leurs ouailles[5]* bien garder,   20
[102] Faulces pastures evader
En chassant les ravissans loups.
Pour ce, pastoureaux, sans tarder
A cecy devez penser tous.

Bon* sens naturel fut exquis   25
Pour monstrer l'art de pastourie.
Il eut bien peu de sens acquis
Ains que hanter la seigneurie ;
Et toutesfois, par industrie,
Son cas rediga par memoire   30
Selon l'estat de bergerie,
Et sans apeter vaine gloire.

11 Nonobstant la vie *BJ*] N. que la vie *TV* (+1)

---

[1] Ou *BJ*
[2] may *BJ*
[3] des bergier [*sic*] *T*
[4] Du *BJ*
[5] oeilles *J*

The simple shepherd Jean de Brie,
Speaking only in good faith,
Prays that all discerning young shepherds
May receive his advice with good will.
He has lived, free from care and anxiety, 5
In town and village,
But he composed under a leafy bough
The Art of Shepherdry from his experience.

At first he experienced many difficulties
And then later great benefits. 10
Nonetheless, the worldly life
He scorned above all else,
Revealing the misfortunes
That can come to shepherds
And how, in many ways, 15
They can minister to their lambs.

The shepherds who carry cross and miter
Wishing to look at this
Will be able to learn many lessons
For guarding well their "sheep," 20
For evading treacherous pastures
While chasing away ravening wolves.
Therefore, Pastors, without delay,
You should all think about this.

His natural good sense was perfect 25
To demonstrate the art of sheep husbandry.
He had acquired very little knowledge
Before associating with the nobility.
Nevertheless, with great endeavor,
From memory he has set down his account in writing, 30
About the art of shepherdry
And without seeking vain glory.

Subtilz entendemens font rage
De distinguer d'aucunes choses.
Le fol peult enseigner le saige;*   35
Sur ung texte sont plusieurs gloses.
Tost se gaste chapeau de roses,
Peu de vin souvent l'homme enyvre :
Par quoy Jehan de Brie en ses proses
Requiert qu'on excuse son livre.   40

[103] Cy fine la vie du bon bergier Jehan de Brie, nouvellement imprimee pour Symon Vostre libraire, demourant a la rue neufve Nostre Dame a l'ymage Saint Jehan l'Evangeliste.[1]

---

[1] Colophons: Fin de Jehan de Brie le bon berger. Ce livre contenant le vray regime des Bergers se polra imprimer sans offense de la Religion Catholicque. Nicolas de Leuze à Fraxinis, Licentié en Theologie, commis à la visitation des Livres *B*. Fin de Jehan de Brie le bon berger *J*. Cy finist la vie du bon bergier Jehan de Brie nouvellement imprimee a Paris par la veufve feu Jehan Trepperel et Jehan Jehannot demourans en la rue neufve Notre Dame a l'enseigne de l'escu de France *T*.

Clever minds make a huge fuss
About finding distinctions between things.
The fool can teach the wise man;‡						35
A text may have many interpretations,
The stingy dowry[1] is soon spent;
A little wine often intoxicates the man:
Which is why, in his discourse, Jean de Brie
Begs indulgence for his book.							40

Here ends the life of the Good Shepherd, Jean de Brie, newly printed for Simon Vostre bookseller, residing on New Notre Dame Street at the sign of Saint John the Evangelist.

---

[1] "A sleight incompetent, or lesse-then due Portion, given a maid by the father unto her mariage" (Cotgrave).

Textual Notes

All page and line references are to Vostre unless preceded by *B, J,* or *T* to indicate readings from Bogart, Jonot, and Trepperel, respectively.

Prologue

2.03   *du tresexcellent prince*: The context seems to require the definite article.

2.07   The adjective *grant* (plural *grans*) was still epicene at the time of our text, i.e., the same form was used before both masculine and feminine nouns. We find only one occurrence of *grande* (17.06) and two occurrences of *grandes* (22.25, 30.10), whereas *grant* occurs frequently before feminine nouns, as here. Cf. Marchello-Nizia: "Dans presque tous les textes, les deux formes [*grant* and *grande* as feminine adjectives] coexistent, dans des proportions variées" [In almost all texts the two forms coexist, in varying proportion (*Langue,* 126).]

2.08–09   Villers sur Rongnon, Coulommiers en Brie: Villers is about three kilometers north of Coulommiers, in the *département* of Seine-et-Marne, about 50 kilometers due east of Paris (Meyer, review, 450 n. 1; Holmér, "Jean de Brie," 136 n. 1).

2.12   *V* regularly prints *fust* for the preterite (*passé simple,* 33 occurrences), though we also find one occurrence each of *fut* (7.21) and *fu* (8.19).

3.03   For the impersonal subject pronoun, *V* uses both *on* (85 occurrences) and *l'en* (69), as well as a single instance of *l'on,* 90.06.

3.07   For the form *pouoir,* see Jodogne.

3.18   *V* uniformly prints *sicomme* as a single word; we have separated it into two words, in accordance with customary practice. See the discussion of variants in the section entitled "Editing Principles".

3.24   *deveroit*: apparently an example of svarabhakti or epenthesis, involving the insertion of a vowel. Cf. *devera,* 4.04. *B* has the modern forms, *devroit* and *devra,* whereas *T* has *devroit* and *devera.*

4.12   The third-person singular present indicative of the verb *dire* is normally *dit,* as in Modern French (ten occurrences in *V,* e.g., 6.03, 6.12, 7.23). We find two more occurrences of *dist*—normally a preterite form—in a

present-tense context, 59.03 and 86.23. The confusion between the two forms is already found in Old French manuscripts.

Table

4.23   There are several discrepancies between *V*'s table and the contents of the text. What is here listed as the first chapter is entitled *Prologue de la vie et estat de Jehan de Brie* and is unnumbered in the text. The table assigns numbers to chapters 1–34 only, whereas the text itself bears chapter numbers through 39. The table includes chapter 24 (whereas in the text chapter 23 is immediately followed by chapter 25), but it repeats the number 32, so that numbers 24–32 in the table correspond to numbers 25–34 in the text. See also the note to 6.15–16.

4.25   *B* adds "Chap.i.", "Chap.ii.", etc. following each title and omits the ordinal numbers (*Le deuziesme, Le tiers*, etc.) found in *V*. Chapters 1–23 are numbered as in *V*.

5.04   The noun *reigle* could be either masculine or feminine. The expression *reigles generaulx* occurs three times in our text: here and in 30.17 and 80.25. On the other hand, we find *les reigles qui cy aprés seront recitees* (30.21), *Toutes ces reigles* (35.14–15), and *par rigle [sic] generale* (86.15–16), where *reigles* and *rigle* are clearly marked as feminine. *B* and *T* present the same readings as *V* in all these cases.

5.19   For chapters 10–20 *B*'s table uses the phrasing *Du moys de* followed by the name of the month.

6.01   *l'en*: see note to 3.03.

6.04–05 In the text, the chapter *Du clavel* is erroneously numbered 25. As a result, the chapters numbered 25–39 are in reality chapters 24–38. The tables in *B* and *J* skip the number 24 and assign numbers 25–33 to what are chapters 24–32 in *V*.

6.09   *V* prints *evertin* here and in 70.17, but *avertin* later, 89.07, 89.09 and 95.03. We have retained *V*'s variable spellings.

6.10   *T*'s table does not list *enfleure*; the remaining chapters in *T* are as follows:

> 30 de la maladie du ronge perdu par herbe que l'en dit poncel (31 in *V*)
>
> 31 De [la] maladie que l'en appelle yrengnier (32 in *V*)
>
> 32 des cures et remedes des maladies dessusdictes (also numbered 32 in *V*)
>
> 33 des ongnemens et de la maniere de la confection (33 in *V*)
>
> 34 des seignies et de la maniere de seigner et amender les petis aygneaulx (34 in *V*).

6.12   *V* prints *poncel* here, but *poucel* in 78.08 and *poucet* in 90.01 and 96.17. We have retained *V*'s variable spellings.

6.15–16   *Le xxxiii^e^*: There is no separate chapter on the subject of ointments and their preparation; these topics are discussed in chapters 38 and 39. The last two chapters are unnumbered in *B*.

6.16–17   Bloodletting and castrating are treated in the third-last and second-last paragraphs of *V*, unnumbered in the text itself.

6.17   Following *les petis aigniaux B* adds *Fin de la table*.

Prologue (Chapter 1)

6.18   *V*'s *vie a estat* is clearly erroneous and may be considered a printer's error.

6.25   This is but the first of 21 cases where *il* is used with a plural verb, compared to 38 cases of *ilz* as plural. We have retained *V*'s usage in this matter and have indicated differing readings in the variants. See Introduction, "Language of the Vostre Text." Subsequent cases are not mentioned in these notes.

7.13   This is the first occurrence of *l'en* in the text proper, though it occurs four times in the Table. See introduction and note to 3.03.

7.21   *fut*: see note to 2.12.

8.07–08   *V*'s usual spelling is *toutesfois* (12 occurrences); this is the only occurrence of *toutefois*.

8.09   ses merites *BT*] ser m. *V* (printer's error).

8.17   *leurs premiers dens* (*B* = *V*): *dent* could be either masculine or feminine at this time. *T* has *premieres*.

8.19   *fu*: see note to 2.12.

8.20   *V* prints *audit* here and in six other occurrences, but more frequently uses the older form *oudit* (22 occurrences).

8.22   *pouoir*: see note to 3.07.

8.24   The form *piees* seems unlikely, given *pye* in 38.14 and 38.15.

9.04   Nolongne: Nolongue, in the commune of Jouarre, some 2.5 kilometers to the north-east of Villers (Meyer, 450 n. 2; Holmér, 136 n. 1). We have retained *V*'s spellings for all place-names.

9.06   We interpret *peust* as a preterite here. Elsewhere *V* prints *peult* for this tense (4 occurrences: 10.12, 11.04, 11.19, 17.01)—but much more frequently *peult* is the present indicative (38 occurrences: 3.04, 3.21, 7.04, etc.).

9.13   For the form *pouoit*, see Jodogne, "*Povoir* ou *pouoir?*"

10.01   The noun *honneur* was commonly feminine.

10.12   *peult*: see note to 9.06.

10.23   d'une *BT*] duue *V* (printer's error).

11.13   *B*, like *V*, prints *auquelles* here, whereas *T* prints *ausquelles*. As the word does not occur elsewhere in our text, we have decided to preserve *V*'s spelling.

11.15   *desdictz aigneaux*: *V*'s reading is clearly erroneous (the number of sheep is specified as 80 in the preceding lines), and we have emended for the sake of consistency. Presumably the error resulted from auditory confusion, *des dix* and *desdictz* being pronounced alike. The spelling *desdictz* occurs in 24.16.

12.22   *V*'s usually prints *deux* (25 occurrences), using *deulx* just twice, here and in 13.16.

13.11   fouc] foue *TV*. Elsewhere *V* has the expected spelling, *fouc* (32.03, 40.06, 63.23). We treat this as a printer's error.

13.16   Messy: village some 23 kilometers to the north-east of Paris (Holmér, 136 n. 1).

13.17   Cloye: Claye-Souilly, some 21 kilometers to the north-east of Paris (Holmér, 136 n. 1).

13.23–24 The omission in *B* is likely the result of eye-skip (*a toutes . . . a toutes*).

14.11   Tueil: Le Theil, in the commune of Coulommiers (Holmér, 136 n. 1).

14.12   *nostredist* (*-dict B*, *-dit T*) may be a misprint here, given *nostredit* in 19.20 (*-dict B*, *nostre dit T*). Cf. *audit, dudit, ledit, oudit*. *V* uses an unusual abbreviation, *seignr* with the same sort of slightly curved line above the letter *n* as is usual above a vowel letter to indicate a missing *m* or *n*. There can be no doubt that the word *seigneur* is intended.

14.18   *V*'s reading, *pars ses ans*, makes no sense. We assume that the intended reading is parallel to *par trois ans* (12.12, 14.14–15) and *par quatorze ans* (19.14), as well as several occurrences of *par l'espace de . . . ans*.

14.19   *V*'s usual spelling is *oeilles* (38 occurrences: 7.17, 13.01, 13.07, 13.13, etc.); this is the only occurrence of *oilles*.

14.22   *V* prints *age* here, whereas he uses *aage* elsewhere (four occurrences, all in the Prologue: 8.15, 11.17, 12.05, and 13.15).

15.22   The context clearly requires the plural, *hommes*.

16.06   *Virgiles* here, but *Virgile* in 10.04. This may have been influenced by the abundance of other proper names in this list ending in *-es*.

16.24   *V* prints *Neys*, with a capital *N*, perhaps under the impression that this was a proper name (though capitalization in this long list, 15.23–16.11, is far from consistent).

16.25   *V*'s *mome* likely resulted from a misreading of *moine*, clearly required by the context. We correct following *B* (*moyne*), whereas *T* prints *nome*.

17.02   The repetition of the possessive adjective seems odd, but *BTV* all have "*ses faictz de ses croniques*" (*faitz B*).

17.06   This is the sole occurrence of *grande* in our text. Elsewhere *V* prints *grant* modifying a feminine singular noun (23 occurrences, including *grant science*, 8.09). Cf. the note to 2.07.

17.16–17 All four printings treat *Marcus Terencius Varro* as if it were a set of names, as indicated by the plural forms of *a leur temps escrivirent* (*B*15.15–16, *T*17.16–17; *J* fol. vi verso, 2–3 lines from bottom). *T* makes it especially clear that these were thought to be three separate names, using virgules: *Marcus / Terencius / Varro*.

18.11   *interpretez*. It is unusual to find -*z* as a plural marker in our text, except for words like *necessitez* and *proprietez*, stressed on the final vowel, or in masculine plural past participles like those at the end of this sentence: *interpretez et manifestez, referez et revelez*.

18.21   *V*'s *reserez*, shared by *T*, is likely a misreading of *referez*, which we adopt from *B*.

19.20   The form *Hetomesnil* is attested in various sources (Lacroix, *Bon Berger*, xx; Meyer, 451; Prevost; Thomas; *Grande Encyclopédie*; Quignon prints *Hétomesnil*). The substitution of *u* for *n* also occurs in 19.23–24 and may have resulted from misreading.

20.03   This is the first of nine instances in which *V* prints *quil* where we might expect *qui*, suggesting that the two were pronounced alike (Marchello-Nizia, *Langue*, 204, 223). We have systematically emended, in the interest of providing a more readable text. Subsequent cases are not mentioned in these notes.

Chapter 2

22.03–04 The presence of the feminine *toutes* with the masculine noun *personnages* is puzzling. We have corrected the disagreement by adopting *B*'s reading.

22.15   *venderoit*: another example of vowel insertion in *V* (shared by *T*). Cf. note to 3.24. *B* has the modern form *vendroit*.

22.25   *grandes*: cf. the note to 2.07.

23.21–22 Elsewhere *V* regularly prints *aucunesfois* (15 occurrences with -*s*-, as in 26.02, 36.04, 38.18, etc.). This is the only occurrence of *aucunefois*. *BT*

likewise omit the -*s*- in this occurrence. In 94.08–09 the word is divided between two lines, with the usual sort of slanted equal sign as a hyphen, showing clearly that the printer considered this a single word.

23.22 The form *oignemen(s)* occurs again in chapter 38 (two more occurrences), whereas in chapters 8 and 39 we find the spelling *ongne-* (5 occurrences), and in the table the word is printed *oingnemens* (6.15). We have retained *V*'s forms throughout.

24.18 *chieveres*: another example of vowel insertion in *V* (*chevres B*, *chievres T*). Cf. note to 3.24.

25.10–11 One might expect an infinitive, such as *defendre*, here, but *BTV* all have "*pour les oeilles contre leurs adversaires.*"

25.12 *ou livre Ezechiel*. For the possessive without *de*, see the section discussing the language of the text.

25.19 Elsewhere *V* prints *fiens* (nine occurrences); this is the sole occurrence of *fient*.

25.22–23 The context requires the feminine singular: *la crote . . . est . . . donnee.*

26.05 Since *raisons* is clearly marked as feminine elsewhere (9.19, 75.18), the correction seems justified. The same situation arises in 41.12. *BT*, like *V*, print *meilleurs* here.

26.11 The form *apparestra* is shared by *T*, whereas *B* has the more usual spelling *apparoistra*.

Chapter 3

28.06 *aroit*: cf. *auroit* in 18.06.

28.18 The conjunction *ou* seems necessary here. The two nouns, *brebis* and *moutons*, are contrasted elsewhere, e.g. 22.20, 23.12, 73.15–16, 76.07–08, 77.21, etc.

29.09–10 *voulut*: we find the older form, *voult*, in 1.03.

30.05 Elsewhere *V* prints *fust* for the imperfect subjunctive (three occurrences: 10.21, 16.16, 60.18); this is the sole occurrence of *feust*. Much more frequently, *fust* occurs as the simple past (Modern French *fut*), as in the next two sentences. Cf. note to 2.12.

30.10 *grandes*: cf. the note to 2.07.

Chapter 4

30.17 *reigles generaulx*: see note to 5.04.

31.01   The preposition *de* seems indispensable here, as in *BT* and preceding the other items in the series.

31.13   Elsewhere *V* prints *laisser* (ten occurrences); this is the sole occurrence of *lesser*. We find *lessoit* in 28.17, but *laisse* and *laissent* for present-tense forms.

31.20   The definite article seems out of place here; cf. *ou de cordeles menues* in the same sentence.

31.24   *V* seems to attempt to combine the ideas of *T, tirer . . . hors par la laine*, and *B, tirer . . . hors par violence*, either of which makes more sense than *V*'s *tirer . . . hors de la laine par violence*. We have emended in order to provide a more readable text.

33.10   Elsewhere *V* prints *mois* (76 occurrences), with but two exceptions, here and in 73.07. (Curiously, both of these involve the phrase *moys de may*—but there are also nine occurrences of this phrase with the spelling *mois*.)

34.17   We find several cases of confusion between *ces* and *ses* (also between *ce* and *se*) in our text and we have systematically emended according to the sense of each passage. All are indicated in the rejected readings. Such confusion is not rare in Middle French texts. Cf. Thiry, "les nombreuses confusions entre *se* et *ce, ses* et *ces*" (introduction to François Villon, *Poésies complètes*, 47).

34.21   The present subjunctive forms *voisent*, used here and in 66.14, and *voist* (41.15) are still the most frequent in fourteenth- and fifteenth-century texts, according to Marchello-Nizia (*Langue*, 264).

35.01   *BJT* all show the expected agreement with *laine*.

35.11   *V* prints both *bestial* (seven occurrences) and *bestail* (2); we have retained *V*'s forms throughout.

Chapter 5

36.01   The author discusses nine kinds of birds in this chapter, introducing each with a title in the form *de* + definite article + noun naming the bird. Given the plural *estourneaux*, we have corrected *V*'s *De* to *Des*. The remaining eight headings all contain singular nouns.

37.06   These two names appear in 8.23–24 (*escoufles, huas*), where they refer to two different birds (Meyer 453).

Chapter 6

41.12   *meilleurs*: see note to 26.05. *B* has the expected form, *meilleures*, here.

41.15   *voist*: see note to 34.21.

42.02–03   *nulz hommes mortelz*: see Introduction, "Language of the Vostre Text".

44.13–14   Cf. Morawski, *Proverbes*, 2224: *Rouge vespre et blanc matin est la joye au pelerin.*

45.02   Our conjectural emendation, *four* to *fouc* (used poetically), is based on Lacroix (62), who was presumably following Jonot. We were unable to verify this reading.

Chapter 7

45.24   The masculine plural *egaulz* is puzzling, given the phrase *l'une a l'autre*. Elsewhere there are numerous passages where *partie(s)* is clearly feminine, e.g., 3.03, 3.20, 22.15, etc.

47.24   The word *manieres* is clearly wrong for the context and may have resulted from a misreading of the model from which the typesetter was working.

48.02   *V* prints *vvest*, using the lower-case letter *v* twice in succession, probably because the typesetter had no capital *W* in the font he was using. *T* does the same, whereas *B* prints *vuest*.

Chapter 8

49.16   This correction was suggested by Paul Meyer (452). Cf. Marchello-Nizia: "Les formes de pluriel *uns* et *unes* . . . servent à déterminer soit un collectif, . . . soit un groupe de deux objets formant paire" [The plural forms *uns* and *unes* serve to modify either a collective . . . or a group of two objects that form a pair (*Langue*, 145–46)]. It is the latter situation we find here.

50.05   pennoncel (pannoncel *T*)] pennoucel *BV* (printer's error).

50.25   Possessive without *de*: see note to 25.12.

51.05   The context makes it clear that this is the same garment referred to in 50.18 and 51.01. We have emended for the sake of clarity.

51.21   Elsewhere *V* prints *rongne* (14 occurrences); this is the sole occurrence of *roingne*.

51.24   *ungs*: see note to 49.16.

52.17   Cf. 49.18–19, *gros fil de chanvre bien cyré de cire blanche.*

53.03   The paragraph symbol and *Et* appear to be a printing error. Although what precedes could constitute a sentence, what follows (*Et du bergier . . . quantité des flaiaux*) could not.

53.23   contre *BJ*] contres *TV* (printer's error)

54.03   We have emended in order to make the adjective agree with *cloux*.

56.13   We feel the need for a conjunction linking the last two elements of this series. *B* prints a virgule after each noun: *aux champs / a la ville / au monstier / se entre aydent . . . .*

58.07–08   Elsewhere *V* prints *prouffit* (20 occurrences); this is the sole occurrence of *profit*.

Chapter 9

60.05   *V*'s typesetter improvised the letter *k* in this word by using a lower-case *l* and a round *r*—presumably because the letter *k* did not exist in the font he was using. This improvisation occurs in *T* as well, whereas *B* and *J* print an upper-case *K*. This is the only occurrence of the letter *k* in our text.

61.11   Elsewhere *V* prints *blanche* (49.19–20, 61.04, and 61.09), but given *mance* (four occurrences) and *mances* (3), this appears to be a case of free variation.

Chapter 10

62.02   Since there is no subject for the plural verb *souloient*, the emendation seems desirable.

62.19   *pouoir*: see note to 3.07.

64.04   The definite article seems necessary here.

64.23   The word *couleur* is clearly wrong for the context and presumably resulted from a misreading of the model from which the typesetter was working.

65.01   Given the condition introduced by *se*, the context requires the imperfect indicative here. The printer may have misinterpreted *en* as a preposition, introducing the present participle, rather than as the adverbial pronoun.

65.07   This is the only occurrence of *aignel*. Elsewhere we find *aignelet* (five occurrences) or *aigneau* (73). *BJT* also have *aignel* at this point.

66.04   *souloient.* Since the subject of this verb is clearly singular (*la longue demeure*), it seems advisable to emend. The same verb form occurs in 72.12 and 72.25, each time with a singular subject..

66.06   In chapter 22 (87.08–16) *V* prints *poucet*. The context makes it clear that the two forms refer to the same illness.

66.14   *voisent*: see note to 34.21.

67.07   *V* prints both *menguent* and *mengent*, preferring the former, 11 occurrences, to just four of the latter. Similarly for the singular: we find two occurrences of *mengue* and just one of *menge*.

67.08   The absence of the definite article seems incorrect. *T*'s reading would also
          be acceptable.

Chapter 11

67.16   In this chapter *V* prints *bouveraude* (five occurrences), but elsewhere we
          find *bouverande* (six occurrences, including the initial Table). *BJT* all have
          bouveraude here. We have retained *V*'s variable spellings.

68.01   The context requires an adjective, rather than a noun.

68.04–05 laquelle *BJT*] laquelles *V*. (printer's error).

68.07   *V* generally prints *tost* (16 occurrences), but prints *tot* here and in 74.12
          (*BT* have *tost* in both places; *J* has *tost* here).

68.08   *T* has the expected feminine singular past participle, *avalee*; *B* prints *avale*.

68.19   Here, too, we find the expected feminine past participles in *T*, *receue*
          and *mengee*, whereas *BJV* do not show this agreement. *V*'s *mengie* may be
          considered a printer's error.

69.10   *commencent*. The context is clearly plural, as indicated by *les aigneaux ont*
          and *leurs membres*.

70.03   For the confusion between *ces* and *ses*, see note to 34.17.

70.17   *evertin*: see note to 6.09.

Chapter 12

71.23   champs *BT*] chmaps *V* (printer's error).

72.07   Elsewhere *V* prints *air* (14 occurrences, e.g. 71.21, 72.05). *T* also prints *er*
          here, whereas *BJ* have *air*.

72.12   All four printings have *souloient*, but since the subject of this verb is clearly
          singular (*ung vent*), it seems advisable to emend. Cf. note to 66.04.

72.24   This passage is puzzling, since the name *Nort* would seem to contradict
          the explanation that this wind comes from the south ("*vient de devers
          Midy*").

72.25   Although the subject pronoun *il* is frequently used for the plural, here it
          seems to refer clearly to *le vent de solerre* (cf. the singular verb *vient* and the
          singular possessive adjective *son*), and we have therefore emended accord-
          ingly. *T* shares *V*'s reading, whereas *BJ* have *fait*. Cf. notes to 66.04 and
          72.12.

Chapter 13

73.11   Another instance of non-agreement of a past participle. *B* and *T* share *V*'s reading.

74.10   Though *berbier* is a recognized form, it refers to the sheep (Lachiver). Since the reference here is to the shepherd, we have emended for the sake of clarity and consistency.

74.12   *tot*: see note to 68.07.

74.25   The relative pronoun *qui* seems necessary here. *B* prints a colon after *hommes*. Alternatively, one could emend by inserting *et* after *raisonnables*.

75.23   The verb *laver* seems indispensable for the context.

76.01   We might rather expect *aucuns* here, the antecedent being *aigneaux*, but *BT* also have *aucunes*.

76.11–12   *J* presents the bizarre form *curieurieux*. A possible explanation is that the typesetter had to break the word at the end of the line after the first *u*, *cu-*. He then remembered breaking the word at *u*, but when he got to the second *u* (*rieu*), he thought he was at the first one, and so went on from there, adding *rieux*.

76.15   The subject of the verb is *la poudre*, singular. Elsewhere *V* prints both *prengne* (4.08) and *preigne* (93.18, 95.09, 97.24). We have adopted the more frequent spelling for this emendation

76.24   Elsewhere *V* prints *puissent* (4 occurrences: 31.03, 50.23, 70.08, 85.15). This is the only occurrence of *peussent*.

77.24   The antecedent for this pronoun is presumably *bestes antenoises*, 77.21–22, the feminine plural agreement being with the last noun of the series rather than with the series as a whole.

Chapter 14

78.02   juing *BJT*] junig *V* (printer's error).

78.20   All four printings have the singular, *icelle*, yet the context clearly requires the plural.

Chapter 15

80.25   *reigles generaulx*: see note to 5.04.

Chapter 16

81.03   *berbier*: see note to 74.10.

Chapter 17

82.07   *V* prints the cardinal number here, rather than the ordinal.

83.04   Since the verb *encourir* normally takes a direct object, we have emended by removing the preposition *en* following *enqueurent*.

83.05   The confusion between *donc* and *dont* is already found in Old French manuscripts. Cf. J.-M. Fritz, ed., Chrétien de Troyes, *Erec et Enide*: "*donc* et *dont* s'emploient indifféremment l'un pour l'autre" (introduction, 20) ["*donc* and *dont* are used indifferently for one another"]. Marchello-Nizia presents them as equivalent forms, *dont/donc* (*Langue*, 216).

Chapter 18

84.13   refroidies *BJT*] refroidiees *V* (printer's error).

84.14   The erroneous reading *pitie*, in *B*, could be the result of a misreading of the abbreviated form *ptie* (with barred p), as the word is printed in *J*.

Chapter 19

85.05   Another case of plural verb with a singular subject (*la doulceur*). The plural continues with the following adjectives, *nourrisans et prouffitables*. *B* and *T* also have plurals for these three words.

85.05   Elsewhere in *V* we find the expected *-ss-* spellings (*nourrissent* 83.01; *nourrissant* 80.05–06).

85.07   medecine *BJT*] mediciue *V* (printer's error). We find the expected spelling in 25.22 (plural), 80.09, and 84.18.

85.18   *V* prints the usual form, *chiet*, in 35.02; cf. *eschiet*, 77.01. One would expect a plural verb, the subject being *les degoustz*. Perhaps the subject is understood to be *la pluye*.

Chapter 20

86.02   *V* prints cardinal numbers for chapters xx through xxxix.

86.15   Elsewhere *V* prints *reigles* (six occurrences, e.g., 5.04, 80.25). *BT* also print *rigle* here.

Chapter 21

87.04   Previously *V* prints *piz* (four occurrences, all in ch. 10, 64.13–65.08).

Chapter 22

87.08 Previously *V* prints *pousset* (66.06, 66.08). We have retained *V*'s spelling in all cases.

87.10 Previously *V* prints *prendent* (nine occurrences, including the first sentence of Ch. 21, 86.25); *preignent* occurs just once more, also in a context where one would expect the indicative, 97.06. All four texts print *preignent* here.

87.11 Given the use of *continuelz* in a very similar context in 14.18–19, it seems likely that *continues* is an error here.

Chapter 23

87.21 In *J* the word *aigniaux* begins on the last line of fol. lxii, with the letters *ai* followed by a sort of hyphen; the complete word then appears in the top line of the next page (lxii verso).

Chapter 25

88.01 Chapters 25 onward are misnumbered in all four printings. See note to 6.04–05. We have reproduced *V*'s chapter numbers.

Chapter 28

88.17 *bouverande*: see note to 67.16 (*BJ* print *bouveraude* here).

88.22 *V* prints *guoitron* in 67.18.

Chapter 29

88.25 *T* prints *douve* (*douue*) throughout the following paragraph, but prints *dauue*(*s*) elsewhere (nine occurrences), except for *dou-* in 70.08.

89.03 nommee *BJ*] nommé *TV*. The past participle should agree with *herbe*.

Chapter 31

89.22 We feel the need of a conjunction linking the final clause to what precedes.

Chapter 32

90.01–02 This plant is called *poucel* in 78.08. Note that both *poucel* and *poucet* are used for the plant, whereas *poucet* and *pousset* are used for the illness.

90.02–03 *V*'s reading, *et cest le test aux bestes le gout de menger,* seems to make no sense, yet it is shared by all four printings. Our conjectural emendation is based on Lacroix, who printed ". . . et cette herbe oste aux bestes le gout de menger" (135). Subsequently *V* prints *goust,* a more usual form for the time (four occurrences, 94.20–98.08; similarly, six occurrences of forms of the verb *gouster* are printed with *-st-,* compared to just one occurrence without the *s: gouté,* 67.19 — and also *desgoutees,* 98.03–04).

Chapter 33

90.06   This is the only occurrence of the form *l'on* in *V,* which generally prints *l'en.* See note to 3.03.

90.09   *muguet:* earlier we find *mugue* (82.16, 82.25).

90.10   Another case of a singular verb with a plural subject. *B* alone prints *descendent* here. Though all four printings have *que,* the context requires *qui* and we have emended in order to provide a more readable text.

Chapter 34

90.15   For the confusion between *ces* and *ses,* see note to 34.17.

90.16   All four printings literally read *la filee* (twice) in this sentence. We have adopted the form found in the six previous occurrences (6.02, 65.02, etc.).

Chapter 35

91.02   The verb *est* is indispensable here. The expression *si comme est dit* reappears in 94.11; *comme dit est* appears more frequently: 11.12, 19.10, 34.09, etc. — eight occurrences in all.

Chapter 36

91.11   *V* prints both *puist* (8 occurrences, 49.10–64.12) and the modern form *puisse* (3 occurrences, the others being 94.213 and 96.04). It is curious to note that the latter form occurs exclusively in the last ten pages of the text.

Chapter 37

91.22   *TV*'s *comme* is likely a misreading for *commune. V*'s *a trouve* (which could be read as *a trouvé*) seems unlikely; both *T* and *BJ* present acceptable readings.

92.03   *que* for *qui* (*BJT* = *V*). See note to 90.10.

Chapter 38

92.10   The context seems to require the infinitive *mesler*, depending on *doit* and parallel to *faire*.

92.18   There is no plural subject to support the verb *praignent*; we find the form *preigne* used similarly in 93.18.

92.23   Elsewhere *V* prints *aigneaux* (60 occurrences); this is the sole occurrence of *aigneaulx*.

92.24   For the form *pouoit*, see Jodogne.

92.25   prendre *BJT*] pendre *V* (printer's error). The context seems to require the infinitive *copper*, depending on *doit* and parallel to *prendre*.

93.02   The preposition *de* seems necessary here, as in Lacroix (142), though it is not present in any of the four printings. *BJ* print *Dauves*, with an oddly placed upper-case *D*.

Chapter 39

93.08   This is the last numbered chapter heading in any of the printings. The two-line capital letters beginning the subsequent paragraphs (94.11, 94.22, 95.03, 95.13, 96.15, 97.05, 98.15, 99.04, 100.07) and the disparate topics treated (seven illnesses, bloodletting, castrating, and the shepherd's dog) suggest that the remaining sections might have been numbered as separate chapters.

93.10–11   *V* generally prints *-ez* for second-person plural verb endings, as for *prenez* and *mettez* in this same sentence, and for *broyez* just above, 93.02. The sole other case of an *-és* verb ending in *V* is *querés*, 95.01. *BT* both print *broyez* here and *querez* in 95.01.

94.05   In all seven previous occurrences *V* prints *poacre*.

94.05–06   The word *ceste* is divided between two lines, but with a virgule (/), rather than the usual "slanting equal sign", to mark the division.

94.18   The conjunction *et* seems necessary here, *terre* and *tampiere* indicating two different materials.

95.01   *querés*: see note to 93.10–11.

95.15   The emendation is based on 89.18–21: "... *quant les brebis menguent une herbe que l'en appelle feuvrel a la petite fleur janne ainçois que ladicte herbe soit fleurie*". It seems likely that *V*'s *l'enfleure* is an inadvertent repetition influenced by the similarity of sound. Confusion between *si* and *s'il* parallels that between *qui* and *qu'il*; it occurs again in 96.20. See note to 20.03.

95.16 *V*'s reading, *du chief de la veue*, shared by *B* and *T*, makes little sense; the emendation is based on 98.16–17, ". . . *on les seigne du chief de la vaine sur l'oeil*".

95.17 In *T* the letter *t* of *cheut* is fainter and appears to be crossed out.

95.21 Generally we find *se* introducing a hypothesis (3.19, 10.21, etc.); *si* occurs here and in 97.01, as well as *sil* (emended to *si*) in 95.15 and 96.20.

96.20 *sil* for *si*: see note to 95.15.

97.01 *V* varies between *runge* (five occurrences) and *ronge* (three).

97.03 ou *BT*] au *V* (printer's error). The context requires the conjunction *ou*.

97.06–07 The structure of the sentence requires an adverbial clause, rather than a second present-tense verb parallel to *preignent*.

97.14 The form *visaige* contrasts with *V*'s usual usage, which is *-age*: we find 42 occurrences of the latter spelling, to which may be added another ten occurrences of plurals in *-ages*; by contrast there are just three other occurrences of *-aige*, all of which occur in the concluding poem, and one of *-aigent*, 75.01. (The word *naige*, 43.15, is a separate case, presumably pronounced much as in Modern French.)

98.02 *blecez*. Elsewhere *V* prints *-cie-* for similar forms: *blecier* 31.03–04, 63.01, 74.01; *blecié* 23.15. In this line *T* also prints *blecez*, whereas *B* has *blessez*.

100.20 *V*'s *congier* is a doubtful form; we have replaced it by the more usual spelling, found in *T*.

Poem (line numbers)

1 Though present in all four printings, this poem is of doubtful authorship: "le poème . . . forme une sorte d'épilogue . . . et . . . n'est peut-être pas de l'auteur" (Möhren, 139 n. 53) [the poem forms a sort of epilogue and may not be by the author]. Cf. the vocabulary and spelling differences discussed in the following notes.

8 In the prose text we find four occurrences of *usage* and one of *usages*. The form *usaige* is unique to the poem.

9 This is the unique occurrence of *beaucop* in our text, *moult* still being the usual word at this time (Baldinger, "Le remplacement," 59). The fact that it occurs only in the poem may indicate a difference in authorship.

11 As printed in *TV*, the line is hypermetric (one syllable too long).

14 Another case of plural subject and singular verb; in this case it may be considered a matter of poetic license.

20 *V* usually prints *oeilles* (38 occurrences). The use of the spelling *ouailles*, unique to this line, is presumably to ensure the proper number of syllables

in the line (*ou* forming a separate syllable). The form *oeilles*, found in *J*, would seem to create a seven-syllable line.

25   Lacroix printed *Son* here, and though it may make better sense, this reading is unsupported by any of the printings.

35   The form *saige*, unique to the poem, contrasts with *sage* and *sages*, each of which is found three times in the text. The fact that *saige* is rhymed with *rage* is evidence that both words were pronounced with the same vowel.

Supplementary Comments

Second Prologue

4.10–13   "Verily, verily I say unto you, He that entereth not by the door into the sheepfold, but climbeth up some other way, the same is a thief and a robber. But he that entereth in by the door is the shepherd of the sheep" (John 10:1–2).

Prologue (Chapter 1)

7.22–24   Ovid's *Metamorphoses*, 2. 531–632, tells how the crow's plumage changed from white to black; the allusion here may be an inaccurate recollection of that passage. The French proverb says: "Qui lave le corbeau ne le fait pas blanc" (Pierron 338). [Washing the crow does not make it white].

9.15   Accurate counting of animals is very important, especially in the case of sheep where, if one is "cast" or down and unable to get up, fluid will collect in its lungs and it will drown.

9.21   The phrase *livres des proprietez des choses* may be a reference to *De proprietatibus rerum* (*On the Properties of Things*), composed around 1240 by Bartholomaeus Anglicus (Bartholomew the Englishman), "the most widely read and quoted of all late-medieval encyclopedias" (Lawler, "Encyclopedias," 448b).

12.09   Although unable to reproduce, the wethers grew more wool than the ewes and thus had greater economic value.

18.22–24   This passage is not to be taken literally, that Jean de Brie had formally studied his subject, but rather simply as a way of saying that he had mastered his craft (Hauser; Holmér 139 n.1).

Chapter 2

20.15–16   ". . . thou hast put all things under his feet, all sheep and oxen, yea, and also beasts of the field; the fowl of the air, and the fish of the sea, and whatever passeth through the paths of the seas" (Psalms 8:7–8).

22.01–04   "Kermes, now commonly called grain (*granum*), from Asia Minor,
            Spain and Portugal was (in the Middle Ages) used in the North as
            it had been in the South in Roman days; it was used to dye the costly
            scarlet robes worn by kings" (Postan and Miller, *Cambridge Econom-
            ic History*, 2: 629). "Kermes, red dye stuff consisting of the bodies of
            pregnant insects *Coccus ilicus*, formerly considered to be a berry" (*Ox-
            ford Universal Dictionary*).

23.07–10   The sheep that grazed on the salt marshes of western France were in-
            deed well known for their superior taste, as evidenced by this state-
            ment from Delisle: "Dès le XIᵉ siècle, la réputation de pré-salé était
            bien établie" (*Etudes*, 240). [From the 11th century onward, the repu-
            tation of salt-meadow mutton was well established]. And this from
            Dumas: "Et ces gigots de mouton des marais salants ! fit Porthos en
            passant sa langue sur ses lèvres" (*Vingt Ans Après* II, 407). ["'And the
            legs of mutton from the salt marshes,' said Porthos, smacking his lips"
            (*Twenty Years After*, 524)].

23.16   *Dauve*: Buttercup. "La renoncule rampante, *Ranunculus repens* L. com-
            me l'espèce voisine, la renoncule des champs, *R. arvensis* L., est une
            plante toxique qui peut être très dangereuse pour le bétail, surtout à
            l'état frais: consommée en grande quantité, elle entraîne la mort moins
            d'une demi-heure après l'ingestion" (Větvička, *Plantes*, 42). [The ra-
            nunculus; Creeping ranunculus, *Ranunculus repens* L., like the closely
            related species, field ranunculus, *R. arvensis* L., is a toxic plant which
            can be very dangerous for livestock, especially when it is fresh. Consu-
            med in large quantity, it leads to death less than a half hour after in-
            gestion]. In Chapter 10 de Brie says that these flukes are caused by a
            malign plant, *dauve*, or buttercup. In reality the problem is twofold:
            buttercup is toxic, but the liver can also be harmed by worms ingested
            by sheep feeding in marshy places where the buttercup flourishes.

            Dayton tells us that *ranunculus*, the Latin word for little frog, was fa-
            cetiously employed by Cicero to denote the inhabitants of the marshes
            near Rome and was adopted by the Roman naturalist Pliny for these
            plants that like that habitat. He adds that another word in French for
            the ranunculus is *grenouille* (*Notes*, 190), or frog; Lachiver defines *gre-
            nouillet* as "une espèce de renoncule d'eau" [a kind of water ranunculus],
            while Cotgrave defines it as "The Crowfoot, Butter flower, King's Cob,
            golden cup; marsh crowfoot." See also 68.14.

23.20–23   Sheep grease is lanolin, which is processed for a variety of products.
            Raw lanolin from fleeces can actually rot through a pair of leather
            boots over time. Anyone who has worked shearing sheep knows that
            the lanolin from the fleeces is pervasively softening: "Shaking hands
            with a shearer is similar to touching warm velvet. Exposed to raw lan-
            olin day after day, even the heavy logging boots of the shearer become
            so pliable they can be folded into a wad" (Irigaray, *Shepherd*, 194).

24.21   In one ton of sheep manure, there are 15.8 lbs of nitrogen, 6.7 lbs. of phosphorus, and 18 lbs. of potash. Six to seven sheep will produce 7.5 tons per year. In comparison, steer manure yields 15 lbs. of nitrogen, 6 of phosphorus, 8 of potash and one steer produces 8.5 tons per year. Chicken manure has the highest levels of all four chemicals but is very "hot" and can burn crops. (Material condensed from Ensminger's *Stockman's Handbook,* 323–24.)

25.12–14   "Wherever the creatures went, the wheels went beside them . . ." (Ezekiel 1:19).

26.05–06   This wording suggests that Jean did not actually write the book himself, but dictated it to another.

Chapter 3

28.06–08   Laban did this because those having colored wool were less valuable and it would take Jacob longer to win his bride.

28.12–16   Cotgrave lists willows with bark of red, white, yellow, and black.

29.05–06   Tamar was the wife of his son, Er (Genesis 39). Printing *B* is the edition explicitly approved by the Church.

29.15–16   The King James Bible says Moses fled to Midian and that Sephora's father was Reuel (Exodus 2:12–22).

29.18   Sheep, even more than other animals, need water: "The body of an animal such as sheep is composed of about 70% water on average . . . If the supply of water . . . drops off, bodily desiccation sets in" (Keller, *Shepherd,* 49–50). . . . "as soon the fourth hour of the day has brought on thirst . . . give them once more the translucent streams . . ." (Virgil, *Georgics* 3. 327–330). Sheep desperately need water and fights over water rights are legendary, persisting to this day.

Chapter 4

31.04–05   To "fall off" is a common livestock term meaning to lose flesh or vitality and be less "thrifty," another expression meaning to do less well. Rough handling bruises the flesh and reduces its value.

31.07   "There are good herders and not so good herders and very bad and unkind herders and the sheep know the difference. They like sureness and tranquillity" (Irigaray, 12).

31.10   Using the scoop end of the crook to pick up a bit of gravel or dirt, a benign way to get their attention and to turn or move them along. "Un type [de houlette] a semble-t-il disparu en France, bien qu'il paraisse à maintes reprises dans l'iconographie ancienne: la houlette avec cuiller d'un côté et crochet de l'autre": *Bergers de France,* 102). [A type {of

crook which has} seemingly disappeared in France although it appears many times in bygone drawings: the crook with the scoop at one end and the hook at the other].

Chapter 5

Note: Pierre Belon du Mans' *Histoire de la nature des oyseaux* was published in 1555. It has been an invaluable source for the birds mentioned by de Brie. Belon's birds are represented by woodcuts which are generally recognizable and are representative of the time but are not comparable with today's bird guides. The information he offers about birds has been most useful, including the number of birds that were considered edible, such as starlings and herons. He quotes Pliny and Aristotle as affirming that magpies can be taught to speak (but are not good to eat). Belon cites Greek and Latin sources and refers frequently to what "the ancients" have to say about a bird. Some have questioned his scholarship of Greek and Latin, but the book remains a valuable resource and a pleasure to read. Only the line where the bird first appears is listed.

36.01   Starlings: "Ils vont à grandes troupes en toutes saisons . . . et pource qu'on en prend grande quantité, on a acoustumé de les avoir en délices" (Belon, 322). [They go in great bodies in all seasons . . . and because they can be taken in great quantities, people are accustomed to have them in dainty dishes].

36.11   Heron: "Et sa nature est tele ke maintenant k'ele aperçoit ke tempeste doit cheoir, ele vole en haut et s'enfuit en l'air amont la ou la tempeste n'a pooir de monter, et par lui coignoissent mainte gent ke tempeste vient" (Latini, *Tresor*, 141–42). [Such is its nature that when it sees a storm is going to fall, it flies high and flees up into the air where the storm cannot climb, and by knowing about it, many folk know that a storm is coming]. "Quand le héron se lève de la pâture et crie fort en se levant / C'est signe de pluie ou de grand vent" (Pierron, 348). [When the heron rises from the pasture crying loudly as it rises, that is a sign of rain or a great wind]. Belon says: "Lon dit communement, que le Heron est viande Royale (190)." [Everyone says that heron is royal food].

36.23   Swallow: "Quand l'alouette chante de bon matin / Le temps va tourner au vilain" (Pierron, 321). [When the swallow sings early in the day, the weather is going to turn foul].

37.05   Kite: "Milan royal, *Milvus milvus*" (Peterson et al., *Guide*). There has been some confusion because this bird is referred to as *hua* or *huat*, which some have thought to be a foreshortening of *chat huant*, an owl, but here it is referred to as an *escoufle*, which is a kite. Belon calls it a Milan Royal or Red Kite, saying; "Les paisants l'ont nommé autrement: car de son cry l'ont dit Huo: les autres prononcent Huauld: d'autres le nomment ausi un Escoufle" (131). [The peasants call it otherwise: for from its cry they have named it Huo: others say it "huauld":

others call it a Kite]. The *Dictionnaire historique de la langue française* relates *huard* to Old and Middle French *hua*, which it defines as "'chat-huant, hibou, milan' (v. 1200) déréve lui aussi de *huer*" [as above]. Its present-day habitat includes almost all of France, and is most likely the bird to which de Brie is referring. Cotgrave says that the *hua* is the black kite, *Milvus migrans*, and that an *escoufle* is a kite, puttocke, or glead, the last two also kites.

37.14   Green Woodpecker: "Nous cognoissons deux especes de Pics verds communs en touts lieux . . . car en tant qu'il est oyseaux prenant sa pasture des excrements des arbres, & vermines d'iceux, nature luy a baillé pour les ongles moult voultez, & bien crochuz pour se tenir à la renverse, comme pour grimper en montant, & descendre le lon des troncs & rameaux" (Belon, 299–300) [We know two kinds of green woodpeckers common everywhere . . . for, understanding that it is a bird taking its feeding from the excretions of trees and their bugs, nature has endowed him with very arched talons, well hooked for holding itself upside down, as well as for creeping while climbing and descending the length of the trunk and branches]. Belon recogizes both *pimart* and *pivert*. Neither Cotgrave nor Larousse give *pivert* but have *pimart*. Lachiver gives both and says "En Normandie, en Brie, le pivert."

"Quand le pivert done son chant / Signe de pluie ou de grand vent./ Lorsque le pivert crie / Il annonce la pluie." (Pierron, 364). [When the green woodpecker sends forth its song, it is a sign of rain or high wind. When the green woodpecker cries out, he is announcing rain]. Cotgrave calls a pimard a "heighhaw" or woodpecker.

37.19   Green Finch: "L'oyseau que les Françoys nomment Verdier, n'est pas de couleur verde, mais est de couleur jaulne tirant sur le verd" (Belon, 364). [The bird which the French call a green finch is not colored green, but is yellow tending toward green].

38.02   Bittern: Belon says that his call can be heard "d'une demië lieuë de loing" (193) [from a half league away].

38.14   Magpie: C. Kita in Greek, Pica in Latin (Belon, 291). " . . . on ne l'estime de bon manger, & qu'elle a la chair dure, les anciens nomplus que les modernes pour le jourdhuy. La Pie a cela de particuliër, qu'elle devient chauve toutes les annees, en muant les plumes de sa teste" (Belon, 292). [. . . the magpie is not considered good to eat, by the ancients as well as those of today, and has a tough flesh. The magpie has this in particular: it becomes bald each year, molting the feathers from its head].

39.01   Crow, "Carrion Crow, Corneille noire. *Corvus corone corone*" (Peterson). "Quand l'on voit que les Corbeaux se debatent & font voix comme en hoquetant, & continuënt quelque temps, c'est presage de

vent à venir: & s'ils reïterent souvent, comme en reprenant leurs voix, signifient pluye venteuse" (Belon, 281). [When one sees the crows debating among themselves and making a hiccuping voice, continuing for some time, it is an omen of wind to come; and if they repeat often, taking voice again, they are signaling windy rain]. A sign of rain if "the Crow does . . . crie verie much toward evening" (Stevens, *Maison*, 25). Belon mentions other crows but not a *faissie*. Very likely the Rook or Corbeau freux, *Corvus frugilegius* (Peterson).

Chapter 6

40.24–41.03 Medieval attitudes toward the cat were profoundly ambiguous. The animal's usefulness for destroying rodents was appreciated, and almost every part of the cat was used in medicinal preparations (Bobis, *Chat*, 92), but at the same time the cat was associated with sorcery and evil, and it was considered unclean because of its traditional food (135–36). The idea of the cat's attitude while washing as a sign of imminent rain reappears in almost the same terms used here, in the fifteenth-century *Evangiles des quenouilles* (Jeay, lines 637–42; Bobis, *Chat*, 637–42), and Dournon lists two modern versions of the same idea: "Quant le chat se débarbouille / Bientôt le temps se brouille" [When the cat washes itself, there will soon be troubled weather] and "Si le chat se frotte l'oreille / Le mistral se reveille" [If the cat rubs its ear, the north wind awakens] (*Proverbes*, 112).

41.09–12 . . . (when) "Flies, wasps and Hornets, Fleas and Gnats bite more keenly than ordinarily they are wont" (Stevens 25).

Chapter 7

45.05 ". . . *ventos et varium caeli praediscere morem*" (Virgil, *Georgics*, 1.51–53) [To learn beforehand the varying winds and moods of heaven]. The American Basque sheepherder Irigaray echoes this image when he says that his "man from Baïgorry could read the clouds and wind too, staring around the bowl of the sky; sniffing the wind" (143). Dictons from Pierron, 469–72:

> "Lorsque souffle le vent de bise / Il perce la peau et la chemise." [When the north wind blows, it cuts right through your skin and shirt].

> "Vent du nord: pluie bientôt / Vent d'ouest: pluie aussitôt; / Vent d'antan: pluie demain." [Wind from the north, rain soon; wind from the west, rain right now; wind yesterday, rain tomorrow.]

> "Le vent de soulaire / Fait geler six pieds sous terre." [The east wind makes it freeze six feet below the ground.]

"Dis-moi les vents / Je te dirai les temps." [Tell me the winds, I will tell you the weather.]

46.21–22　From this name comes "foehn winds . . . dry, high velocity, usually warm winds that originate in continental interiors . . . all compete with moderating marine air, temporarily driving out its moisture and quickly generating conditions that favor fire" (Pyne, *Fire*, 413).

47.05　　　" . . . or whence grim Auster arises, and saddens the sky with bleak rain" (Virgil, *Eclogues and Georgics,* trans. Buckley, 77).

47.06　　　"Ouvre ta fenêtre à aquilon et orient; / Ferme à midi et occident" (Pierron, 473). [Open your window to North and East winds; shut it to the South and West].

47.11　　　World Map is the old name. Mercator "devoted more than three decades to his famous 'Atlas' (which he named after the Titan of Roman mythology) . . . issued in three parts, starting in 1585" (Monmonier, *Mercator,* 33).

47.15–16　For most medieval writers, the year was divided into just two seasons, summer and winter.

48.09–11　Cotgrave lists at least 17 winds, showing their importance to sailors, millers, and husbandrymen.

Chapter 8

49.03　　　" . . . games of chance were the most popular, although . . . forbidden both by ecclesiastical and royal authority . . . especially . . . those in which dice were used . . . The law of 1396 is aimed particularly against loaded dice . . ." (Lacroix, *France,* 234–35).

49.12–18　"La signification sociale du vêtement est encore plus grande. Il désigne chaque catégorie sociale, il est un véritable uniforme. Porter celui d'une autre condition que la sienne, c'est commettre le péché majeur d'ambition ou de déchéance" (Le Goff, *Civilization,* 441). [Clothing was of even greater social significance. It designated each social class and amounted to a uniform. To wear the clothes of a social condition other than one's own was to commit a serious sin of ambition or of derogation]. This lengthy description not only paints the picture of the working man, but also places him in the societal hierarchy.

50.13　　　"Fourteenth-century language manuals considered 'camelin' to be some colour probably a shade between white and grey" (van Uyten, "Cloth," 177). "A l'origine, drap de laine fine, rarement teint, dont la couleur variait du gris clair au brun, sans rayures ni dessins. On a ensuite donné ce nom à des tissus grossiers, sans doute à cause de leur couleur poil de chameau" (Lachiver). [Originally a cloth of fine wool, rarely dyed, whose color varied from light gray to brown, with neither

stripes nor patterns. Later this name was given to coarser material, doubtless because of the camel's-hair color].

50.25   Aaron's ephod: "And they shall make the ephod of gold, of blue and purple and scarlet, and of fine twined linen, with cunning work. It shall have the two shoulder-pieces thereof joined at the two edges thereof, and so it shall be joined together." (King James Bible, Exodus 28:6–7). It is, in essence, a tunic.

51.11–12   "Le berger sédentaire a sur lui tout un 'équipement portatif,' instruments variés pendus à sa ceinture ou suspendus les uns aux autres, à moins qu'il ne les tienne à la main. Du simple couteau à la houlette, chacun a une fonction précise. Cet équipment a trois buts, faciliter la vie du berger en plein champ, en faire un bon vétérinaire, l'aider dans sa tâche de gardeur" (Kaiser-Guyot, *Berger*, 39). [The sedentary shepherd has on him a whole set of 'portable equipment,' various instruments hung from his belt or some suspended from others, except when he has them in his hands. From a simple knife to his crook, each has a precise function. This equipment has three purposes: to facilitate the life of the shepherd in the field, to make him a good veterinarian, and to help him in his job as guardian].

51.21   Mange is caused by parasitic mites burrowing under the skin. "Il ne faut qu'une brebis galeuse pour gâter un troupeau" (Dournon 32). [It takes only one mangy ewe to spoil the flock]. Mange is highly contagious and sheep are essentially comminglers. Since it is mentioned fifteen times in the book, it was obviously an important problem.

52.02   Clévenot's translation omits *bobelins*, presumably as a duplication. It is possible de Brie was indicating that the shepherd was patching already patched shoes, certainly not an unlikely occurrence.

53.08   "*Eau et pain est la viande du chien*: Bread and water is meat good ynough for a dog (though not for a man)." "*Qui veut avoir bon chien il faut qu'il le nourrisse bien*: He that will have a good dog must feed him well; he that desires a good servant must use him well" (Cotgrave).

54.02–03   Varro describes the collars used by dogs in his time (B.C. 116–28): "To protect them from wounds from wild beasts we place collars on them, of the kind which we call *meliu*, which is a girth around the neck made from strong leather studded with nails and lined with soft leather to protect the neck from being chafed by the hard iron heads of the nails: for if a wolf or other wild beast is once wounded by these nails all the other dogs are safe from his attack, even if they have no collars" (254). "A good dog will sense trouble, shooting a look toward the herder . . . Often, the dogs spot trouble long before the herder does" (Irigaray, 63–64).

54.16–17   The statement "Tel est amy a la despense qui ne l'est pas a la defense" sounds proverbial, but we have found no corroborating citations.

54.22 "Jesus also spoke of himself as the 'good shepherd,' and was often represented as such in early Christian art. Following this example, bishops, his representatives on earth, carry as the badge of authority and emblem of commitment a pastoral staff in the form of a shepherd's crook . . . to be memorialized as the faithful guardian of the flock was the only tribute that really counted." (Henisch, *Calendar*, 86.)

58.14–59.03 "Then, under colour of shepherds, somewhile / There crept in wolves, full of fraud and guile, / That often devoured their own sheep, / And often the shepherds that did them keep" (Spenser, *The Shepherd's Calendar*, 126–29). This passage may have been omitted in *B* because of its criticism of prelates.

Chapter 9

60.14 "Au xive et au xve siècle, nos campagnes furent continuellement infestées par des bandes de loups. Une imposition particulière fut établie sur les paysans pour faciliter la destruction de ces terribles animaux" (Delisle, *Etudes*, 114). [In the fourteenth and in the fifteenth century, our countryside was continually infested by packs of wolves. A special tax was levied on the peasants to facilitate the destruction of these terrible animals].

61.04 "Natural events such as freezing, wilting, or crushing may cause hydrocyanic acid (HCN) to be formed in the plant . . . Once HCN is absorbed in the animal body, it stops the red blood cells from releasing oxygen to the tissue cells" (Scott, *Handbook*, 129).

Chapter 10

62.03 *Noire gelée* is black frost and is dry, while hoar frost, *gelée blanche*, brings moisture.

64.09 As the mother cleans the lamb, she is also giving encouragement to its life forces.

64.11 He could do this more easily when sheep were smaller. Toynbee says the weight of sheep in traveling flocks in 13th-century England was about 32 pounds, including the fleece (8). One can presume that size had not changed a great deal at the time of our shepherd.

64.12–13 When the ewe first lambs, there is a waxen plug in the teat which has served to prevent infection between lambings. This must be expelled before any milk will flow.

64.24–25 "The first milk secreted by a mammal after parturition; the 'greenings' or 'green milk'" (*Oxford Universal Dictionary*). While Jean de Brie thought the milk was harmful, today sheep ranchers save colostrum milk in the freezer for newborn lambs that are in need.

65.02   The disease usually affects young lambs 1 to 4 weeks of age. Most frequently the disease attacks vigorous, single lambs whose mothers are
giving an abundance of milk" (Scott, 80). What caused the scours was
the milk and its abundance.

66.23   "A contagious disease affecting susceptible sheep of all ages but primarily nursing or recently weaned lambs" (Scott, 840). "A kind of erysipe-
las surrounds their mouths and lips with filthy sores" (Columella, 277).
Possibly a very painful condition, it can be transmitted to humans as
"orf." It can also affect the ewe, causing mastitis.

Chapter 11

67.16   Spiny shrubs. Furze, common gorse of France (Coombes). Seeds of the
common gorse yield a poisonous alkaloid, ulexine, which was formerly
used as a local anesthetic and diuretic (*Encarta*).

68.03   *Dauve.* See 23.16.

68.14–15   A form of parasitic internal flatworm about an inch long that gravitates
to the liver and takes hold (Scott, 119). *Douve*: "Genre de vers némato-
des qui vivent en parasites dans le tube digestif des vertébrés; l'espèce la
plus commune et la plus dangereuse est la douve du foie ou distome du
foie qui ravage les troupeaux de mouton" (Lachiver). [Kind of worm living parasitically in the digestive tract of vertebrates; the most common
and most dangerous is the liver fluke or sheep fluke that ravages sheep
herds].

69.12   "Some hay" expresses the idea that the lambs get small quantities at
first to accustom their stomachs to "grown-up" food.

69.14   Vetch is considered "hot," which means that it can cause diarrhea and
other upset.

70.17   "Tournis: maladie des moutons . . . dont le principal symptôme consis-
te à tourner et qui dépend de la présence de cénures dans un point quelconque de l'axe cérébro-spinal, du cerveau surtout" (Lachiver). [Sheep
illness, commonly known as staggers; staggers: sheep illness, whose
main symptom consists of turning and which results from the presence
of the larvae of tapeworms at some point in the cerebral-spinal axis,
above all in the brain]. De Brie attributes *avertin* to sunstroke.

Chapter 12

71.01–02   "Le pasteur a la responsabilité des parcours de ses bêtes; il décide de
l'heure propice au départ ou au retour, il choisit les prés. Cette connais-
sance du moment et du lieu favorables constituait la technique fonda-
mentale du berger médiéval" (Kaiser-Guyot, 29). [The shepherd is responsible for the grazing area for his animals; he decides the favorable

hour for going out and returning, he chooses the meadows. This knowledge of favorable time and place constituted the fundamental technique of the medieval shepherd].

72.22–24   This passage is puzzling, since the name *Nort* would seem to contradict the explanation that this wind comes from the south (*vient de devers Midy*).

73.04   In his book *Sheep and Man*, M. L. Ryder discusses Lacroix's 1879 edition of *Le Bon Berger*. Ryder interprets Lacroix as saying that *la seignee* is the "marking" of sheep to make them easily recognizable by their owners (412). Clévenot interpreted *la seignee* correctly in his 1979 translation.

Chapter 13

73.17   Cotgrave quotes the adage that "Il n'est pas toujours saison de brebis tondre: everything in its season; waiting can bring more benefit." "Among the sheep there is a high proportion of rams. They carry a thicker fleece than the ewes, and since . . . wool production was the principal aim of sheep-farming, a certain preference for rams and wethers is understandable" (Slicher van Bath, *Agrarian History*, 67).

74.21–75.03   While it is possible that this thorny bush could be another, still it is likely that it is the one identified by Belon.

75.06   That even the slightest loss of wool could be significant is shown by the admonition of Virgil: "If the woolen manufacture be thy care, first let prickly woods and burs, and caltrops, be far away" (*Georgics*, trans. Buckley, 80).

Chapter 14

78.08   Jean de Brie says that there are two kinds of *poucel*, one of which is harmful for his flock, the other good. *P. rhoeas* is presumably the latter.

78.13   The ewes must chew their cud in order for the food to descend to the third stomach and be available to them for nourishment.

78.15   Jean de Brie uses *faire traire* (to have milked) to indicate that he did not do the milking. "Du lait, le berger sédentaire ne s'en occupe jamais; il ne trait pas ses bêtes, il ne fabrique pas le fromage. Ce double travail s'ajoute à ceux de la ferme, une femme, le plus souvent, l'accomplit (appendice VI). Jean de Brie, dans tout son traité ne parle qu'une fois, et incidemment, de la traite des brebis. . . . Il est clair qu'il ne les trait pas lui-même. Mais il travaille dans une grande exploitation située, qui plus est, dans une région qui produit un fromage renommé" (Kaiser-Guyot, 34). [The sedentary shepherd never concerns himself with

milking: he does not milk his animals, he does not make cheese. These twin tasks belong to those of the large farming operation; a woman does it most often. In his whole treatise Jean de Brie speaks only once [in June's chapter], and then incidentally, of the milking of ewes. It is clear that he does no milking himself. But he worked on a large manor situated, moreover, in a region which produced a renowned cheese].

79.13–15   Two teasels mentioned in *Plantes des champs et des forêts* are both members of the *Asteraceae* family, while Fuller's teasel is *Dipsacus sativa* L. and a member of the *Dipsacaceae* family. To further confound the issue, one of them, the *Chardon Fausse-Acanthe*, is often confused with the thistle *Cirse des champs*. However, Větvička specifically mentions teasels and says they are good for the sheep when young and tender. *Pouchelet*: "En Boulonnais, chardon à foulon ou cardère sauvage" (Lachiver). [In the region of Boulogne, fuller's teasel or wild teasel]. *Dipsacus fullonum* L. (Niehaus & Ripper). *Dipsacus sativus* L.: used by fullers to tease cloth. Europe, Asia. (Coombes). Větvička offers three teasels: *Onopordum acanthium* L., *Carduus acanthoides* L., and *Carduus nutans* L. Fuller's teasel was grown commercially because it was very useful in the manufacture of wool. The spines of the plant, also called teasels, are flexible with recurved barbs that could "full" or raise the nap of woolen cloth. From George de Mestral's observations of teasel in the 1940s we now have Velcro® and its many uses.

80.05   *Matricaria chamomilla* L.: "l'une des plus utiles plantes médicinales . . ." (Větvička, 40). [one of the most useful medicinal plants]. Hunt says that it is probably henbane ("Lexique," 397), but Culpeper says henbane is never to be taken internally.

Chapter 15

80.18–20   ". . . au nord de la Loire, crucifère des champs plus connue sous les noms de *moutarde des champs, sénevé sauvage, ravenelle*. En Picardie: colza" (Lachiver). [. . . north of the Loire, a cruciferous plant of the field better known under the names of *field mustard, wild mustard, wallflower*. In Picardy, rape]. When freshly cut, mustard can cause digestive problems for livestock. Of its cousin, *Ravenelle (Raphanus raphanistrum* L.), Větvička writes: ". . . la ravenelle n'est quand même pas une bonne plante fourragère car elle irrite les voies digestives. . . Une fois défleurie, elle est même légèrement toxique et on connaît des cas d'empoisonnement de chevaux, de bétail, et d'agneaux directement au pré" (34). [Mustard is not at all a good forage plant, for it irritates the digestive passages . . . Once having flowered, it is even slightly toxic and there are known cases of poisoning of horses, cattle, and lambs directly in the meadow]. The drawing in Větvička shows the upper leaves having a yellowish tinge.

Chapter 16

81.12–13   "Si le chaume n'est pas arraché, il est brûlé ou enterré en novembre après le passage des moutons" (Lachiver). [If the stubble is not uprooted, it is burned or turned under in November after the passage of the sheep]. Because the crops had been harvested with a hand sickle which allowed only for the ears of grain to be harvested, this left a tall stalk behind for the sheep to feed on as they fertilized the land, a situation that Crosby says is "an example of 'sustainable farming' that would delight an old Yankee farmer and a new organic farmer equally" (337).

81.24   *Une lieue* (var. *heure*) *de nuyt. Lieue,* a measure of distance, was also used as a measure of time. Cf. Greimas and Keane, *Dictionnaire,* s.v. *lieue:* "L'espace d'une lieue de terre, c'est-à-dire une heure de temps." It recurs in Chapter 18, 84.11–12.

82.04–05   Overeating of grain left behind can result in bloat.

Chapter 17

82.12–14   Wheat is the stronger of the two: about 80% total digestive nutrient versus 70% for oats.

82.16–17   "Plante de sous-bois qui fleurit au printemps, vers le 1er mai, et qui porte de petites fleurs blanches en clochettes d'une odeur très agréable . . . lis de mai, lis des vallées, clochettes des bois" (Lachiver). [Plant of the forest undergrowth which blooms in spring, around May first, and which has white bell-like flowers with a very pleasant fragrance . . . May lily, lily of the valley, wood bellflowers]. He adds that present-day medicine uses the stem to produce a cardiac-regulating drug, which can have the drawback of side effects and that the water from a bouquet of lily of the valley is toxic. However, Lachiver lists a plant named *araignée* and defines it as *"cheveux de Vénus* ou nigelle de Damas." This plant is found in Větvička (76) as Nigelle des champs, *Nigella arvensis* L., and is known in English as Love-in-a-mist. Its pictures show suspended balls that correlate with what de Brie describes. While *muguet* in modern French is lily-of-the-valley, Cotgrave offers "woodruff, cheese-running and Ladies Bedstraw" (*Galium odorata* L.). Another definition of *muguet* is thrush, a condition that young children get in the throat and on the lips that is caused by a fungus. Horses can also get a disease called thrush on the frog of their hoof.

83.03–04   ". . . finding the thicke Dew, Cobwebs, Meldews, and such filthiness upon the grass, they will with all greedinesse devoure and eat it, than which nothing in the world sooner procureth rotting" (Stevens, 114).

83.05   *Yrengnier:* Lacking any modern equivalent, we have dubbed this "cobweb disease."

Chapter 18

84.05   "Holding" is a term meaning to keep animals together as a unit in a specific area for a definite purpose, for example, grazing, sorting or doctoring.

84.07   *Chardon.* See 79.13.

84.11–12   *Une lieue* (var. *heure*) *de nuyt.* See 81.24.

84.17   *La seignee*, bloodletting, is forbidden at this time to avoid sapping the strength of the breeding animals.

Chapter 19

85.16   "Les loups sont fort nombreux et n'hésitent pas à attaquer; aussi le berger est-il toujours armé d'un solide couteau, et accompagné de grands chiens" (Lorcin, *France*, 39). [The wolves are extremely numerous and do not hesitate to attack; thus the shepherd is always armed with a stout knife, and accompanied by large dogs].

85.23–24   [In the atmosphere of rain] "the sound of the belle be more lowd and shrill, and heard further off, than they were wont" (Stevens 25).

Chapter 21

86.23   *Affilee.* See 65.02.

Chapter 22

87.08   *Poucet (Pousset).* See 66.06.

Chapter 23

87.17   *Bouchet.* See 66.23.

Chapter 25

88.01   *Clavel, clavelée*: sheep pox is specific to sheep and spreads by contact. It can be followed by secondary infections causing death. It appears in Asia and Europe, but not in the U.S. (*Newsom's*, 116).

Chapter 26

88.07   *Rongne.* See 51.21.

Chapter 27

88.10   *Poacre*: oral lesions: De Brie says it is like mange and Lachiver says it is mange. However, Cotgrave does not specify a name but remarks on its symptoms and references its cause exactly as de Brie does. It has been suggested that it is vesicular dermatitis.

Chapter 28

88.23–24   *Guoiteron de la gorge*: Swollen throat, an affliction caused when the sheep eat gorse.

Chapter 29

89.01   *Dauve*. See liver fluke, 68.14.

89.03–04   *Dauve*. See 23.16.

Chapter 30

89.07   *Avertin*. See 70.17

Chapter 31

89.15   *Enfleure*: bloat.

Chapter 32

89.23   *Runge, rungot perdu*: lost cud. It is possible to swallow a cud and all ruminants need their cuds to process their food. See also 78.13

90.01–02   *Poucet*. See pousset, 78.08.

Chapter 33

90.04   *Yrengnier*. See 83.05.

90.09   *Muguet*. See 82.16.

Chapter 34

90.13   In only one of the previous chapters has he actually suggested a remedy: number 12. In the others he has merely said that dire things will occur unless a remedy is applied. This does not include his instructions for ameliorating the condition of newly shorn animals or other ideas of illness prevention, but applies only to remedies.

90.17–18   *Affilee.* See 65.02.

Chapter 35

90.22   *Pousset.* See 66.06.

Chapter 36

91.04   *Bouchet.* See 66.23. For sore mouth, Columella advocates "hyssop and salt crushed together in equal quantities, the palate, tongue and the whole mouth being rubbed with this mixture." Next sores are washed with vinegar and "thoroughly anointed with liquid pitch and lard" (277). Other mixes are of crushed cypress leaves and water.

Chapter 37

91.15   *Clavel.* See 88.01.

91.19   June 23, St. John's feast-day being June 24. St John is the protector of sheep (Wilmart, "Pratiques," 152).

91.20   A member of the nightshade family, it has "caused occasional livestock poisoning. Henbane alkaloids have been used in the past, and are currently used, as medicines at controlled dosages. It is considered a poisonous plant to humans" (Whitson et al., *Weeds*). Confusion has frequently arisen in trying to find the names of the plants that de Brie has mentioned, even when he has described them. Often he has mentioned only their healing properties. In this case he has given us a wealth of information, three names for the same plant: *hennebone, juscarime,* and *tume*: henbane, *Hyoscyamus niger* L. In Tony Hunt's book, *Popular Medicine in Thirteenth-Century England* (Cambridge: D. S. Brewer, 1990), he mentions even more names for henbane: chanilee, canellie, chanelee, chanlee.

Chapter 38

92.05   *Roingne.* See 51.21.

92.09   *Alun de glace*: Cotgrave indicates that this is rock alum, "Roche Allum," that has been first melted and made into flakes like ice.

   Copperas: a metallic sulphate (*Oxford Universal Dictionary*). Columella describes taking green hemlock cut in the spring, crushing the stem, pressing out the juice in an earthenware vessel, and mixing it with dried salt, sealing, burying in a dung pit for a year to heat and mature, and then using it (267). Hunt says it is common or potash alum (428).

93.02 Whereas buttercup may be poisonous when ingested, its irritant qualities may be useful in a salve.

Chapter 39

94.01 "Goutte-rose: An extreme redness of the face; pimpled, and set thick with rubies, or fiery speckles" (Cotgrave). Gout: a spot of color resembling a drop *(Oxford Universal Dictionary)*.

94.11 *Bouverande.* See swollen throat, 88.23.

94.22 *Dauve.* See 68.14.

95.03 *Avertin.* See 70.17.

95.05 The seeds and leaves are used in eye lotions (Coombes). Hunt says this is a name applied to a variety of plants, including clary. Cotgrave calls it "clarie or cleere-eye."

95.13 *Enfleure.* See 89.15.

95.13 A small bean more often called *féverole*, intended for animals. *Heath's* defines *féverole* as horse beans.

96.15 *Runge perdu.* See 78.13.

96.17 *Poucet.* See poucel, 78.08.

97.05–06 *Yrengnier.* See 83.05.

97.07 *Muguet.* See 82.16.

98.10 Some plants are considered "hot" or "cold" in their effect: e.g., oats are thought to be hot and barley less so. See Chaps. 11 and 17.

98.15–16 *Seignee.* See 73.04.

98.17 "We also draw off blood beneath the eyes and from the ears" (Columella, 269).

99.08 The birth of the Virgin Mary was and is traditionally celebrated on September 8. We have been unable to identify a date in March associated with this event.

99.11 There is some doubt as to whether this means three finger breadths from the body or from the end of the tail. Present custom is from the body.

Poem

35   "*Un fol advise bien le sage* [A foole may sometimes give a wise man counsaile]." (Cotgrave). Cf. Morawski, *Proverbes,* 2450, *Ung foul* [sic] *conseille bien le sage.* The following three lines sound proverbial as well, but we have found no corroborating citations.

APPENDIX: PRINTER'S ERRORS

In a number of cases, *B* or *T* presents a reading which is clearly a typesetter's error, rather than a true variant. We have grouped these here, in order to show the sorts of mistakes that occurred and, secondarily, to reduce the number of variants. These errors usually result in impossible forms, involving omitted or (rarely) added letters, transposed letters, or substitution of one letter for another. In all cases the result is a recognizable deformation of the intended word. (Such errors in *V*, relatively rare, are discussed in the textual notes.) In case of doubt, or where additional differences from *V*'s text are involved, we have retained the reading from *B* or *T* among the variants. In the following table we have made the usual distinction between *i* and *j*, *u* and *v*, and have added the acute accent on stressed final *e*.

Reading in text	chap-ter	page & line	erroneous form	edition page & line
philosophie	J. de B.	3.20	phitosophie	*T* 2.21
attribué	J. de B.	3.22	artribué	*B* 3.27–28 (A ii)
pousset	Table	6.03	poussat	*T* 6.03
Le vingtsiziesme	Table	6.06	L vingtsiziesme	*T* 6.06
maladie	Table	6.07	mlladie	*T* 6.07
jactance	1	6.19–20	jactanee	*B* 7.03–04 (A iiii)
Jehan	1	8.13	Hehan	*T* 8.13
bonnes	1	9.19	bonnnes	*T* 9.19
exciter	1	10.04	excicer	*T* 10.04
tellement	1	11.03–04	teltement	*T* 11.04
fust	1	11.08	sust	*B* 11.01
oings	1	11.25	onigs	*B* 11.19
l'acroissement	1	12.19–20	la croissement	*B* 12.09
ses	1	13.06	sen	*B* 12.21
moult	1	15.16	nout	*T* 15.16
Hamon	1	16.19	Gamon	*T* 16.19
Mengeour, ne	1	16.23	mengeourne ne	*T* 16.23
Helynant	1	16.24–25	helymant	*T* 16.24–25
hardiesse	1	18.18	hardtesse	*T* 18.18

champs	2	20.19	chumps	*T* 20.19
eaues	2	21.04	eanes	*T* 21.04
Premierement	2	22.01	Premierent	*B* 21.12 (B iii)
traictons	2	22.21	traiceons	*T* 22.21
a faire	2	22.21	r faire	*T* 22.21
et	2	22.23	te	*T* 22.22
tanner	2	22.23	lanner	*T* 22.23
en plusieurs	2	22.24	n plusieus	*T* 22.24
ailleurs	2	23.08	ailliers	*T* 23.08
pour	2	23.23	puor	*T* 23.23
prouffitable	2	26.09	poruffitable	*T* 26.09
figures	3	27.04	f gures	*T* 27.03–04
principalement	3	27.19–20	principallemene	*T* 27.19–20
a abruver	3	29.18	a bruver	*B* 28.14
enfraindre	4	30.19–20	en faindre	*B* 29.13
de corgies	4	31.02	ce corgies	*T* 31.02
ont esté	4	31.12	ont estés	*T* 31.12
veulent	4	31.22	vullent	*T* 31.22
fouc	4	32.03	fonc	*T* 32.03
esté	4	32.10	estre	*T* 32.10
may	4	32.11	moy	*T* 32.11
vers	4	32.24	ves	*B* 31.08
l'uys	4	33.01	l'hius	*T* 33.01
expedient	4	33.23	experient	*T* 33.23
mieulx	4	34.13	myeuly	*T* 34.13
tondre	4	35.01	londre	*B* 33.01 (C)
mieulx	4	35.01	myenlx	*T* 35.01
pluye	5	36.11	pluve	*T* 36.11
longs	5	36.25	loingtz	*T* 36.25
quant	5	37.09	quat	*T* 37.09
pluye	5	37.22	pulye	*T* 37.22
diligemment	5	39.21	deligemment	*B* 38.02
fruit	6	41.07	furit	*T* 41.07
trepent	6	41.08	treppet	*T* 41.08
muees	6	43.13	nuees	*T* 43.13
naige	6	43.15	niege	*B* 41.26
ferveur	6	43.17	freveur	*T* 43.17
appellé	7	46.14	apppellé	*T* 46.14
blanche	8	49.19–20	blenche	*T* 49.19–20
ses	8	50.14	sen	*B* 48.13
Premierement	8	51.12	Piemierement	*T* 51.12
millieu	8	52.04–05	meillu	*B* 49.23
mance	8	52.05	mauche	*T* 52.05

cousue	8	52.21	conseue	*B* 50.10
anguille	8	53.03	auguille	*T* 53.03
l'Evangile	8	55.11	le vangile	*T* 55.11
prouffit	8	56.03	poruffit	*T* 56.03
l'ung	8	56.05	l'ug	*T* 56.05
aguisant	8	56.15	aguisaut	*T* 56.15
son	8	58.05	so	*T* 58.05
tout	8	58.24	tont	*T* 58.24
mains	8	59.05	mais	*T* 59.05
quant	8	59.13	quanl	*T* 59.13
çainture	8	59.16	cienture	*B* 55.21 (D iiii)
autres	9	60.12	antres	*T* 60.12
effondreroient	9	60.20	effondreroint	*T* 60.20
instruit	9	61.15	iustruit	*T* 61.15
bergiers	9	61.17	begers	*B* 57.17
doulcement	10	63.15	doulcament	*T* 63.15
introduction	10	64.09	introducaion	*T* 64.09
leurs	10	67.05	laurs	*T* 67.05
gorge	11	67.18	gorgue	*T* 67.18
avaler	11	67.23	evaler	*T* 67.23
gorge	11	68.12	gorgue	*T* 68.12
leur	11	69.16	lenr	*T* 69.16
fenestres	12	71.20	fenestraes	*T* 71.20–21
appelle	12	72.09	eppalle	*T* 72.09
de tondre	13	73.22–23	de tondra	*T* 73.22–23
tonsure	13	74.01–02	tousure	*T* 74.01–02
ailleurs	13	74.18	allieurs	*T* 74.18
aux	13	74.24	uux	*T* 74.24
autres	13	75.02	autes	*T* 75.02
grant	13	75.04	gant	*T* 75.04
heure	13	75.11	hure	*T* 75.11
torves	13	76.04	tornes	*T* 76.04
expedient	13	76.06	xepedient	*T* 76.06
pareillement	13	76.08	pareillemenet	*T* 76.08
leurs	13	76.15	lenrs	*T* 76.15
fueille	14	78.09	fueillz	*T* 78.09
L'autre	14	78.10	L'utre	*T* 78.10
faire traire	14	78.15	faire traira	*T* 78.15
pourveoir	14	79.05	pouveoir	*B* 72.23
heure	14	79.21	hiure	*T* 79.20
soleil	14	80.03	foleil	*T* 80.03
juillet	15	80.17	uillet	*T* 80.17
sauvres	15	80.20	fauvres	*T* 80.19–20

fevrier	17	83.19	febvrir	*B* 76.24
emmy	17	83.23	emmyt	*T* 83.23
partie	18	84.14	pitie	*B* 77.17
nuysans	20	86.22	nuiysans	*T* 86.22
rousees	27	88.13	tousees	*T* 88.13
poacre	27	88.14	poacra	*T* 88.14
aux	29	89.02	auy	*B* 82.01
semblablement	29	89.03	semblament	*T* 89.03
sont	31	89.22	sout	*T* 89.22
bouchet	36	91.05	bouchit	*T* 91.05
est tel	37	91.18	estlel	*T* 91.18
gouterose	39	94.01	boutte rose	*T* 94.01
secoure	—	94.13	seceure	*T* 94.13
escourre	—	94.19	asourre	*T* 94.18
force	—	95.04	fore	*T* 95.04
feuvrel	—	95.13	feuvrel	*T* 95.13
doit	—	95.22	doibit	*T* 95.22
perdu	—	96.15	pardu	*T* 96.15
trouvera	—	97.04	trouver ra	*T* 97.03–04
playes	—	99.23	ployes	*T* 99.24
euvrent	—	99.23	euvres	*T* 99.24
usaige	poem	line 8	usaise	*B* 92

Bibliography

A. Works specific to Jean de Brie and *Le Bon Berger*

Catalogue général des livres imprimés de la Bibliothèque nationale. Paris: Imprimerie Nationale, 1923. Tome 77, col. 657.

Clévenot. See Jean de Brie.

Hauser, Henri. "Une Bévue du Bibliophile Jacob sur Jehan de Brie." *Revue d'Histoire Littéraire de la France* 19 (1912): 407–8. [Vol. no. from Holmér, 135 n. 7.]

Holmér, Gustaf. "Jean de Brie et son traité de l'art de bergerie." *Studia Neophilologica* 39 (1967): 128–49.

Hunt, Tony. "L'Art d'élever les moutons: Le Lexique médico-botanique du *Bon Berger* de Jean de Brie." In *"Qui tant savoit d'engin et d'art": Mélanges de philologie médiévale offerts à Gabriel Bianciotto*, ed. Claudio Galderisi and Jean Maurice, 301–10. Poitiers: Université de Poitiers, Centre d'études supérieures de civilisation médiévale, 2006.

Jean de Brie. *Le Bon Berger, ou Le vray régime et gouvernement des bergers et bergères, composé par le rustique Jehan de Brie, le bon berger. Réimprimé sur l'édition de Paris (1541),* avec une notice par Paul Lacroix (Bibliophile Jacob). Paris: Liseux, 1879.

———. *Le Bon Berger.* Trans. Michel Clévenot. Paris: Stock, 1979; repr. Étrépilly: Les Presses du Village, 1986.

Lebert, F. "La Ferme de Nolongues et le bon berger Jehan de Brie." *Bulletin de la Société littéraire et historique de la Brie* 13 (1934): 133–38.

Lebert, S. [Resume of *Le vray regime et gouvernement des bergers et bergeres* par Jehan de Brie.] *Bulletin historique et philologique (jusqu'à 1610) du Comité des Travaux Historiques et Scientifiques* (1967): L–LI.

Martin, Henri. "Jehan de Brie, le bon laboureur [*sic!*]." In *Histoire de France.* 17 vols. 4ᵉ edition. Paris: Furne, 1860–1861. 5: 299.

Meyer, Paul. Review of Jean de Brie, *Le Bon Berger*, ed. Lacroix. *Romania* 8 (1879): 450–54.

Möhren, Frankwalt. "Analyse sémantique structurale et contexte: Les dénominations du mouton dans des textes techniques." In *Actes du IVᵉ Colloque*

International sur le Moyen Français, ed. Anthonij Dees, 119–42. Amsterdam: Rodopi, 1985.

Nais, Hélène. "Jean de Brie (dit le Bon Berger)." *Dictionnaire des lettres françaises*, ed. Robert Bossuat et al., I: 408. Paris: Fayard, 1964.

Polain, Louis. *Catalogue de la Bibliothèque du Musée Thomas Dobrée*. Tome 2, *Imprimés*. Nantes: Musée Thomas Dobrée, 1903.

Prevost, M. "Brie (Jean de)." *Dictionnaire de biographie française*. 20 volumes to date (2011). Paris: Letouzey et Ané, 1933-. 7: col. 295.

Quignon, H. "Jehan de Brie, auteur du *Bon Berger* et son protecteur Jehan de Hétomesnil (xive siècle)." *Procès-verbaux et Mémoires de la Société d'Etudes historiques et scientifiques de l'Oise* 2 (1906): 173–77.

Sarton, G[eorge]. *Introduction to the History of Science*. 3 vols. Baltimore: Williams & Wilkins, for the Carnegie Institution of Washington, 1927–1948. [Jean de Brie, 3: 1164, 1181, 1309, and esp. 1631–32. "A critical edition [of *Le Bon Berger*] is much to be desired": 1632, cited by Holmér, 129].

Strubel, Armand. "Jean de Brie." *Dictionnaire des littératures de langue française*, ed. Jean-Pierre de Beaumarchais et al. 2 vols. Paris: Bordas, 1984. 1: 333.

Thomas, A[ntoine]. "A propos de Jehan de Brie." *Romania* 42 (1913): 85–87.

———. "Brie (Jean de)." *La Grande Encyclopédie: inventaire raisonné des sciences, des lettres et des arts . . .* 31 vols. Paris: Société Anonyme de la Grande Encyclopédie, 1889. 8: 11.

Wilmart, Mickaël. "L'homme face à la mort de l'animal: Pratiques, savoirs et croyances des bergers du xive siècle d'après le traité de Jean de Brie (1379)." In *La Mort écrite: Rites et réthoriques [sic] du trépas au Moyen Âge, textes recueillis par Estelle Doudet*. Actes de la journée d'études du groupe « Questes » (Paris-Sorbonne), 26 avril 2003, 137–53. Paris: Presses de l'Université Paris-Sorbonne, 2005.

B. General and reference works.

We include here a number of works which, while not specifically cited, have been useful in preparing this book.

Abel, Wilhelm. *Agricultural Fluctuations in Europe, from the Thirteenth to the Twentieth Centuries*. Trans. Olive Ordish. New York: St. Martin's Press, 1980.

Arbour, Roméo. *Dictionnaire des femmes libraires en France (1470–1870)*. Histoire et civilisation du livre 26. Genève: Droz, 2003.

Audoin-Rouzeau, Frédérique. "Compter et mesurer les animaux." *Histoire et mesure* 10 (1995): 277–312.

Autrand, Françoise. "France under Charles V and Charles VI." *New Cambridge* 6: 422-41.

Baldinger, Kurt. "Le remplacement de 'moult' par 'beaucoup' (A propos des bases méthodologiques d'un dictionnaire du moyen français)." In *Du mot au texte: Actes du IIIème Colloque International sur le Moyen Français, Düsseldorf, 17–19 septembre 1980*, ed. Peter Wunderli, 57–84. Tübingen: Narr, 1982. [Cited by Möhren, 139 n. 53.]

Bergers de France. Exposition, Musée des Arts et Traditions Populaires, 26 juillet–19 novembre 1962. Catalogue établi par Mariel Jean-Brunhes Delamarre et al. *Arts et Traditions Populaires* 10 (1962).

Bezard, Yvonne. *La Vie rurale, dans le sud de la région parisienne, de 1450 à 1560*. Paris: Firmin-Didot, 1929.

Bobis, Laurence. *Le Chat: Histoire et légendes*. [Paris:] Fayard, 2000.

Bökönyi, Sándor. "The Development of Stockbreeding and Herding in Medieval Europe." In Sweeney, *Agriculture in the Middle Ages*, 41–61.

Bossuat, Robert, et al. *Dictionnaire des lettres françaises*, t. 1: *Le moyen age*. Paris: Fayard, 1964.

Brunet, Jacques-Charles. *Manuel du libraire et de l'amateur de livres*. 5e éd. Paris: Maisonneuve & Larose (undated). Mayenne: Joseph Floch, 1965.

Calmette, Joseph. *Charles V*. Les Grandes Etudes Historiques. Paris: Arthème Fayard, 1945.

Camille, Michael. "When Adam Delved: Laboring on the Land in English Medieval Art." In Sweeney, *Agriculture in the Middle Ages*, 247–76.

Cantor, Norman F. *The Civilization of the Middle Ages*. New York: Harper Perennial, 1993.

Cato. See Varro.

Cherubini, Giovanni. "The Peasant and Agriculture." In Le Goff, *Time, Work, and Culture*, 113–38.

Clapham, J.H., and Eileen Power. *The Cambridge Economic History of Europe from the Decline of the Roman Empire*. 8 vols. New York: Macmillan, 1944.

Clévenot. See Jean de Brie, sec. A.

Columella, Lucius Junius Moderatus. *On Agriculture*. Trans. Harrison Boyd Ash. Cambridge: Harvard University Press, 1960.

Comet, Georges. "Animal Husbandry." *ODMA*. 1: 62.

———. "Stock Breeding and Selection." *ODMA*. 4: 1574–75.

Contamine, Philippe. *La Vie quotidienne pendant la guerre de Cent Ans: France et Angleterre (XIVe siècle)*. [Paris:] Hachette, 1976.

Coombes, Allen J. *Dictionary of Plant Names*. Portland, OR: Timber Press, 1994.

Cotgrave, Randle. *A Dictionarie of the French and English Tongues* [1611]. Columbia: University of South Carolina Press, 1968.

Crosby, Alfred W. "Afterword." In Sweeney, *Agriculture in the Middle Ages*, 337–42.

Culpeper, Nicholas. *Culpeper's Complete Herbal*. London: W. Foulsham and Co., 1952.

Dahmus, Joseph. *A History of the Middle Ages.* New York: Barnes and Noble, 1995.

Davies, Norman. *Europe: A History.* Oxford: Oxford University Press, 1996.

Dayton, William. *Notes on Western Range Forbs: Equisetaceae through Fumariaceae.* Washington, DC: Forest Service, U. S. Department of Agriculture, 1960.

Delisle, Léopold. *Etudes sur la condition de la classe agricole et l'état de l'agriculture en Normandie au Moyen Age.* New York: Burt Franklin, 1969 [original date of publication not indicated].

———. *Recherches sur la librairie de Charles V, roi de France, 1337–1380.* 2 vols. Paris: Champion, 1907. Repr. Amsterdam: van Heusden, 1967.

Delort, Robert, and Frédérique Audoin-Rouzeau, eds. *L'élevage médiéval.* Spec. no. of *Ethnozootechnie* 59 (1997).

Dournon, Jean-Yves, ed. *Mini Encyclopédie des proverbes et dictons de France.* Paris: Hachette, 1986; Édition du Club Loisirs, 1992.

Dresbeck, LeRoy. "Winter Climate and Society in the Northern Middle Ages: The Technological Impact." *On Pre-Modern Technology and Science: A Volume of Studies in Honor of Lynn White, jr,* ed. Bert S. Hall and Delno C. West, 177–99. Malibu: Undena, 1976.

Duby, Georges. *L'Economie rurale et la vie des campagnes dans l'Occident médiéval (France, Angleterre, Empire, IXe–XVe siècles): Essai de synthèse et perspectives de recherches.* 2 vols. Paris: Aubier, 1962. *Rural Economy and Country Life in the Medieval West,* trans. Cynthia Postan. Columbia: University of South Carolina Press; London: Edward Arnold, 1968.

Dumas, Alexandre. *Vingt ans après.* Œuvres de Alexandre Dumas, 30. Paris: Louis Conard, 1925. *Twenty Years After.* Great Illustrated Classics. Translator not credited. New York: Dodd, Mead, 1942.

École nationale des chartes. *Conseils pour l'édition des textes médiévaux.* Fascicule I: *Conseils généraux.* Paris: Ecole nationale des chartes, 2001.

Encarta 98 Encyclopedia. Redmond, WA: Microsoft, 1998.

Ensminger, M. E. *The Stockman's Handbook.* Danville, IL: Interstate Printers and Publishers, 1962.

Evans, Joan. *Life in Medieval France.* London: Phaidon, 1969.

Freedman, Paul. *Images of the Medieval Peasant.* Stanford: Stanford UP, 1999.

———. "Rural Society." *New Cambridge* 6: 82–101.

Fritz. See Chrétien de Troyes, sec. C.

Gardner, Rosalyn, and Marion A. Greene. *A Brief Description of Middle French Syntax.* Studies in the Romance Languages and Literatures 29. Chapel Hill: University of North Carolina Press, 1958.

Gimpel, Jean. *The Medieval Machine: The Industrial Revolution of the Middle Ages.* New York: Holt, Rinehart and Winston, 1976.

Godefroy, Frédéric. *Lexique de l'ancien français.* Paris: Champion, 1965.

Grand, Roger, and Raymond Delatouche. *L'Agriculture au moyen âge de la fin de l'empire romain au XVIe siècle.* Paris: Boccard, 1950.

Grandsaignes d'Hauterive, R. *Dictionnaire d'ancien français.* Paris: Larousse, 1947.

Greimas, A[lgirdas] J[ulien]. *Dictionnaire de l'ancien français jusqu'au milieu du XIVe siècle.* Paris: Larousse, 1980.

———, and Teresa Mary Keane. *Dictionnaire du moyen français: La Renaissance.* Paris: Larousse, 1992.

Guérard, Albert. *France: A Modern History.* New edition, revised and enlarged by Paul A. Gagnon. Ann Arbor: University of Michigan Press, 1969.

Guiraud, Pierre. *Le Moyen Français.* Que sais-je? 1086. Paris: Presses Universitaires de France, 1963.

Hale, J. R., et al, ed. *Europe in the Late Middle Ages.* Evanston: Northwestern UP, 1965.

Hamilton, Edith. *Mythology.* Boston: Little, Brown and Co. 1942.

Harrap's Modern College French and English Dictionary. Rev. M. Ferlin and P. Forbes. Ed. D. M. Ledésert and R. P. L. Ledésert. New York: Scribner, 1972.

Harte, N. B., and K. G. Ponting, eds. *Cloth and Clothing in Medieval Europe: Essays in Memory of Professor E. M. Carus-Wilson.* London: Heinemann Educational Books, 1983.

Hay, Denys. *Europe in the Fourteenth and Fifteenth Centuries.* New York: Holt, Rinehart and Winston, 1966.

Heath's New French and English Dictionary. Ed. Ernest A. Baker. Boston: D. C. Heath, 1932.

Henisch, Bridget Ann. *The Medieval Calendar Year.* University Park: Pennsylvania State University Press, 1999.

———. "In Due Season: Farm Work in the Medieval Calendar Tradition." In Sweeney, *Agriculture in the Middle Ages,* 309–36.

Herlihy, David. "Land, Family and Women in Continental Europe, 701–1200." *Traditio* 18 (1962): 89–120.

Hollister, C. Warren. *Medieval Europe: A Short History.* 5th ed. New York: Alfred A. Knopf, 1982.

Holy Bible, Old and New Testaments. Authorized King James Version. . . Thomas Nelson, 2003. [No place of publication indicated.]

Hüe, Denis. "Le berger à la fin du Moyen Âge: remarques sur une figure trifonctionnelle." In *Remembrances et resveries: Hommage à Jean Batany,* ed. H. Legros et al. Orléans: Paradigme, 2006. 117–38.

Huizinga, J. *The Waning of the Middle Ages.* Trans. F. Hopman. Garden City, NY: Doubleday Anchor, 1954.

Hunt, Tony. *Popular Medicine in Thirteenth-Century England.* Cambridge: D. S. Brewer, 1990.

———. "The Trilingual Glossary in MS London, BL Sloane 146, ff. 69v–72r." *English Studies: A Journal of English Language and Literature* 70 (1989): 289–310.

Irigaray, Louis, and Theodore Taylor. *A Shepherd Watches, a Shepherd Sings.* Garden City, NY: Doubleday, 1977.

Jenkins, David, ed. *The Cambridge History of Western Textiles.* 2 vols. Cambridge: Cambridge University Press, 2003.

Jodogne, Omer. *"Povoir* ou *pouoir?* Le Cas phonétique de l'ancien verbe *pouoir."* *Travaux de Linguistique et de Littérature* 4 (1966): 257–66.

Kaiser-Guyot, Marie-Thérèse. *Le Berger en France aux XIVe et XVe siècles.* Paris: Klincksieck, 1974.

Keller, Phillip. *A Shepherd Looks at Psalm 23.* Grand Rapids: Zondervan, 1970.

King James Bible. See Holy Bible, above.

Lachiver, Marcel. *Dictionnaire du monde rural: Les Mots du passé.* [Paris:] Arthème Fayard, 1997.

Lacroix, Paul. *France in the Middle Ages: Customs, Classes and Conditions.* New York: Ungar, 1963.

———. *Sciences et lettres au Moyen Age et à l'époque de la Renaissance.* Paris: Firmin-Didot, 1877. *Science and Literature in the Middle Ages and the Renaissance.* Translator not credited. New York: Ungar, 1964.

Langdon, John. "Animals, Domestic, Draught, and Wild." *ODMA.* 1: 63.

Lawler, Traugott. "Encyclopedias and Dictionaries, Western European." *Dictionary of the Middle Ages*, ed. Joseph R. Strayer, 4: 447b–50b. New York: Scribner, 1982–1989.

Le Goff, Jacques. *La Civilisation de l'Occident médiéval.* Paris: Arthaud, 1972. *Medieval Civilization 400–1500.* Trans. Julia Barrow. London: Blackwell, 1988.

———. *Pour un autre Moyen Age: Temps, travail et culture en Occident: 18 essais.* [Paris:] Gallimard, 1977. *Time, Work, and Culture in the Middle Ages.* Trans. Arthur Goldhammer. Chicago: University of Chicago Press, 1980.

Lenient, Charles. *La Satire en France au Moyen Âge.* 5e éd. Paris: Hachette, [1912].

Lepage, Yvan G. *Guide de l'édition de textes en ancien français.* Paris: Champion, 2001.

Long, Harold C. *Plants Poisonous to Livestock.* Cambridge: Cambridge UP, 1917.

Lorcin, Marie-Thérèse. *La France au XIIIe siècle.* Millau: Maury, 1981.

Lucas, Henry S. *A Short History of Civilization.* New York: McGraw-Hill, 1943.

Maillet, Germaine. "La Vie rurale et ménagère au Moyen Age d'après les auteurs champenois." *Nouvelle revue de Champagne et de Brie.* April–July 1930.

Mane, Perrine. *Calendriers et techniques agricoles (France-Italie, XIIe–XIIIe siècles).* Paris: Le Sycomore, 1983.

Mansion, J.E. See *Harrap's.*

Marchello-Nizia, Christiane. *La Langue française aux XIVe et XVe siècles.* Paris: Nathan, 1997 [updated version of her *Histoire de la langue française aux XIVe et XVe siècles.* Paris: Bordas, 1979; Dunod, 1992].

Mazzaoui, Maureen Fennell. "Wool." *ODMA.* 4: 1770.

McGee, Timothy J. "Musical Instruments." *ODMA.* 3: 1183–85.

Monmonier, Mark. Review of Nicholas Crane, *Mercator, the Man Who Mapped the Planet. Washington Post Weekly,* 17 Feb. 2003.

Munro, John H. A. *Wool, Cloth, and Gold: The Struggle for Bullion in Anglo-Burgundian Trade, 1340–1478.* Toronto: University of Toronto Press, 1972.

New Cambridge: The New Cambridge Medieval History, vol 6, *c. 1300–c. 1415,* ed. Michael Jones. Cambridge: Cambridge University Press, 2000.

New Grove: The New Grove Dictionary of Music and Musicians, ed. Stanley Sadie; executive editor John Tyrell. 29 vols. 2nd ed. London: Macmillan; New York: Grove's Dictionaries, 2001.

Newsom's Sheep Diseases, ed. Hadleigh Marsh. 3rd ed. Huntington, NY: Kreiger, 1973.

Niehaus, Theodore F., and Charles L. Ripper. *A Field Guide to Pacific States Wildflowers.* Boston: Houghton Mifflin, 1976.

Le Nouveau Petit Robert, dictionnaire alphabétique et analogique de la langue française. Nouvelle édition du *Petit Robert* de Paul Robert. Paris: Dictionnaires Le Robert, 1993.

ODMA: Oxford Dictionary of the Middle Ages, ed. Robert E. Bjork. 4 vols. Oxford: Oxford University Press, 2010.

Ovid. *The Metamorphoses of Ovid.* Trans. Mary M. Innes. Baltimore: Penguin, 1955.

Oxford Universal Dictionary on Historical Principles. 3rd ed. Ed. C. T. Onions. Oxford: Clarendon Press, 1955.

Parker, William Nelson, and E.L. Jones, eds. *European Peasants and Their Markets: Essays in Agrarian Economic History.* Princeton: Princeton University Press, 1975.

Peterson, Roger Tory, et al. *A Field Guide to the Birds of Britain and Europe.* Boston: Houghton Mifflin, 1954.

Pierron, Agnès. *Dictionnaire des dictons.* Alleur, Belgium: Marabout, 1997.

Postan, M. M., with Edward Miller. *The Cambridge Economic History of Europe.* 8 vols. Vol. 2: *Trade and Industry in the Middle Ages.* Cambridge: Cambridge University Press, 1963. Vol. 3: *Economic Organization and Policies in the Middle Ages.* Cambridge: Cambridge University Press, 1963.

Produzione, commercio e consumo dei panni della lanna (secoli XII–XVIII). Ed. M. Spallanzani. Florence: Olschki, 1976.

Pyne, Stephen J. *Fire in America: A Cultural History of Wildland and Rural Fire.* Princeton: Princeton University Press, 1982.

Quillet, Jeannine. *Charles V le roi lettré: Essai sur la pensée politique d'un règne.* Paris: Librairie Académique Perrin, 1984.

Renouard, Philippe. *Documents sur les imprimeurs, libraires . . . ayant exercé à Paris de 1450 à 1600.* Paris: H. Champion, 1901.

———. *Répertoire des imprimeurs parisiens . . . jusqu'à la fin du seizième siècle.* Paris: Minard, 1965.

Rey, Alain. *Dictionnaire historique de la langue française.* 2 vols. Paris: Dictionnaires Robert, 1994.

Robert, Paul. *Le Petit Robert 1: Dictionnaire alphabétique et analogique de la langue française.* Rédaction dirigée par A. Rey et J. Rey-Debove. Paris: Dictionnaire Le Robert, 1987.

Ryder, M. L. *Sheep & Man.* London: Duckworth, 1983.

Scott, George E., project coordinator. *The Sheepman's Production Handbook.* Sheep Industry Development Program. Denver: Abegg Printing, 1970.

Sherman, Claire Richter. *The Portraits of Charles V of France (1338–1380).* New York: NYU Press, for the College Art Association of America, 1979.

Slicher van Bath, B. H. *The Agrarian History of Western Europe, A.D. 500–1850.* Trans. Olive Ordish. London: Edward Arnold, 1963.

Southern, R. W. *The Making of the Middle Ages.* New Haven: Yale University Press, 1953.

Spufford, Peter. "Trade in Fourteenth-century Europe." *New Cambridge* 6: 155–208.

Stephenson, M. J. "Wool Yields in the Medieval Economy." *Economic History Review*, 2nd ser. 41 (1988): 368–91.

Stevens, Charles. *Maison Rustique, or The Countrey Farme.* Compyled in the French tongue by Charles Stevens and John Liebault, . . . and tr. into English by Richard Surflet . . . now newly reviewed, corrected and augmented, . . . with the husbandrie of France, Italie, and Spaine, reconciled and made to agree with ours here in England by Gervase Markham. London: Printed by Adam Islip for John Bill, 1616.

Sweeney, Del, ed. *Agriculture in the Middle Ages: Technology, Practice, and Representation.* Philadelphia: University of Pennsylvania Press, 1995.

Thiry. See Villon, sec. C.

Tobler, Adolf. *Altfranzösisches Wörterbuch: Adolf Toblers nachgelassene Materialien, bearbeitet und mit Unterstützung der Preussischen Akademie der Wissenschaften; herausgegeben von Erhard Lommatzsch.* Wiesbaden: Franz Steiner, 1955–2002.

Toynbee, Arnold. *The Industrial Revolution.* Boston: Beacon Press, 1956 (first published 1884).

Turnau, Irena. "The Diffusion of Knitting in Medieval Europe." In Harte and Ponting, *Cloth and Clothing*, 368–89.

van Uyten, Raymond. "Cloth in Medieval Literature of Western Europe." In Harte and Ponting, *Cloth and Clothing*, 151–83.

Varro, Marcus Terentius. *Roman Farm Management.* Trans. Fairfax Harrison. New York: Macmillan, 1918.

Větvička, Václav. *Plantes des champs et des forêts*. Adapted by Barbora Faure. Paris: Librairie Gründ, 1979.

Virgil. *Eclogues and Georgics: and the Last Six Books of the Aeneid*. Trans. Theodore Alois Buckley. New York: Translation Publishing Co., 1930.

White, Lynn, Jr. *Medieval Technology and Social Change*. London: Oxford University Press, 1971.

Whitson, Tom D., et al, ed. *Weeds of the West*. Jackson Hole: University of Wyoming Press, 1992.

C. Other Medieval and Renaissance Texts

Belon du Mans, Pierre. *L'Histoire de la nature des oyseaux*. Fac-similé de l'édition de 1555, avec introduction et notes par Philippe Glardon. Genève: Droz, 1997.

Chrétien de Troyes. *Erec et Enide*, ed. Jean-Marie Fritz. Lettres gothiques. Livre de Poche. Paris: Librairie Générale Française, 1992; repr. in Chrétien de Troyes, *Romans*. Livre de Poche. La Pochothèque. Paris: Librairie Générale Française, 1994.

Jeay, Madeleine, ed. *Les Evangiles des Quenouilles*. Edition critique, introduction et notes par Madeleine Jeay. Paris: Vrin; Montréal: Presses de l'U. de Montréal, 1985.

La Marche, Olivier de. *Le Chevalier deliberé (The Resolute Knight)*. Ed. Carleton W. Carroll, trans. Lois Hawley Wilson and Carleton W. Carroll. MRTS 199. Tempe: Arizona Center for Medieval and Renaissance Studies, 1999.

Latini, Brunetto. *Li Livres dou Tresor*. Ed. Francis Carmody. Berkeley: University of California Press, 1948.

Morawski, Joseph. *Proverbes français antérieurs au xve siècle*. Classiques Français du Moyen Age 47. Paris: Champion, 1925.

Spenser, Edmund. *The Poetical Works of Edmund Spenser*. British Poets Series. Edinburgh: James Nichol, 1859.

Villon, François. *Poésies complètes*, ed. Claude Thiry. Lettres gothiques. Paris: Librairie Générale Française, 1991.

Index to the Text and Translation of
Le Bon Berger

Note: We have included both Middle French and English forms of proper names whose spelling differs between the text and the translation. We have also included names of plants and diseases and certain other subjects discussed by de Brie. The noun *bergier* ("shepherd") and the various names for sheep (*aigneau, brebis, mouton, oeilles,* etc., and their English equivalents), occurring on nearly every page, are excluded, as are items mentioned in footnotes and references to Vostre's table of contents (p. 38). Words and names whose Middle French and English forms are nearly identical are listed together, French first. The numbers refer to the pages of the edited text.

A
Aaron, 94, 95
Abel, 64, 65
Abraham, 64, 65
Ætes, King, 53
affilee, 112, 144, 150
Affricus, 90, 91
agache, 78
all-good, 159
amender, 164
amont (vent d'), 90
aoust, 106, 136, 138, 140, 150, 160
Aphelotes, 88, 89
April, 81, 123
Aquilo, 90, 91
Aristoteles/Aristotle, 50, 51
Arnoul de Grant/Grand Pont, 54, 55
aronde(s), 76, 80
Asclepiades, 50, 51
asnes, asnesses, 50, 68, 82
August, 107, 137, 139, 141, 151, 161
Augustin(e), Saint, 52, 53
Auster, 82, 83, 90, 91
autompne, 60
Auximenes, 50, 51

aval (vent d'), 76, 90
avaines, 118, 138
avertin, 148, 158 (cf. *evertin*)
avortons, 106
avril, 80, 122

B
Babiloine la Grant, 68
Babylon, 69
Balance, 88
bellwether, 83, 131
bet, 112, 144
beufz, 56
Bias of Priene, 51
bise, vent de, 76, 90, 110
bittern, 79
blez, 138
bloat, 151, 161
bloodletting, 123, 141, 143, 163
Boeces/Boethius, 50, 51
Boetos, 50, 51
Boreas, 90, 91
bouchet, 114, 146, 152
bouverande, -aude, 116, 118, 148, 156
Brie (region), 35, 46, 47, 82, 83, 136, 137

Brie, Jehan/Jean de, 34, 35, 38–55, 62, 63, 86, 87, 90, 91, 124, 125, 164–69
Bucoliques, *Bucolics*, 43, 44
Buridan(s), 50, 51
butor, 78
buttercup, 59, 117, 119, 149, 155
Byaspenis, 50

C
Cæsar, Julius, 51
Calaterius, 52, 53
calf-skinning wind, 91
camomile, 133
Capricorn(e), 88, 89
castrating, 165
cat, 83
Cato(n), 50, 51
Cesar, Jules, 50
chaillie, chailliee, 132
chardons, 130, 140
Charles le Quint, 34
Charles the Fifth, 35
chat, 82
chatrer, 164
chauves soris, 84
chevaux, 42, 44, 82
chien du bergier, 96, 98, 136, 164
Chorus, 90, 91
Chritolaüs, 50
Cicero, 51
clary, 159
clavel, 126, 128, 146, 152
Clio, 51
clocheman, 82, 83
clover, 139
Cloye, 48, 49
Clyo, 50
cobweb disease, 139, 151, 163
colostrum, 113, 145
corbeau(x), 40, 110
corneille(s), 42, 80, 110
Coulommiers en/in Brie, 34, 35
coulons, 80
cows, 45, 57
Crab, sign of, 89
Crete, 50, 51

Cricias/Critias, 50, 51
Chritolaüs/Critolaus, 50, 51
crook, shepherd's, 71, 99, 101, 103, 105, 109, 137
crow(s), 41, 43, 81, 111
Cyceron, 50
Cyrus, 68, 69

D
dauve(s), 58, 116, 118, 148, 154, 158
David, King, 56, 57, 68, 69
de Brie: *See* (Jehan) de Brie
decembre/December, 144, 145
Dieu, 36, 40, 56, 64, 98, 100, 106, 164
dog, shepherd's, 63, 97, 99, 137, 165
doves, 81
dung, 63. *See also* manure
dwarf elder, 145
Dyogenes/Diogenes, 50, 51

E
East (wind), 91
Egypt(e), 52, 53
Eleopoleos, 66, 67
Empedocles, 50, 51
enfleure, 150, 160
Eoüs, 84, 85
Epicurus, 51
Epimenides, 51
Epycurus, 50
Epymenon, 50
Eraclitus, 50
espec, espect, 78
escorchevel, vent d', 90
escoufle(s), 42, 78
Escrevice, signe de l', 88
Esdras, 52, 53
estas, trois, 100
estates, three, 101
estourneaux, 76
Eth (vent), 90
Ethoüs, 84, 85
Euclid(es), 50, 51
Euroauster, 90, 91
Euronochus, 90, 91
Eurus, 88–91

Euzebe de Cesarie/Eusebius of Caesarea, Saint, 52, 53
Evangile(s), 46, 100
evertin (cf. *avertin*), 118
Ezechiel/Ezekiel, 62, 63

F
faissie, 80, 81
Fanonius, 90, 91
February, 107, 109, 111, 139, 145, 153, 159
feuvrel, 150, 160
fevrier, 106, 108, 110, 138, 144, 146, 152, 158
fiens, fient, 60, 62, 72, 74, 144
Filadelphus, 52
finch, green, 79
Fortune, 44, 45
fox, 79
France, 34, 35, 136, 137
France, escu de, 168
France, vent/wind, 90, 91
Fraxinis, 168
Froitmont/Froidmont, 52, 53

G
Galerne, 90, 91, 122, 123
geese, 43
Genesis, 64, 65
God, 37, 41, 57, 65, 99, 101, 107, 165
Golias de Jeth, 68
Goliath of Gath, 69
gorse, 117, 119, 149, 157
goslings, 43
Gospels, 47
gouterose, 156
Grant Pont, Arnoul de, 54, 55
Greeks, 53, 89, 91
Grejois, 52, 88, 90
gruis, 118

H
Hamon, 52, 53
Helynant/Hélinand, 52, 53
henbane, 153
hennebonne, 152
Heraclitus, 51
Hermes/Hermas, 50, 51

Hermogenes, 50, 51
heron, 76–79
Hetomesnil, Jehan/Jean de, 54, 55
Hierosme, Saint, 52
Hippocrates, 51
Holy Scripture, 65
Holy Spirit, 37
Homer, 51
horse beans, 161
horses, 43, 45, 83
horses of the sun, 85, 87
houlette, 70, 98, 100, 101, 102, 104, 108, 136
huas, huat, 42, 78, 110
hyebles, 144
Hypater, 50, 51

I
Isaac, 65
Israel, 65, 67, 69

J
jacks, 83
Jacob, 64–67
janvier/January, 106, 107, 164, 165
Jean (Baptiste), Saint, 36, 46, 152, 168
Jehan/Jean de Hetomesnil, 54, 55
Jehannot, Jehan, 168
jennies, 69, 83
Jerome, Saint, 53
Jesucrist/Jesus Christ, 36, 37
Jeth, 68
Jetro/Jethro, 66, 67
John, Saint, 37, 47, 153, 169
Juda(h), 66, 67
juillet, 134, 150
juing, 130, 134
Jules Cesar/Julius Cæsar, 50, 51
July, 135, 151
jumens, 82
June, 131, 135
Jupiter, 50, 51
juscarime, 152

K
kite(s), 43, 79, 111

L

Laban, 64, 65
Latins, 52, 88, 90
Leah, 65
Leuze, Nicolas de, 168
Libra, sign of, 89
lily of the valley, 151
liver fluke, 149, 159
Livre, signe de la, 88
lost cud, 151, 161
loup(s), 44, 46, 60, 78, 98, 106, 142, 166
louves, 106
love-in-a-mist, 139
Lya, 64
Lybie/Libya, 52, 53
Lybs, 90, 91

M

Macrobes/Macrobius, 50, 51
magpie, 43, 79
mange, 95, 97, 101, 103, 127, 129, 147, 149, 155
manure, 61, 73, 75, 145. *See also* dung
March, 89, 117, 119, 121, 149, 157, 165
mares, 83
mars, 88, 116, 118, 120, 148, 156, 164
mastin, 98
Mathieu de Pommolain, 48, 49
Mathieu/Matthew, Saint, 46, 47
may/May, 70–75, 124–127, 144, 145
Mede/Medes, 68, 69
Mellissus/Mellisus, 50, 51
merelles, 92, 93
Messy, 48, 49
Moses, 53, 67
Mouton, signe du, 88, 118
Moÿses, 52, 66
mugue(t) *(sauvage)*, 138, 150, 162, 163
mustard, 135

N

Nature, 48
Neemias/Nehemiah, 52, 53
New Notre Dame Street, 169
Nolongne, 42–45
Normendie/Normandy, 90, 91

Nort/North (vent/wind), 90, 91, 111, 122, 123
Nostre Dame (feste), 164
Nostre Dame (rue neufve), 168
Nothus, Notus, 90, 91
novembre/November, 142, 143

O

oats, 119, 137, 139
octobre/October, 140–143
Oetes, King, 52
oincture(s), 58, 102, 154
ointment(s), 59, 97, 101, 103, 109, 155, 157
Omers, 50
ongnement, oignemens, 58, 94, 96, 154, 156
oral lesions, 149, 157
Origen(es), 52, 53
Orleans/Orléans, 58, 59
orvalle, 158
oues, 42
Our Lady's Birth (Feast of), 165
Ovides/Ovid, 40, 41, 50, 51
oysons, 42

P

Pamphile/Pamphilus, 52, 53
Paris, 48, 49, 54, 55, 58, 59
Parmenides, 51
Paul, Saint, 93
Pentecost, Penthecoustes, 34, 35
Penthateuque/Pentateuch, 52, 53
Periander, 51
Permenides, 50
Perse, Persians, 68, 69
Peryander, 50
Peter the Glutton [Comestor], 53
Pharés/Pharez, 66, 67
Phebus/Phoebus, 82, 83
Philadelphus, 53
Phylogeüs, 84–87
Picardie/Picardy, 58, 59
Pierre le Mengeour, 52
pies, 42
pigs, 43
Plato(n), 50, 51
Plongel, Plungel, 76, 77, 122, 123
pneumonia, 113, 147, 153

poacre (cf. *pouacre*), 148, 156
Pol, Saint, 92
Pommolain, Mathieu de, 48, 49
poppy, 131, 151, 161
poreaulx, 162
Posidonius, 51
Possedemus, 50
pouacre (cf. *poacre*), 156
poucel, poucet (herbe/plant), 130, 150, 160
poucet, pousset (maladie/illness), 112, 146, 152
pourceaux, 42
pox (sheep pox), 127, 129, 147, 153
printemps, 60, 120
Psalms, Book of, 57
Ptholomees/Ptolemy, 52, 53
pye, 78
pymart, 78
Pyroüs, 84, 85
Pytagoras/Pythagoras, 50, 51

Q
queen of the meadows, 163

R
Rachel, 64, 65
Ram, sign of, 89, 119
rampaille, 40, 41
ranunculus, 117
ravens, 111
rebbardeure, 58, 59
renart, 78
roingne, 94
Romans, 53, 89, 91
ronge (cf. *runge*), 160
rongne, 96, 100, 102, 126, 128, 146, 148, 154, 156
roynette, 162
runge, rungot perdu, 116, 130, 150, 160

S
sage, 159
Saincte/Sainte Chapelle, 54, 55
Saincte Escripture, 64
Saint Augustin(e), 52, 53
Saint Esperit, 36

Saint Euzebe de Cesarie/Eusebius of Cæsarea, 52, 53
Saint Hierosme, 52
Saint Jehan (Baptiste), 36, 46, 152, 168
Saint Jerome, 53
Saint John (the Baptist, the Evangelist), 37, 47, 153, 169
Saint Mathieu/Matthew, 46, 47
Saint Pol/Paul, 92, 93
Salomon, 50
Saül/Saul, 68, 69
sauvres, 134
scabies, 157
Scale (sign of), 89
scours, 113, 145, 151
Secons, 50, 51
seignee, 122, 140, 142, 162
Seneque/Seneca, 50, 51
Sephora, 66, 67
septembre/September, 67, 70, 71, 88, 89, 106, 107, 138, 139, 150, 151, 162, 163
shearing, 59, 75, 103, 125, 127, 129
Socrates, 50, 51
Solerre, 122, 123
Solius/Solinus, 52, 53
Solomon, 51
sonnaillier, 82, 83, 130
sore mouth, 115, 147, 153
South (wind), 91, 123
Souverain Pasteur/Sovereign Shepherd, 34, 35, 138, 139
staggers, 119, 149, 159
starlings, 77
Straw Lane, 55
Subsolain/Subsolanus, 88–91
Sut (vent), 90
swollen throat, 149, 157

T
teasel(s), 131, 141
Thamar/Tamar, 66, 67
Theophrastus/Theostratus, 50, 51
three estates, 101
tierceul, 118
Titus, 93
tondre, 74, 98, 124, 126

tonsure, 58, 74, 102, 124, 126, 128
toutebonne, 158
treffle, 138
Trepperel, veufve feu Jehan, 168
trippes/tripe, 58, 59
trois estas, 100
Tueil, 48, 49
Tulle/Tullus, 50, 51
tume, 152
Tyton, 92

V
vaches, 44, 56
Varro, Marcus Terencius/Terentius, 52, 53
ver (printemps), 120
verdiere, 78
vervaine/vervain, 162, 163
vesche/vetch, 118, 119
Villers (sur Rongnon), 34, 35, 42, 43
Virgil, Virgile(s), 42, 43, 50, 51
Vostre, Symon, 168, 169
Vultur, Vulturus, 90, 91

W
West (vent/wind), 90, 91
wheat, 109, 119, 137, 139
wolf, wolves, 45, 47, 61, 79, 99, 107, 143, 167
woodpecker, green, 79
wood sorrel, 151

X
Xenocrates, 50, 51
Xenophantes, 50, 51
Xenoplyn/Xenophon, 50, 51

Y
Ypocras, 50
yrengnier, 138, 150, 162
Ysaac, 64
Ysrael, 64, 66, 68

Z
Zaran/Zarah, 66, 67
Zeno(n), 50, 51
Zephirus, 90, 91